The Genetic Basis
of Selection

The Genetic Basis
of Selection

I. MICHAEL LERNER
University of California
Berkeley

New York · John Wiley & Sons, Inc.
London · Chapman & Hall, Ltd.

Many laws regulate variation,
some few of which can be dimly seen.

Preface

Had this book been published in earlier days, it would have borne on the title page a lengthy description of what is and what is not to be found between its covers. Such a subtitle might have contained a disclaimer stating that the volume is not intended to be either a handbook of data or a manual of breeding practice. It would have included a warning that the discussion of selection is limited to diploid sexually reproducing populations, that only the intraspecific level of biological organization is dealt with in detail, that artificial selection is accorded rather fuller treatment than natural selection, and that examples, forming the core around which the text is written, are confined to experimental data on the domestic fowl. Finally, the subtitle would have suggested that it is the author's hope that this work will prove to be of interest and value to advanced students of both evolution and breeding, and, in particular, to those who, having a thorough knowledge of modern genetics, lack an extensive background in mathematics and statistics.

In pursuit of this goal a compromise between a romantic (in the sense of free and imaginative) and a classical (i.e. traditionally accepted or long-established) outlook on selection has been adopted. General concepts are introduced at the beginning on a theoretical and sometimes conjectural level. A gradually increasing dosage of empirical observations is then given in their support. Many terms are defined in a special sense or carry an intentionally vague meaning. Statistical descriptions of different aspects of the subject are segregated in inserts, called *boxes* (some containing lists of literature), which do not form an integral part of the text. They may be taken or left alone according to the reader's inclination. But most of the statistics used are homespun and therefore need not hold terror for any biologist. Standard errors and tests of significance are not given, because nearly all the data cited are used to illustrate ideas and not to adduce proof of precise quantitative relations.

vii

In short, the biological phenomenon of selection is approached without either the naturalist's disdain of or the mathematician's reverence for statistical formulation.

The restriction of experimental data presented in detail to those gathered on the chicken may be thought to circumscribe the utility of this work. I view it, however, as giving the book a greater unity of outlook and coherence of exposition than would otherwise be possible, even though this procedure leads to an overemphasis of my own work. The reader need not know much about poultry. Reading the book will not make him an expert poultry geneticist. But I hope that when he has finished it he will have acquired enough understanding of the biology of chickens, and of their advantages and limitations as material for the study of selection, to be able to apply freely the principles discussed here to the species of his own interest. The emphasis on artificial as against natural selection and the number of specific references to poultry become greater as the discussion unfolds. The reader can determine for himself the point at which his willingness to reason from chickens to higher or lower forms of life fails him.

This book was written while I was a Fellow of the U. S. Guggenheim Foundation (Dr. Henry Allen Moe, Secretary-General) on sabbatical leave from the University of California. I am very grateful to Professors A. A. Buzzati-Traverso, G. E. Magni, and R. E. Scossiroli of the University of Pavia and to the staff of the Poultry Research Centre (Dr. A. W. Greenwood, Director) and the Animal Breeding Research Organization (Dr. H. P. Donald, Director), both at Edinburgh, for their hospitality and much help in various tangible and intangible ways. I also wish to thank Mrs. Dorothy C. Lowry for the computations underlying figures 5.3–5.14; Professor E. R. Dempster for some of the material in boxes 2 and 3; Dr. Alan Robertson for a critical reading of the manuscript; and Dr. D. S. Falconer for a number of constructive suggestions.

To the greatest degree I am indebted to Dr. H. P. Donald, who once again, by virtue of his indefatigable editorial labors, bears more responsibility for what may be good in form and content of this book than a mere acknowledgment of help can convey, and to my wife, Ruth S. Lerner, for her infinite patience in wielding a blue pencil, redrawing the drafts of the figures, retyping the seemingly endless revisions of the manuscript, and much else that enters the making of a book.

Lastly, it should be, but probably is not, superfluous to note that all the epigraphs are from the pen of Charles Darwin.

I. MICHAEL LERNER

Pavia–Edinburgh

Contents

Chapter 1

THE MENDELIAN POPULATION   1

   1   Population genetics   3
   2   Selection within populations   5
   3   Artificial versus natural selection   10
   4   The gene pool   15
   5   Selection progress   22
   6   The roles of mutation and migration   30
   7   Coadaptation   32

Chapter 2

POLYGENIC INHERITANCE   36

   8   Polygenic balance   37
   9   Gene interaction   42
  10   Partitioning phenotypic variance   51
  11   Heritability   57
  12   Special cases of non-additive gene action   65

Chapter 3

CONSERVATION OF GENETIC VARIANCE   70

  13   Population equilibrium   73
  14   Fitness of intermediates   81
  15   Inbreeding   85
  16   Overdominance   95
  17   Population size and the effects of chance   103

Chapter 4

RESPONSE TO SELECTION PRESSURE   109

  18   Gains under selection   112
  19   Types of selection response   125
  20   A detailed case history   132
  21   Correlated response   144

Chapter 5

SELECTION BASED ON ADDITIVELY GENETIC ACTION   153
22   The basis of family selection   156
23   Non-random environmental effects   165
24   Combined selection   169
25   Multiple objectives   176
26   Auxiliary selection methods   184
27   Optimum structure of breeding populations   191

Chapter 6

SELECTION WHEN VARIANCE IS NON-ADDITIVE   197
28   Genotype-environment interaction   199
29   Interpopulation and cross-performance selection   204
30   General and specific combining ability   217

Chapter 7

IMPROVEMENT OF SPECIFIC TRAITS   224
31   Egg number   227
32   Other fitness components   238
33   Egg production traits   248
34   Meat production traits   254

Chapter 8

PROSPECTS   259
35   Research in artificial selection   260
36   Selection limits   265
37   Macroevolutionary horizons   267
38   Envoy   269

LITERATURE CITED   274

INDEX OF NAMES   285

SUBJECT INDEX   291

List of Figures

1·1   Types of selection   7
1·2   Continuity of genetic material   8
1·3   The gene pool   17
1·4   Selection progress in the absence of dominance   26
1·5   Selection for a dominant allele   27
1·6   Selection for a recessive allele   28
1·7   Selection for a heterozygote   29
1·8   Selection between and within populations   31

2·1   Examples of polygenic balance   40
2·2   Genotype-environment interaction   44
2·3   Genotypic interactions   49
2·4   Partitioning epistatic variance   50
2·5   Relationship between parents and offspring   53
2·6   Relationship between sibs   53
2·7   An example of simple scale transformation   57
2·8   Variance components in heritability estimation   60
2·9   Variance components in a diallel system   61
2·10   Selection progress as a function of heritability   62
2·11   Range of heritability estimates for economic traits of chickens   64
2·12   Epistatic variance of an all-or-none trait   67

3·1   Equilibrium value of q_A when selection favors the heterozygote   76
3·2   Incidence of recessive lethals maintained in a population by heterozygote superiority   77
3·3   Selection for the number of comb blades in chickens   80
3·4   Relation between egg weight and fitness in chickens   82
3·5   Model of allelic fixation when selection favors an intermediate phenotype   83

3·6   A pedigree showing irregular inbreeding   86
3·7   Increase in homozygosity under inbreeding   90
3·8   Rise in inbreeding in a flock of chickens   91
3·9   Effect of inbreeding on reproductive fitness of chickens   92
3·10   Effects of inbreeding on viability of chickens   93
3·11   Theoretical loss in egg production as a result of
       restriction of flock size   94
3·12   A model of genetic homeostasis   96
3·13   The relation between metrical traits and fitness   98
3·14   A model of developmental homeostasis   101
3·15   The effect of population size on the distribution of
       allelic frequencies   105
3·16   Distribution of allelic frequencies in polygamous
       populations   106

4·1   The selection differential   112
4·2   The selection differential as a function of selection intensity   115
4·3   Gains expected from selection for egg production in relation
       to the age structure of the breeding flock   118
4·4   Asymmetry of selection response   120
4·5   The gains expected when heritability or intensity decline
       under selection   124
4·6   Schematic representation of selection progress   127
4·7   Selection for the shank growth ratio   128
4·8   Selection for slow rate of sexual maturity   129
4·9   Selection for increased incidence of crooked toes   131
4·10   Selection for increased shank length   134
4·11   Frequency distributions in the shank length experiment   136
4·12   Shank length frequency distribution in the eighteenth
       generation of selection   137
4·13   Inbreeding and hatchability under selection for
       shank length   138
4·14   Attenuation of the selection differential by natural
       selection   139
4·15   Gains in shank length as a function of the realized
       selection differential   140
4·16   Fitness and gains under selection for shank length   141
4·17   Correlated response to suspension of selection for
       shank length   143
4·18   Correlated response to selection for body weight   146
4·19   The basis of phenotypic correlation between traits   150

5·1   Maximum rate of gain as a function of heritability   156

5·2   Biometric basis of family selection   160
5·3   Ratio of family to individual heritability   161
5·4   Ratio of family to individual standard deviation   162
5·5   Efficiency of full-sib family selection   163
5·6   Efficiency of half-sib selection   164
5·7   Efficiency of full-sib selection in the presence of non-
       random environmental effects   167
5·8   Efficiency of half-sib selection in the presence of non-
       random environmental effects   168
5·9   Weighting factors in combined full-sib family and mass
       selection   171
5·10   Weighting factors in combined full-sib family and mass
       selection in the presence of non-random environmental
       effects   172
5·11   Weighting factors in combined full-sib, half-sib, and
       mass selection   173
5·12   Efficiency of combined full-sib and mass selection   174
5·13   Relative efficiency of combined full-sib, half-sib and
       mass selection   175
5·14   Relative efficiency of half-sister selection for a sex-
       limited trait   176
5·15   Selection for two uncorrelated traits   178
5·16   Relative efficiency of different selection methods   179
5·17   Selection based on an index   180
5·18   Inbreeding coefficients of dams and daughters   190
5·19   Efficiency of family selection as a function of family size   192
5·20   Relative selection differentials in relation to population size 194
5·21   Suspension of selection   195

6·1   Growth of poultry crossbreeding in the United States   198
6·2   Genotype-year-location interaction   203
6·3   Intra- versus interpopulation selection   208
6·4   Intrapopulation selection based on performance in a cross   209
6·5   Selection between inbred lines on the basis of incrossbred
       performance   209
6·6   Two-population rotation scheme   210
6·7   Four-way cross between inbred lines   212
6·8   Selection for egg weight under inbreeding   215
6·9   Selection for egg number under inbreeding   216
6·10   One-way recurrent selection   220
6·11   Recurrent and intrapopulation selection   221
6·12   Prediction of combining ability   230

7·1   Selection for increased egg number   233
7·2   Changes in the part production record under selection   234
7·3   Survivors' production and mortality under selection   235
7·4   Heritability of egg number   236
7·5   Changes in fitness under selection for egg production   237
7·6   Hatchability of the production-bred flock   238
7·7   Elimination of recessive lethals by natural selection   240
7·8   Selection for disease susceptibility   244
7·9   Selection for resistance and susceptibility to lymphomatosis   245
7·10   Changes in egg production of the lymphomatosis-resistant
          line   245
7·11   Selection for persistency of egg production   250
7·12   Selection for increased egg weight   251
7·13   Selection for shell thickness   252
7·14   Selection for egg shape   253
7·15   Selection for increased incidence of blood spots   254
7·16   Selection for twelve-week body weight   256

List of Boxes

Chapter 1
1   Genetic basis of selection progress   23

Chapter 2
2   Partitioning two-locus interaction   46
3   Examples of gene interaction   47
4   Parent-offspring and sib relationships   54
5   Estimation of heritability   58

Chapter 3
6   Selection favoring heterozygotes   74
7   Symbolization of dominance   78
8   The inbreeding coefficient   87
9   The effect of inbreeding on variance   89
10   Sampling variance of allelic frequencies   107

Chapter 4
11   The selection differential   113
12   Prediction of gains under mass selection   116
13   Numbers of birds in the shank length experiment   133
14   Genetic correlation   149
15   Expected correlated response   150

Chapter 5
16   Family selection   158
17   Combined selection   169
18   Selection indexes   181
19   Repeatability   185
20   Overcorrection   188

Chapter 6
21   Legal definitions of inbred and hybrid stock   206
22   Literature on mating schemes in poultry   211
23   Inbreeding crises   213

Chapter 7

24 The pioneers of poultry genetics   226
25 The University of California production-bred
      flock   228
26 Recent data from the University of California
      flock   230
27 Inheritance of disease resistance   241
28 Genetic differences in nutritional requirements   247

Chapter 8

29 Literature on selection experiments   270
30 Miscellaneous references   271

1

The Mendelian Population

> No one definition has satisfied all
> naturalists ; yet every naturalist
> knows vaguely what he means...

The practice of selection as a means of modifying the properties of plants and animals dates from prehistory. Citations of references to selection procedures from classical antiquity and Biblical sources are frequent in historical resumes of breeding methods. The famous makers of livestock breeds and fanciers, to an even greater degree, accumulated a store of empirical experience in the practice of selection, although the results they obtained were often confounded with the consequences of different mating systems. Darwin's extensive documentation of examples of artificial and assumed natural selection leaves little doubt that knowledge, if not understanding, of selection effects reached a high level long before genetics became a science. The success of many breeders in altering the genetic properties of various species of useful organisms without the benefit of acquaintance with Mendelian or probability theory testifies to the same fact.

The theoretical study of selection based on Mendelian inheritance was initiated less than half a century ago. This development prepared the ground for a multitude of experimental investigations and increasingly elaborate refinements of theory, which on many occasions have been adapted for practical ends. It is impossible to say precisely how much the growing comprehension of the bases of selection has contributed to the progress of breeding. With enough qualifications it can, however, be asserted that genetics has narrowed the limits of predictions of population behavior, often made possible rational choices between alternative selection procedures, swept away much of the folklore of both breeders and naturalists, and, above all, immeasurably advanced our understanding of evolution on all levels.

Fifty years is not a long time on the evolutionary scale, especially in dealing with long-lived animals. Experimental verification of all that current genetic theory supposes to be true is impossible in such a brief period. Hence the respectably large islands of organized information on selection are still surrounded by vaster expanses of relative ignorance.

Much of the experimental work with useful animals in the past was in want of systematic foundations, so that data of significance were frequently reported in a manner deceptively free from any premises. Of course, closer inspection of such material invariably reveals a variety of concealed assumptions. Some of them are relatively innocuous and disregard of their character has little consequence; others may eventually visit the unwary, who may put into practice a deduction without realizing the postulates on which it rests. This hazard arises from the fact that Mendelian inheritance, viewed comprehensively, is a statistical phenomenon, and evolution, in nature or under man's control, is a process depending on a subtle balance of forces which can largely be described in probability terms. Hence, models of varying degrees of intricacy are needed to represent different aspects of genetics and breeding, if practical consequences are to be drawn from empirical observations.

In fact, the ingenuity and mathematical proficiency of the recent builders of such models have already produced many hypothetical constructs of a complexity considerably beyond the powers of experimental resolution. Yet genetics must still deal with living organisms and not only with manipulation of symbols. A fusion of abstract theory and concrete experimental facts is therefore needed in the study of evolutionary change. Indeed, it is the field of selection especially which demands that the biological and mathematical approaches become verily integrated, rather than merely find a mode of coexistence.

The first step of an inquiry into the genetic basis of selection is then to examine from a point of view uniting biological experience, agricultural practice, and statistical theory the relevant properties of the material on which selection acts. This material displays a hierarchy of organized levels proceeding from possibly intra-allelic structures, through alleles, chromosomes, genomes, and individual organisms, to populations. The last of these is the main focus of attention in viewing nearly every aspect of selection. The discussion to follow deals with a particular type of population or spatio-temporal entity, which consists of a group of inter-breeding organisms, is characterized by Mendelian inheritance, possesses by virtue of its prior evolutionary history an integrated genetic structure, and is statistically specifiable by systems of allelic or genotypic frequencies.

This kind of population was succinctly defined by Dobzhansky (1950) as "a reproductive community of sexual and cross-fertilized individuals which share in a common gene pool," and was called by him the *Mendelian population.* The implications of this definition should gradu-ally become apparent from the review of the effects of selection on the composition and parameters of Mendelian populations, which occupies the major part of this volume. However, before embarking on the con-sideration of this topic, it may be desirable to orient the general subject of selection within the field of genetics.

1. Population Genetics

The study of selection belongs to the branch of genetics known as *population genetics.* It is a discipline that is supplemented by, and over-laps in different ways, other compartments of the science of heredity and variation, which are designated as *mathematical genetics* and as *biometrical genetics.* These three expressions are not to be taken as synonymous as is assumed by some, nor do they refer to completely separate disciplines as has been asserted by others. Formal definition of these terms is not necessarily desirable, but an idea of the differences between them may be given here in order to indicate their respective scopes.

Mathematical genetics is basically a *descriptive science.* Its function is to construct mathematical models that can account as adequately as possible for the processes involved in hereditary transmission and in evolutionary change. Biometrical genetics pursues an *analytical* ap-proach. It may deal with tests of linkage relationships, with goodness of fit to Mendelian ratios, with analyses of the inheritance of quantitative traits, or with other aspects of genetics requiring statistical manipulation of data. Population genetics embraces many phases of both mathematical genetics and biometrical genetics, but it should be primarily an *experimen-tal* science. It must be rooted as much in a biological outlook as in a statistical one, even when it deals with theory or with material not always susceptible to experimentation, such as that in human genetics and in studies of evolutionary changes in geological time.

All three of these branches of genetics are distinguished from others in that they deal with groups rather than with individuals. In contrast, *biochemical genetics, physiological genetics, developmental genetics* all occupy themselves with successively more complex analyses of pathways from the gene to the character, that is to say, with aspects of gene function observable in single organisms. Again, some phases of *cytogenetics*, and of the field that may be called *biophysical genetics*, concern themselves with the reproduction of the units of heredity, the genes and the chromosomes, i.e. with functions of the gene exercised within a cell.

Thus, the biological phenomena of primary interest to geneticists can be arranged on three planes. First, there are the physicochemical aspects of self-propagation of the fundamental bearers of inheritance, the *intracellular* level. Second, there is the behavior of the material transmitted by parents to their offspring through the uniting gametes in the process leading to the phenotypic expressions of traits. This is a level which can be studied within cells, tissues, and organs but may more generally be said to be the one dealing with *individual* organisms. Finally, observations on the properties of groups, including means and variances of different metric traits and attributes which bind aggregates of individuals in time and space and thus transform them into organized entities, must be treated on the *population* level. In particular, when cross-fertilized diploid organisms are dealt with, the kind of population to be considered is the Mendelian one, characterized by a cohesive structure.

The current interest of investigators in the field of population genetics is, however, directed not only to the population level itself but also to attempts to bridge the gap between it and the level of individual organisms. The understanding of the phenomena included in the general concept of selection is basic for such a purpose. This is true whether the student of the subject is concerned with long-range evolutionary phenomena covering centuries and thousands of generations, with middle-range aspects of experimental work lasting tens of generations, or with short-range results of breeding practices where the number of generations is very limited.

There are no strict lines of demarcation to be drawn between short- and long-range alterations in the composition and properties of populations. The short-term changes are often referred to as *microevolutionary* in rank. They are, generally speaking, reversible, repeatable, and comprise events occurring within single populations or races. At the other extreme, *macroevolution* deals with non-reversible and unrepeatable phylogenetic modifications of such radical nature as to produce new genera or higher categories. The forces and the actual processes that lead to macroevolutionary changes are basically the same as those that operate at the microevolutionary level.[1] However, in the course of gradual transformation

---

[1] For a dissenting view see Goldschmidt (1940); one of several counter-critiques may be found in Simpson's (1953) book.

occurring over periods of geological time, the weight of accumulated sequential changes in the population becomes so great that a point of no return is reached.

Between the two extremes of the continuum from the microevolutionary to the macroevolutionary order of change lies an area for which Dobzhansky (1954) has coined the word *mesoevolution*. Here, drastic modification in the average or corporate genotype of a population may occur, and formation of new varieties, or perhaps even species, takes place. The degrees of determinacy and reversibility of processes of this type are intermediate between those at the extremes.

The discussion to follow is directed mainly toward changes in allelic and genotypic frequencies on the microevolutionary level. It will then neglect to a considerable extent, on the one side, the origin of new genetic variation or mutation in the broad sense, and disregard, on the other, the processes of fixation of interpopulation differences which are responsible for speciation.

2. Selection within Populations

Selection can be defined in terms of its observable consequences as the *non-random differential reproduction of genotypes*. This definition avoids the confusion created by the use of the term "selection" in reference to the differential reproduction of phenotypes which may or may not be reflected in the genetic composition of the following generation. Haldane (1957b), in commenting on this difficulty, was led to propose a set of terms to distinguish between phenotypic and genotypic differential reproduction. But his usage of *phenotypic selection* and *genotypic selection* is in conflict with the vocabulary of breeders in which these terms refer to the criteria of selection (e.g. phenotypic performance of an individual as against a progeny test as an estimate of genetic merit) and not to the levels at which differential reproduction is considered.

In order to avoid cumbersome circumlocution, *selection* may also be used in the lay sense of *choice*, to indicate the actual procedure by which discrimination between individuals with respect to their reproductive rate is arrived at. Darwin's (1872) definition of natural selection as the "preservation of favourable individual differences and variations and the destruction of those which are injurious" clearly must be taken today as a description of a phylogenetic process. In the words of Wright (1955), "selection is a wastebasket category that includes all causes of directed change in gene frequencies that do not involve mutation or introduction from without. Biologically, it includes such diverse phenomena as differential viability at any stage, dispersal beyond the range of inbreeding, differential maturity, differences in mating tendencies, fecundity and duration of reproductive capacity."

For the time being we shall consider selection only within breeding populations, rather than between such groups.   The individuals comprising a population are usually represented by a variable number of offspring in the next generation.   If such variation is entirely due to chance, or to other reasons not connected with genetic differences between individuals, then in a sufficiently large population the proportion of genotypes in successive generations will remain unchanged, and no selection will have taken place.   Conversely, if the reasons why one individual leaves fewer or more offspring than the average for all individuals in the population are in some way based on the dissimilarities among the genotypes of the respective parents, selection has occurred.   In this situation, the proportions of the various genotypes in the following generation may be modified, although not inevitably.   The consequences to be expected from different types of selection can be deduced on the assumption of Mendelian inheritance.   They are illustrated in a schematic fashion in figure 1.1, from which it may be seen that the average for a trait under selection can either change or remain constant.   But even when the average stays the same, genotypic proportions in the population may be altered.

In the first example shown in the figure, selection is *stabilizing* (Schmalhausen, 1949): individuals near the mean of the population reproduce themselves but the extreme types do not.   Under the simplest conditions the next generation will have the same mean as the previous one, but a narrower range.   The next two examples also show stabilizing selection. In II the intermediate types are heterozygous; in III extremes are preferred. In both instances the mean and the range of the filial generation may be expected to be equal to those of the parental generation.

The next illustration (IV) is of *disruptive selection*, in the course of which parents are chosen from both extremes but are mated like to like.   It is a form not likely to be encountered in ordinary breeding operations, although it does have considerable evolutionary significance, particularly in connection with the origin of polymorphism (Mather, 1955).

The last example (V) is of greatest pertinence to plant and animal improvement.   It illustrates *directional*[2] (also called *dynamic*) selection, or selection for an extreme expression of a given character.   The mean of the filial generation here is displaced in the direction of the selection pressure applied, whereas the range may be somewhat contracted (although the effect of reduction in variance due to selection is, generally speaking, very small).

[2] The designations for different kinds of selection given here follow Mather's (1953) usage.   Simpson (1953) applies other names to the phenomena pictured in figure 1.1.

It is important to realize that, although selection refers to changes in the genetic composition of a population brought about by the differential propagation of genotypes, it is a particular phenotypic expression, or the phenotype in its totality, that may be the agent of selective discrimination between the members of the parental generation. This is why the subject of selection includes the problem of genotype-phenotype relationship and

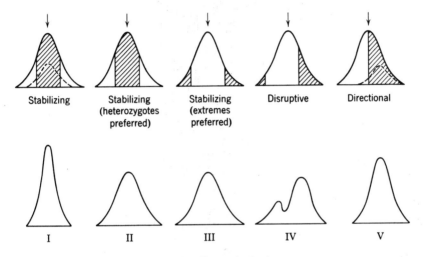

Figure 1.1. Types of selection

In each of the five examples the top curve represents the frequency distribution of the parental generation for a phenotypic property. The arrows indicate the mean for this character. The selected parents are included in the shaded portions of the areas under the curve; the individuals outside these areas are rejected and do not leave any offspring. The curves in the bottom row show the expected frequency distributions of the next generation on the assumption that all parents have the same probability of contributing a given number of offspring to it, that (except for type IV) they are mated at random, and that no further selection among gametes or progeny occurs. The dashed lines in the first and fifth examples are more representative of the distribution of the prospective parents under natural selection, where selection based on sharp vertical truncation is not a common occurrence.

why the bridge spanning the individual and the population levels of genetics is of such importance.

The phenotypic expression of a certain character at any stage in the lifetime of a given individual may be viewed as the combined result of its genetic constitution and the environment in which it develops and lives. Environment must be defined here so as to include all extrachromosomal sources of variation. Then it may be said that, for instance, the uppermost individual (T) in the pedigree represented in figure 1.2 has a phenotype (P_T) which is a product of interaction of its genotype (Ge_T) and its environment (E_T). When the population of which T is a member is subjected to artificial selection, the decision whether T will leave any offspring, and if so, how many, may often be based not on its genotypic merit but on one or more properties of its phenotype.

Suppose that all individuals of a population are genotypically identical

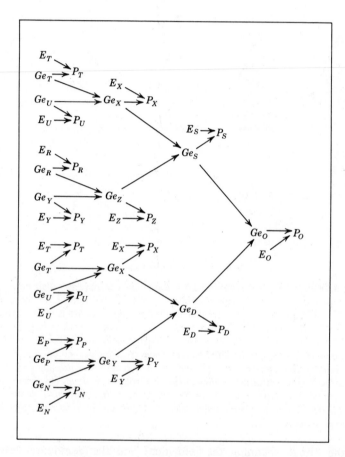

Figure I.2.   Continuity of genetic material

This pedigree illustrates the continuity of genetic material from one generation to the next. Each individual in it is portrayed as having a phenotype (P with an identifying subscript) which is a product of the environment specific to it (E) and of its genotype (Ge). The E of any parent, however, is not connected with either the environment or the genotype of its offspring. On the other hand, the genotype of every parent makes an immediate contribution to the genotype of its offspring (the direction of the arrows proceeding from cause to effect).

with respect to loci contributing to the character under selection, or that the variation between genotypes is very small compared to that between the individual environments. Differential reproduction within this population will then depend on individual differences of non-genetic origin. As already noted, this will not be a selective process, since the causes of variability in the number of offspring will not affect the genetic composition of the succeeding generation. In figure 1.2 the direction of the arrows from each Ge and E to the appropriate P indicates that the latter is the effect of the former. It may also be noted that the continuity of hereditary transmission is based only on pathways joining the Ge components. The E component, although contributing to the P, does not affect the genotypes of any subsequent generation. Hence, selection can be said to have occurred only when the relation between P and Ge is so strong that decisions made on the basis of P values are reflected in a differential reproduction of individuals differing in their values of Ge.

The situation represented here is oversimplified in at least two respects. First, the environment of a parent may directly influence the phenotype of the offspring, as is observed in non-genetically determined maternal effects. Thus, the body weight of young suckling a dam of poor nutritional status, the level of which may, at least in part, be assumed to be environmentally determined, will, no doubt, be lower than that of their contemporaries nursed by better-fed mothers. This kind of influence falls into a special category of environmental variation designated as C effects (see section 10). They also include cytoplasmic contributions of the dam to the offspring, which are hereditary but not genetic, as the term has been defined here.

Second, it is possible that environment, although without influence on the actual genotype of the parent, may modify the genetic material transmitted to the offspring. For example, exposure of the parental population to X-rays may produce mutations. Should one of the gametes contributed to the next generation include germinal material thus changed, it may be said that parental environment has, indeed, influenced the variability of the genotypes of the progeny. This, however, is not a directed effect as is selection, nor should it be confused with the inheritance of acquired characters in higher organisms, belief in which seems to be without foundation. Although various experimental results, bearing a superficial resemblance to the vulgar notions of inheritance of acquired characters have been described, they can usually be proved to have a different explanation. Chemical mutagenesis and the process called genetic assimilation by Waddington (1953a) are examples in point. On the other hand, the relevance to genetics of the claims that hereditary changes may be produced by such means as albumen transfer in eggs or by blood transfusions remains to be established.

3. Artificial versus Natural Selection

So far, we have failed to distinguish between natural and artificial selection, although there is a profound difference between the two concepts. Unfortunately, it is only too often obscured by the terminology used in discussing these phenomena. It must be understood that *natural selection* is really not an *a priori* cause of any phenomenon observed in nature, in the laboratory, or on the farm. Natural selection is a term serving to say that some genotypes leave more offspring than others. Natural selection has no purpose. It can be deduced to have existed and its intensity can be measured only *ex post facto*. For any given generation, natural selection is a consequence of the differences between individuals with respect to their capacity to produce progeny. The individuals who have more offspring are *fitter* in the Darwinian sense. To speak of natural selection as causing one array of individuals (such as the extremes on the right side of the third example in figure 1.1) to have offspring, and another (such as that on the left) not to, is a tautology. This fact, however, should not prevent us from attributing a major part of evolutionary change, viewed in retrospect, to natural selection.

Artificial selection, in contrast, is a purposeful process. It has a goal that can be visualized. It may, indeed, be the immediate cause of changes in the genetic composition of populations. The breeder or the experimenter can prevent at will certain individuals in the population under his control from reproducing themselves, thereby decreasing the frequency of their particular kind in the next generation. The fitness of the group of individuals selected, that is, the number of offspring it will leave, is predetermined by the selector to be greater than that of the group rejected.

At this point a comment on the measurement of fitness must be interjected. The number of descendants which characterizes the fitness of an individual may be counted in any of the successive generations, but it is usually most convenient to do so in the generation immediately following its own. For many purposes, particularly those concerned with mathematical formulations of evolutionary processes, it is best to express the fitness of a given zygote in terms of the relative number of zygotes it contributes to the next generation. Under artificial selection a more appropriate measure of the fitness of an animal chosen for reproduction is the absolute or relative number of offspring surviving to breeding age. The weakness of this method lies in the fact that it does not strictly measure the fitness of a given zygote or individual but depends on a combination of properties of the genotype of the parent (its fecundity) and of the genetic constitution of the offspring (viability of the young). But truncation of the population under artificial selection (see later) makes it possible to determine only the fitness of the individuals selected for mating. Hence the generation span considered must perforce be from breeding animal to breeding animal rather than from zygote to zygote.

Let us consider an experiment in which a flock of chickens is to be propagated without artificial incubation. What is the likely outcome of such a test in which natural selection is to occur without interference by man, at least with respect to reproduction? Presumably the females in the experimental flock which have the capacity to become broody and raise chicks will be favored to a degree over their non-broody flockmates. Yet since the latter will, no doubt, produce more eggs than the former, they will continue to be represented in the successive generations because the sitting hen will not discriminate between its own eggs and those of others. Eventually, some sort of balance between the advantages of egg number and broodiness will be attained, which might be described as "the result" of natural selection under artificial conditions.

Should artificial selection be applied for broodiness, the outcome would very likely not be the same. Since non-broody individuals can be entirely removed from the population, a flock in which all birds become broody is an attainable objective. In other words, the goal of artificial selection can be defined as a change in certain specific phenotypic traits of a population. The goal of natural selection, on the contrary, cannot be defined in any way except by saying that natural selection favors the fitter individuals. This statement is redundant except in a special sense deriving from Fisher's (1930) so-called fundamental theorem of natural selection, which states that the "rate of increase in fitness of any organism at any time is equal to its genetic variance in fitness at that time." This formulation can be interpreted as signifying that the "goal" of natural selection is to maximize fitness. In fact, however, as noted by Crow and Kimura (1956), fitness may decrease under natural selection in the presence of particular circumstances involving changes in the degree of inbreeding and in the selection coefficients (see section 5).

Although the distinction between natural and artificial selection is of major importance, it must be realized that these processes are not clear-cut alternatives but present a continuum. That is, although the extreme forms of the two types of selection are clearly distinguishable, there is an intermediate area where one form merges into the other without a threshold. This is particularly true when natural selection is allowed to occur under artificial or laboratory conditions.

The various differences between the two kinds of selection are more easily discerned when selection in nature is compared with artificial selection in the laboratory. For example, it has been estimated that in *rapidly* evolving lines of descent, changes in body length or shape are in the range of 1 to 2 per cent per million years (Haldane, 1949). This order of magnitude is of limited interest to a person practicing artificial selection. The purposive changes that he can obtain are of spectacular velocity compared to the rate deducible from the paleontological record. Yet in the wild, circumstances can no doubt cause a great acceleration in the average speed of evolutionary change, although on the farm a slowing down to a rate the breeder will not be able to distinguish from a dead stop can most certainly occur.

Natural selection, even under laboratory or farm conditions, can proceed without artificial selection. The latter, generally speaking, does not exist in pure form. Man can decide which individuals are to be discarded or prevented from reproducing themselves (i.e. which individuals will have a fitness of zero). Yet, among the individuals he wishes to be represented by offspring in the next generation, there may still be natural selection. Some of those chosen to be parents may be found to be sterile and thus are destined to join their culled contemporaries in leaving no progeny; among the others there may be a wide variation in fitness, attributable to differences between their genotypes. The fact that natural selection usually accompanies artificial selection may, as will be noted later, play a role of considerable importance in attempts to improve domestic animals.

In breeding practice it is common to cull or reject as parents a certain proportion of the population (as shown in figure 1.1). In nature such truncation may also happen, especially in species with a capacity for producing a large number of offspring. In species with a lesser reproduction potential, only a relatively small proportion of the population remains childless, and individual fitness tends to vary within narrow limits (see the reference to effective population size in section 17). Here, instead of truncation of the population into selected and rejected parts, selection must be represented by a continuous function, the probability of having offspring varying along the independent coordinate of the frequency distribution.

In the discussion to follow, artificial selection may be viewed as a two-step process. First there is the truncation between prospective parents and the rejects. This is the artificial selection that is being attempted. Then, among the parents chosen, variation in the number of offspring (with zero as the lower limit) will occur because of natural selection. This second step determines how much of the selection attempted has been realized. Only when the fitness values of selected parents do not vary, except due to operation of chance, can it be said that pure artificial selection has occurred.

We may list, simply as food for thought, a number of other factors contributing to the difference between the extremes of artificial and natural selection, without entering into details or precise qualifications:

1. Laboratory and experimental populations are usually maintained under reasonably constant environments. They are shielded from environmental fluctuations of various kinds and from predators; they are often provided with shelter and food. In nature, selection may operate much more strongly in favor of individuals able to fend for themselves and overcome unexpected stresses. This fact does not merely change the criteria by which fitness is determined in the two situations; it may be responsible for profound modifications in the whole genetic system of artificially selected populations.

2. Interspecific competition is part of natural selection but is seldom involved in artificial selection, especially in animals. Laboratory experiments concerned with interspecific competition have been performed, but in genetic improvement projects it is not an issue. Hence part of the environment (consisting of the competitors) which is itself modifiable by selection of the population under observation is absent in animal breeding.

3. Sexual selection as a rule does not play a significant role in breeding operations. When it does, it falls into the second (or natural selection) phase of the artificial selection process.

4. Under both natural and artificial selection, reversal of direction of selection pressure may occur. In the former, such irresolution is governed entirely by temporal changes in the contribution to fitness of the trait in question. In artificial selection, man's demands may be capricious and arbitrary, often leading to decreased reproductive fitness of the population, although, as already noted, there are also circumstances in which fitness under natural selection may be reduced.

5. In artificial selection, selective advantage is conferred on some members of the population in preference to others because they or their relatives exhibit certain phenotypic traits which are visible, measurable, or can be evaluated in some manner by the agency of control over relative reproductive rates, i.e. by the breeder. In natural selection, selective advantage is the property of the totality of all phenotypic expressions of the genotype, among which the decisive role as often as not is played by subtle differences at the physiological or biochemical level which cannot be discerned by the human observer and whose existence is often not suspected by him. A clear exposition of this point may be found in Dobzhansky's (1956) essay on what is an adaptive trait.

6. Members of many natural populations can to a certain degree choose their own environments. For domesticated organisms, microenvironments are (after proper experimental tests) made suitable for the average, or sometimes the poorest, genotype, but within a population all the individuals are, as a rule, confined to the same milieu.

Still other points bearing on this issue could be mentioned. The important consideration is that all the circumstances and facts noted are of a kind that leave an imprint on the various properties of populations exposed to them. The biology of any population, flock, or herd is, at the time of observation, the result of its genetic biography. The evolutionary forces which a population encounters in its history, and the peculiarities of the pattern of their action, cause it to differ from other populations. This is why it is often dangerous to attempt too broad generalizations about population behavior.

To close the discussion of the differences between artificial and natural selection, it may be noted that Lerner and Dempster (1948) suggested that the former can be made more efficient than the latter by the use of genotypic instead of phenotypic information. Their suggestion is valid only if efficiency is measured by the rate of immediate gains from selection. From the long-range operational point of view, selection for a single trait can be overefficient in the sense that undesirable changes in other characters (particularly in fitness) may occur, so that the population loses its plasticity or capacity of responding to varying environmental pressures (and for other reasons noted in Dempster's 1955b abstract). It is true that a breeder of domestic animals faced with such a problem can seek remedy by altering the mating system, by immigration, or by a suspension or relaxation of selection pressure. Not all these measures are open to nature. Therefore the efficiency of natural selection is not to be measured by rapidity of evolutionary change but by the possibilities of adjustment of the total phenotype to the new demands of the immediate situation without destroying the population's genetic reserves. As will be seen from later discussion, this conception is often valid for artificial selection as well.

Finally, it may be noted that for those who wish to explore more profoundly the whole question of artificial versus natural selection, acquaintance with the general problem of genetic structure of populations under domestic conditions as contrasted with that in nature is mandatory. Spurway's (1955) discussion of domestication in the light of evolutionary theory may be consulted for the purpose. The particular factors noted by her as operative in captivity but absent in the wild are: (a) an environment drastically different from the one in which prior selection for stable developmental patterns has occurred, (*b*) an initial reduction in the number of potential mates and hence inevitable inbreeding, and (*c*) artificial selection by man.   All three factors are, of course, germane to the central subject of this volume and will be referred to either directly or indirectly in the course of the following discussion.

4. The Gene Pool

So far selection has been considered to be based on differences between genotypes rather than between alleles.   However, before descendants of any genotype actually come into being, gametes must be formed.   During this process the diploid genotypic combinations, inseparably united in the soma of the parents, are dissolved.   The assemblage of different diploid genotypes, which is the Mendelian population, is rebuilt every generation from a collection of haploid gametes.

With respect to any locus, a description of the population in its diploid phase can be made in terms of frequencies of different genotypes which it contains.   Thus if three alleles (designated as 1, 2, and 3) segregate at a locus, the population can be specified by listing the proportions of individuals in it which have the respective genotypes of 11, 12, 13, 22, 23, and 33.

For the gametic population, the pertinent frequencies are not those of the diploid genotypes but of the alleles 1, 2, and 3.   If it is assumed that each parent has an equal probability of contributing progeny to the next generation, and that there is no selection between the gametes produced by each parent, the allelic frequencies characterizing the population of selected parents will be the same as those of the gametes to be produced by their unselected offspring.

The totality of alleles distributed among the members of an interbreeding population constitutes the *gene pool*.   The elaboration of the concept of such a pool has been one of the most fruitful developments in population genetics.   A great deal of the Mendelian algebra, on which our understanding of secular processes in genetics is based, depends on computations referring to the haploid stage rather than the diploid stage of the life cycle.   Indeed, quantitative descriptions of evolutionary processes are generally expressed in terms of changes in allelic frequencies.[3]   It is, however, also important to bear in mind that gametic frequencies do not always tell the whole story about a Mendelian population.   When mating

[3] Although most readers of this volume very likely lack, in common with the writer, the background to appreciate the complicated mathematical formulations which have been constructed for this purpose, they may find it of interest to examine them.   The paper of Kimura (1955a) provides possibilities for such intellectual window-shopping.

is at random and no further selection occurs between the time the parents are chosen and the time the offspring reach breeding age or are measured for a phenotypic trait, genotypic frequencies can be computed from allelic frequencies and vice versa. Otherwise, the simple relationship between them on which this computation is based does not necessarily remain valid.

Figure 1.3 schematizes the process of selection, showing for each generation the genotypic, as well as the allelic, frequencies. The upper three circles represent the gene pool for a locus at which three alleles (1, 2, and 3) are segregating in the original population considered. The three large circles in the lower row represent the population of genotypes in three successive generations. The smaller circles in the same row represent the individuals selected for reproduction. The numbers in the squares in the upper circles refer to the alleles present in the gene pool; their respective frequencies in each generation are also shown. The figures in the bottom row indicate frequencies of the genotypes described by the encircled two-digit numbers.

Many simplifying assumptions are made about the genetic picture in this illustration. Selection is taken to be all-or-none, i.e. all selected individuals are assumed to have an equal number of offspring, whereas the rejected individuals have none. The selective values of different genotypes are arbitrary, since they serve only the purpose of illustration. Mating is taken to be at random. No disturbing factors (e.g. mutation) are considered to be present, nor is sampling variability assumed to exist. This is a very important point to remember in looking at this figure, as well as at the later ones portraying various models. They represent abstractions, simplifications, or parts of a whole rather than reality.

In the first generation portrayed (n), 25 per cent of the individuals may be seen to be homozygous for allele 1, nine per cent for allele 2, and 4 per cent for allele 3. The proportions of the various types of heterozygotes are similarly indicated. It may be noted that individuals carrying allele 1 are preferred in the selection, since only genotypes 11, 12, and 13 are represented in the group destined to produce generation $n + 1$. It may also be noted that some preference for heterozygotes, at least for those of constitution 12, is manifested here, since this type is relatively more numerous among the parents selected than among the population from which they originate.

From the proportions shown for the parents, the composition of the gene pool represented by the gametes is readily computable. Thus, allele 1 is present in 60 per cent of all the gametes, allele 2 in 32 per cent, and allele 3 in 8 per cent.

Assuming, as already noted, random union of gametes, the composition

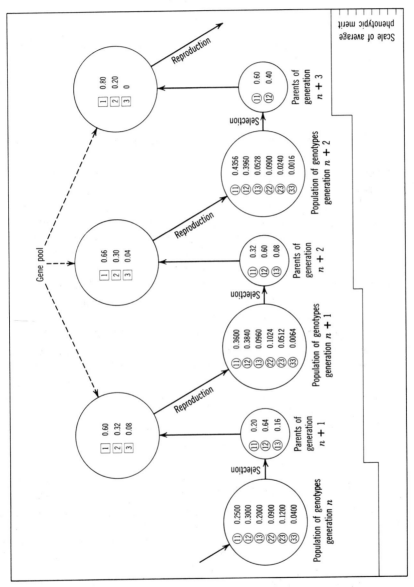

Figure 1.3.   The gene pool (see text for explanation)

of the next generation of phenotypes is easily calculated from the simple expression,

$$(p + q + r)^2 = p^2 + q^2 + r^2 + 2pq + 2pr + 2qr$$

where p, q, and r respectively represent the gametic frequencies of alleles 1, 2, and 3.   For example, the expected frequency of genotype 11 is 0.6^2 or 36 per cent, that of 12 is $2(0.60 \times 0.32) = 38.4$ per cent, and so forth. Of course, the more familiar form of the expression used here is the Hardy-Weinberg binomial,

$$(p + q)^2 = p^2 + 2pq + q^2$$

for situations in which only two alleles are present at a locus.[4]   This formula can be used for computing genotypic frequencies in generation $n + 3$, since by then one of the alleles has been completely eliminated from the gene pool.

The lines connected in a step-like fashion at the bottom of the figure depict the changes in the mean phenotypic values produced by selection in a hypothetical metric character.   For the sake of simplicity it is assumed that no dominance is exhibited by the locus in question, that the average environment is identical throughout the period chosen, and that the effect of substituting allele 1 for allele 2 on the expression of trait in question is double that of the substitution of allele 2 for allele 3.

Whether we refer to alleles or to genotypes, complete specification of the genetic composition of a population is an impossibility.   Even if all loci were identifiable, and it were known precisely how many different alleles (many of which, e.g. isoalleles, are ordinarily not distinguishable from each other) exist, an all-inclusive catalogue of allelic frequencies of a particular population would be so long as to lose any meaningfulness. On the genotypic level the numbers of potential diploid combinations is, of course, of such an immense magnitude (when several thousand loci are concerned) as to make a full census of frequencies impossible.

The gene pool and the system of genotypic frequencies are therefore usually described only with reference to one (as in figure 1.3) or few loci with a limited number of alleles rather than to a great many having an indefinitely great variety of alleles at each.   This procedure is adequate for traits having phenotypic expressions governed by a few major gene differences.   For metric and meristic characters, populations must be described in terms of means, variances, and, on occasion, other statistical

---

[4] When the population is inbred, these proportions must be modified.   Anticipating here the definition of the inbreeding coefficient, F (see box 4), we note that the respective proportions of the three genotypes stated in a general form which allows for inbreeding are $[p^2 + Fpq]$, $[2(1 - F)pq]$, and $[q^2 + Fpq]$.

attributes (e.g. skewness and kurtosis).   The distribution of phenotypic values of these traits is usually continuous instead of falling into distinctly separate classes, as is often true of characters based on gene differences at single loci.   Yet, underlying the continuous distributions of phenotypic expressions of metric traits, there are discrete genetic units.

It may be recalled that the great significance of Mendel's discovery was that it introduced the principle of *particulate inheritance*.   The unit of hereditary transmission, deduced to exist on the basis of a long series of experiments of Bateson and his associates, of the school of Morgan, and of many others came to be known by Johannsen's term, *gene*.   From the very early days of Mendelism, the particulate nature of hereditary units, i.e. the units of transmission of potentialities from parent to offspring, was open to confusion with the particulate nature of character expression. The word *factor* was often used synonymously with gene, although it was at the same time intended to convey the idea of a "unit" phenotypic trait (e.g. "rose-comb factor").

So long as experimenters or breeders dealt with all-or-none characters, i.e. traits generally described as qualitative, this ambiguity was a help rather than a hindrance.   In fact, it has been said that had Mendel measured and not merely counted, his name would be unknown to us. But as soon as continuously distributed characters were subjected to intensive study, it became necessary to distinguish between the units of transmission and those of character expression.   Whereas the former could be considered to be particulate in some manner (e.g. genes carried on separate chromosomes in organisms of interest to breeders very likely exhibit largely independent assortment), the latter, on the scale of phenotypic metric value, most often appeared to act in crosses in a blending fashion.

In reality, the difference between the two types of behavior is superficial. In both instances there is a unit of primary action with a specific function. When allelic (to take the simplest unit in general usage when discussing this question) substitution produces a clearly identifiable effect on the phenotype, a discontinuous distribution, or clear-cut unit-Mendelian behavior, is observable.   In continuously distributed characters, although each allele still has a specific primary function at the level of gene action, by the time the end product of development (fitness, body weight, number of eggs produced, average egg shape, etc.) is measured, the individual contributions of the separate loci are no longer discernible.   The physiological interactions between the primary and the subsequent products of gene action at the different loci are exceedingly complex.   The effects of many loci are interchangeable so far as the phenotypic scale of measurements is concerned.   As a result, the development of quantitative characters, initiated as it may be by particulate units, is a process not amenable to description in discrete terms.

This fact was responsible for the vigorous controversy between the Mendelians and the Biometricians at the beginning of the century. The satisfactory resolution of the apparent discrepancy between the model of inheritance of major character differentials and that of quantitative traits was due to the early work of Fisher (1918) and Wright (1921), followed by Haldane's studies (summarized by him in 1932). The treatment of metric traits on the basis of a particulate transmission of their hereditary components provides the fundamental basis of selection theory. There are, however, two qualifications that must be noted here.

First, there is, of course, no doubt that the cytoplasm and its inclusions play a role in heredity. But, with a few possible exceptions, effects of cytoplasmic differences in populations of higher animals sharing a common gene pool have not been demonstrated to be of particular significance in the variability of metric traits, especially of economic interest. Hence, although cytoplasmic transmission cannot be described by Mendelian algebra and therefore calls for a different treatment, no special consideration will be given to this phenomenon in this book apart from passing references to maternal effects.

The second qualification needs a somewhat more extended discussion. It refers to the fact that the meaning attached to the word *gene* has now become ambiguous. When used to describe an entity having the capacity to mutate, *gene* does not refer to the same physical unit which is considered in a discussion of crossing over. Nor is the unit of physiological action (at the level of the immediate gene product) necessarily coincident spatially with the unit of mutation or that of crossing over. It has indeed been suggested that different designations should be given to each type of entity (Benzer, 1957). This procedure would still leave the unit involved in evolutionary change unnamed.

It is the latter unit with which selection theory is basically concerned. It is different from the others in that it has much less permanence. At one time it may be a single locus (which might be defined as a section of a chromosome within which no crossing over occurs); at another, it may be a linked block of loci subject to breakup, or perhaps an entire chromosome, or, even, the whole complex of chromosomes derived from one parent. As yet, too little is known about the actual nature of segregating units in many of the species dealt with in artificial selection studies to permit generalization on this point to be made. It may, therefore, be best to remain at present intentionally vague in defining the ultimate factors dealt with in population genetics. Hence the terms allele or allelic frequency refer in the following dicussions to somewhat uncertainly delimited units of segregation and transmission. Whether they are really alleles in the classic sense of the word, or sections of chromosomes, or even more complex entities is, of course, a matter of importance in considering long-term behavior of populations. In the contemplation of long-range evolutionary processes, indiscriminate usage of *allele*, *block*, *chromosome*, *genome*, etc., must therefore be avoided. However, when only a few generations of segregation are considered (as is the rule in artificial selection of economic animals), the use of *allele* as a synonym for "unit of hereditary transmission" is less objectionable and in fact may be of great help in simplifying the examination of the principles and the consequences of selection.

Not too long ago the classical gene served as the basic unit of all the processes mentioned above. It was also supposed to have two different functions, an autocatalytic one of self-propagation, i.e. making replicates of itself, and a heterocatalytic one of manufacturing an enzyme or another product held responsible for certain biochemical or physiological processes in the organism containing it. It is not at all clear at present whether the autocatalytic and the heterocatalytic functions are exercised by identical "units." From the standpoint of selection, neither of these probably different units is the operational one. Mutations, at least those viewed as errors of self-reproduction, are part of the autocatalytic gene physiology; the pathway from the genotype to the phenotype is part of the heterocatalytic gene physiology. In as much as these aspects of genetics enter selection theory, they are of interest in the context of the present discussion. But the focus of our attention must be the segregating entity which may vary from time to time in its physical dimensions and which at this stage of our knowledge must perforce be left without precise definition.[5]

Because of these terminological difficulties, which unfortunately are more than merely semantic, a number of conventions about the gene and the genotype must be adopted. It shall then be assumed here that each allele has a measurable value for metric characters. This value need not be constant in all genetic combinations. The average (weighted for the number of doses present in an individual) that an allele has in all genotypes in the population carrying it is defined, following Fisher's usage, as its *genetic* or *additively genetic value*. The deviation from it exhibited by a particular individual carrying the given allele may be due not only to the effect of environment but also to gene interaction (to be discussed in section 9).

[5] Consideration of McClintock's (1956) "controlling elements," which induce hereditary modifications affecting gene action and apparently operate as integrated systems, may be premature in discussing broad features of selection. In time, however, they will have to be incorporated into the framework of population genetics.

Each particular genotype will be considered to have a constant *genotypic value* equal to the phenotypic average of all individuals of the particular genotype in the population. This definition implies that the environmental components of phenotypes are on the average zero. The deviation of any individual of a given genotype for the diploid genome from its genotypic value is then of environmental origin. Deviations from the genotypic value of a particular locus or group of loci may be due, in addition to such environmental effects, to genotypic effects of other loci.

5. Selection Progress

The effect on a metric trait of directional selection depicted in figure 1.3 may be judged from the scale of phenotypic merit appearing at the bottom of that diagram. It must be recognized, however, that underlying the changes produced by selection in the mean phenotypic expression of a character, there are, as shown in the figure, always changes in frequencies of genotypes or, even more basically, of alleles at relevant loci.

When many loci contribute to the genetic variability of a trait, it is usually impossible to estimate accurately either the respective frequencies of the segregating alleles or their total number. But granting certain simplifying assumptions, estimates may be obtained of such properties of quantitative traits as the number of loci, the average degree and direction of dominance, and the types of interlocus interaction. At the same time, there is not a single instance on record where an adequate allelic analysis of a continuously distributed trait in a domestic animal has been performed. The hope expressed by the early Mendelians that all characters are potentially analyzable in terms of individual loci, and occasionally still voiced by workers trained only in formal genetics, has long been extinguished in the minds of population geneticists. It is even improbable that practical techniques for the simultaneous determination of the number of effective units, the linkage relationships between them, the number and relative effects of different alternatives forms at each, and other features of the hereditary basis of any metric trait of larger animals will soon be forthcoming.

Nevertheless a theoretical model for frequency changes at single loci is essential for an understanding of the forces governing selection progress. In its barest form it must neglect the complications due to the environmental component of the phenotype and deal with the problem entirely on the genotypic level. For monogenic characters, not susceptible to modification by random environmental differences between individuals (e.g. differences in the exhibition Standard comb shapes of pure-bred poultry), such a model may correspond rather closely to reality.   In more complicated instances it will not.

One of the fundamental determinants of the rate at which allelic frequencies are changed under *selection pressure* is the degree of selective advantage that the preferred allele or genotype enjoys over the others, i.e. the amount of selection.   This factor can be measured in a number of ways.   Thus it may be convenient to describe the relative number of offspring produced by different genotypes by a system of *selection coefficients*, such as are given in box 1.   Under artificial selection, where only a

---

BOX I

Genetic Basis of Selection Progress

There are many sources of reference for general formulas describing rates of selection progress under differential reproduction at single loci. The three great pioneers of mathematical genetics, R. A. Fisher, Sewall Wright, and J. B. S. Haldane, have all presented and discussed various aspects of this question in many publications.   Li's (1955a) book cites much of their work and includes derivations of many expressions for determining changes in allelic and genotypic frequencies under various conditions.

The simplest model assumes random mating in an indefinitely large population of constant size, two alleles at a locus, and a constant selective advantage of the most desirable genotype over the others.   Let q stand for the frequency of allele A (under random mating, q^2 will be the frequency of genotype AA), and $1-q$ for the frequency of the alternative allele a.   When A is completely dominant, the respective reproductive rates of $AA:Aa:aa$ are as $1:1:1-s$, s being the selection coefficient.   It has a positive value if selection is directed toward the dominant and aa is discriminated against (when aa is lethal, s is at its maximum of 1).   The change per generation in the frequencies of A and a can be readily determined for any generation of selection when q and s are known.   The obvious procedure is to consider the gene pool derived from the selected parents in the following fashion.

Genotype	AA	Aa	aa	Total
Initial frequency	q^2	$2q(1-q)$	$(1-q)^2$	1
Selective value	1	1	$1-s$	–
Parents selected	q^2	$2q(1-q)$	$(1-q)^2(1-s)$	$1-s(1-q)^2$

The AA group of parents will contribute proportionally

$$q^2/[1 - s(1 - q)^2]$$

A gametes to the pool; the Aa parents will contribute

$$q(1 - q)/[1 - s(1 - q)^2]$$

gametes of the same kind; the aa individuals will produce only a-bearing gametes. Thus, the fraction of all gametes in the pool which contains the A allele will be the sum of these two expressions, equal to $q/[1 - s(1 - q)^2]$. The increase in the frequency of allele A from the parental to the filial generation is then

$$\Delta q = \frac{q}{1 - s(1 - q)^2} - q = \frac{sq(1 - q)^2}{1 - s(1 - q)^2} \tag{1}$$

showing the amount of change in q per generation of selection. Expressions for selection favoring the recessive allele and the heterozygote (see box 6) can be derived in the same manner.

Similar computations can also be made for selection between gametes or between non-interbreeding populations. Assuming a selective disadvantage of the $(1 - q)$ gametes carrying a (or populations homozygous for a) relative to the q gametes (or populations) carrying A, Δq is readily seen to be equal to

$$\frac{sq(1 - q)}{1 - s(1 - q)} \tag{2}$$

There is no evidence that gametic selection is of significance in domestic animals, although the possibility of its occurrence cannot be entirely neglected.

In figures 1.4–1.7 the selection coefficients vary with allelic frequency, becoming larger as the proportion of the desired type approaches the fraction of the population to be selected for reproduction. In a multigenic situation where the effect of allelic substitution at each locus is very small compared to the standard deviation, s is independent of q.

The simplest way to construct the curves in figures 1.4–1.7 is to calculate directly the composition of each successive generation. Formulas for estimating the number of generations needed to produce a given change in allelic frequency are given by Lush (1948). Haldane (1958) may be consulted for generalizations regarding the number of individuals that must be culled over all generations of selection to substitute one allele for another in a gene pool.

Expressions for the construction of selection curves without the various restrictions applied here are available. They may be used for populations of expanding or contracting size, for multiple alleles, inbreeding, different degrees of dominance, and in a variety of other situations. The works of Li and Lush cited contain these formulas.

fraction of the population is permitted to reproduce itself, *selection intensity* may be expressed as the proportion of the population thus favored. This value can also be translated into the *selection differential*, or the amount by which individuals chosen as parents exceed their generation with respect to the metric trait under selection. Consideration of the quantitative relationships between selection coefficients, selection intensity, and the selection differential must be deferred to chapter 4 (box 11).

Selection intensity depends among other things on the reproductive capacity of the species in question. If the population is to remain constant in size, selection intensity cannot be higher than the reciprocal of the maximum possible number of offspring per parent. Thus if each couple in a population with a monogamous system of mating can produce no more than ten offspring, then at least one-fifth of the parental population must be retained for breeding.

The illustrations of selection progress shown in figures 1.4–1.7 are based on theoretical considerations embodied by the model described in box 1. They portray changes in genotypic frequencies under a series of different conditions. Infinitely large populations, sexual reproduction, Mendelian behavior, and random mating are assumed. It is considered that there are two alleles, *A* and *a*, segregating at each locus. In every instance, the desirable allele has an initial frequency of 1 per cent. In the case of figure 1.7 where the heterozygote is preferred, either *A* or *a* can be taken as the rarer allele. Examples of two levels of reproductive capacity are given in each figure: (*a*) where one-tenth of the population of each sex has to be selected to maintain population size, i.e. where each monogamous couple is able to produce on the average 10 surviving offspring of each sex, or a total of 20; (*b*) where one-half of the population needs to be bred from, each couple having on the average 4 offspring reaching breeding age. The identical curves can illustrate selection progress in polygamous systems, but the reproductive rates which correspond to them are different from those given here.

The scale on the left shows in all but figure 1.7 the percentage of homozygotes of the desirable type present in each generation. The values for the solid lines can be read from it. They represent the squares of allelic frequencies, in accordance with the binomial expression already cited.

The dashed lines refer to the average desirability score (right-hand scale), which is based on somewhat different values in each instance. In figure 1.4, where no dominance is postulated and the selection is assumed to favor *A*, the respective values for the three genotypes are taken as

$$AA = 1$$
$$Aa = 0$$
$$aa = -1$$

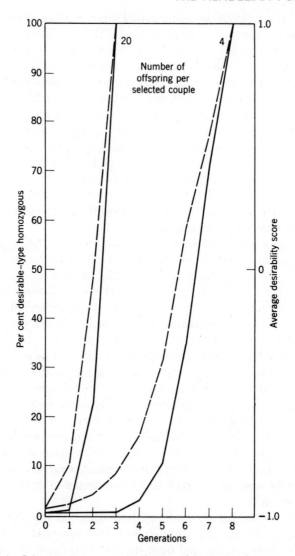

Figure I.4. Selection progress in the absence of dominance (see text and box I)

In 1.5, complete dominance is assumed, and accordingly the values are

$$AA \text{ and } Aa = 1$$
$$aa = -1$$

Since under complete dominance it is impossible to distinguish the desirable homozygote from the heterozygote, the later stages of selection (when the frequency of *A* becomes high) are in this example exceedingly inefficient. Although the average desirability score can reach unity, fixation of the allele selected for is a virtual impossibility without resorting to devices auxiliary to simple phenotypic selection (e.g. progeny testing). It might also be noted that after approximately ten generations, the actual

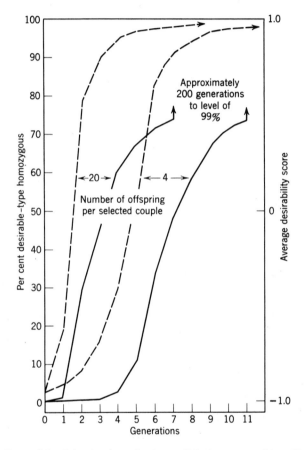

Figure 1.5. Selection for a dominant allele (see text and box 1)

reproductive rate is of less importance in determining the rate of progress than it is in the early stages of selection.

In figure 1.6, selection is directed toward the recessive type. The genotypic values are

$$AA \text{ and } Aa = -1$$
$$aa = 1$$

Here, because of the original rarity of *aa* individuals in the early generations, most of the parents bred from are of necessity of the undesirable
type (*AA* and *Aa*, being undistinguishable, enter the group of parents
proportionally to their numbers in each generation).   However, as soon
as the incidence of *aa* offspring reaches a level of about 5 per cent, rapid

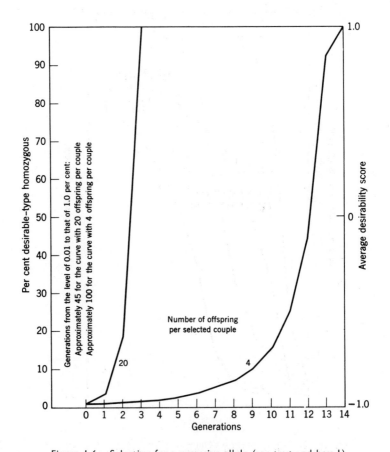

Figure 1.6.   Selection for a recessive allele (see text and box 1)

progress results.   Differences in reproductive rates are very important in
this instance.   Thus, at the point where some 3 per cent of the population
are of the *aa* type, only two generations of selection produce fixation when
10 per cent of the population suffice to reproduce it as against nine generations needed for fixation when only one-half of the population can be
discarded.

Figure 1.7 shows the selection progress attained when the heterozygote is preferred.   Here the genotypic values are taken as

$$Aa = 1$$
$$AA \text{ and } aa = -1$$

Because fixation is an impossibility when the heterozygote is the goal of selection, at best only 50 per cent of the population will be of the desired

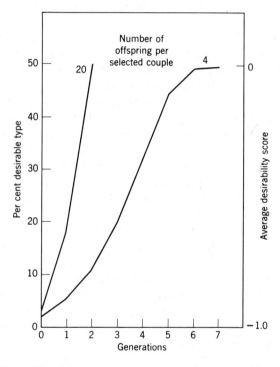

Figure I.7.   Selection for a heterozygote (see text and box I)

type, and the average score has zero as a maximum.   In this instance, no dashed lines are shown, since the curves for genotypic frequency and desirability score coincide.   It should be pointed out that a proportion higher than 50 per cent of desirable phenotypes in the population can be arrived at by the use of disassortative mating.   For example, if genotype *Aa* is the only one of value to the breeder, he can mate the *AA* individuals of each generation to the *aa* ones and thereby maintain a higher percentage of the heterozygotes in the population than is possible with random mating.

6. The Roles of Mutation and Migration

In short-range selection programs the process of mutation is of little importance because of its comparative rarity. This statement must be qualified in two respects. First, there are artificial means of inducing genetic changes. Many chemical and physical mutagenic agents are known, and it is not outside the realm of probability that sooner or later they will be resorted to, in order to replenish genetic variation exhausted by inbreeding.

The second qualification arises from the fact that genetic variation currently found in any population must have originated, even if only in the dimmest past, by a process of mutation. Strong evidence has been presented for the view that the most significant source of presently observed variation in many instances investigated is hybridization between normally non-interbreeding populations, rather than recent mutation (Anderson, 1953). Such process of infiltration of genetic material from one interbreeding group into another, as a rule separate from it, is termed gene flow, introgression, or introgressive hybridization (when the groups are considered to be distinct species). It is entirely possible that introgression has contributed a good share of the variation found in domestic animals. Yet the first appearance of difference between the various alleles at any given locus still needs to be explained, and mutation processes of some sort seem to be the only logical possibility at present. But the remoteness and rarity of such events as well as difficulties in recognizing and evaluating them, although not detracting from the very great importance of the subject of mutation in evolutionary studies, make it of only casual interest in a discussion centering on artificial selection.

Gene flow or migration between populations of the same species, race, or variety concerns us much more closely than mutation. The two kinds of selection used in breeding practice are (a) within populations, illustrations of which have already been given, and (b) between populations. The latter consists of discarding populations judged to be inferior by whatever criterion of selection is adopted, and of propagating the superior ones without interchange of genetic material between the groups compared. In mathematical terms selection between non-interbreeding populations can be described in the same manner as selection between gametes in a gene pool (see box 1).

A more general model is one in which both intrapopulation selection and interpopulation selection play a part. For the former the units of selection are alleles, individuals, and families; for the latter they are lines, strains, breeds, and interbreeding isolates of higher categories. In succeeding chapters the details of intrapopulation selection are dealt with for the most part.   There shall also be occasion to consider some of the forms of selection between such non-interbreeding groups as inbred lines, and

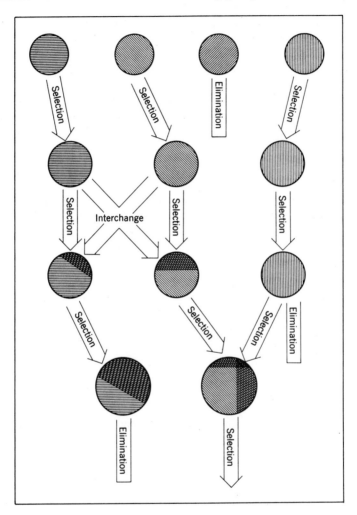

Figure 1.8.   Selection between and within populations (see text)

some limited examples of the situation in which selection on both intra- and interpopulation bases occurs.   However, detailed quantitative consideration of their joint action combined with migration is difficult. Hence, only a schematization of the elements of a model which includes both processes is presented in figure 1.8.

The top row shows four isolates or previously non-interbreeding groups. Within three of them selection is initiated, and the fourth one, presumably inferior for the trait under selection, is discarded. The overall population size is taken to be constant in each generation, the circles representing the different groups increasing in area as a population is eliminated. Thus each remaining isolate becomes larger at the expense of those culled.

To produce the third generation, reciprocal introduction of genetic material between the first two remaining populations is made. At the same time, selection within populations is continued in all groups left. In the following generation, one-way migration is depicted, with elimination of the non-migrating remainder of the population supplying the immigrants.

Only a single group is continued beyond the fourth generation. However, it is assumed to have incorporated some genetic material from two of the others. Exactly how much they have contributed to the gene pool from which the following generations are to arise depends on the amount of intrapopulation selection exercised. In practice the fate of the migrating alleles can be followed only if they are individually recognizable. For continuously distributed traits only very rough estimates of the effects of migration can be made. Thus, in general, although both mutation and migration provide the raw material for selection and their significance in evolutionary change cannot be denied, the scope of the discussion undertaken here limits the consideration of these processes to occasional mention.

7. Coadaptation

A gene pool that maintains a constant composition through a series of generations is said to be in *equilibrium*. The nature of Mendelian inheritance leads, in the absence of disturbing pressures, to constancy of gene frequencies and genotypic combinations. This is clear from the Hardy-Weinberg law, which, however, has validity, as any other statistically formulated principle, only within limits of sampling error. When disturbing pressures operate, they may balance each other so as to produce an equilibrium state. The counterpoise between selection and mutation pressure (see Li, 1955a) is a classical example of such a situation. When pressures in some directions are stronger than in the others tending to counterbalance them, the composition of the gene pool changes. These pressures can be of diverse kinds and may be classified in a variety of ways. Among them is Wright's (1955) systematic listing of the various forces of evolutionary significance which amended his earlier treatments of the subject.

For the present purposes, it will suffice to make note only of three general kinds of factors operating to produce evolutionary change: (a) directed processes which effect a determinate change (recurrent mutation, migration and hybridization, and selection); (b) random processes whose variance is determinate (including fluctuations in the directed processes and accidents of sampling); (c) unique events (i.e. those that occur only once and hence cannot be incorporated into probability-based prediction equations). The last category includes the occurrence of single favorable mutations, accidental reductions of the population to a very small number of individuals, the swamping of the original population by mass immigration, "unique selection incidents," and similar phenomena.

Selection falls into the first of these classes. Wright defines it, as has already been noted in section 2, by exclusion. That is to say, selection is considered by him as comprising all directed processes not covered by the terms mutation and migration. It differs from these phenomena in one very important respect: selection can operate only when at least two different alleles are present at a given locus in the population. Thus it depends on the existence of genetic variation, a topic to which chapter 3 is devoted.

The changes under selection which have been illustrated so far refer to allelic frequencies at single loci. In reality it is unlikely that selection can very often be such a simple process. Mendelian populations share a gene pool which contains variants at numerous loci. Their frequencies are not independent of each other. The gene pool has a delicately balanced structure, and its components are, in Dobzhansky's term, coadapted. Hence, displacement of allelic frequencies at one locus by selection or by another force is bound to produce in its wake a displacement of allelic frequencies at other loci. The secondary effect may in turn generate further changes at the original locus, until either the old balance is regained or a new one achieved.

The process of coadaptation is probably a continuous one. It is reflected by the great fluidity of the genetic composition of Mendelian populations, which, in spite of the fact that each population may be uniform and constant in phenotypic appearance, are usually genetically extremely heterogeneous. Under artificial selection, or, indeed in nature, it may happen that the selection presssure applied too strongly to some single trait outstrips the coadaptation process. The lag may be so great as to result in an unbalanced population which is in danger of extinction.

The evolutionary significance of the concept of coadaptation cannot be overstressed (see Dobzhansky, 1955, for a review, and Wallace and Vetukhiv, 1955, for some specific evidence). In general, it is based on selective processes which build up and maintain a gene pool of alleles acting in a synergistic manner to produce desirable genotypic combinations, and which endow the genetic system of a population with the property of *integration* (Darlington, 1939). Coadaptation exists on two different levels. The interchromosomal one refers to interdependences between frequencies of alleles or more complex structures on non-homologous chromosomes (e.g. White, 1957); the intrachromosomal level deals with single loci or with segments and arms of a particular chromosome.

At the interchromosomal level, shifts in frequency of an allele at one locus may be due to the origin of a new mutant on a different chromosome, with which the allele in question "nicks" or combines well. Selection acts not to *adapt* the gene frequency at a given locus to the background or residual genotype (all other loci) but to *coadapt* all loci on all chromosomes, so that a coherent gene pool is created and perpetuated.

On the intrachromosomal level, coadaptation may be of two kinds. One, which may be called *internal*, relates to the accumulation of alleles at neighboring loci or along a chromosome segment. For instance, the sequence of four loci of $a_1b_2c_1d_3$ may gradually replace, by the process of internal coadaptation, segments of the constitution $a_1b_3c_2d_3$ and $a_2b_2c_1d_1$.

The second type of intrachromosomal coadaptation may be called *relational*. It refers to the attainment of optimal combinations not along a stretch of a chromosome but between homologous loci in the diploid state. Thus, maintenance of heterozygosity at a given locus by selection in a population may be described as a result of one form of relational coadaptation. It is this type which has been particularly emphasized by Dobzhansky and which more than any other factor makes the gene pool an organized whole.

Coadaptation was a term used by Darwin (1872) in discussing correlated modification of different structures of an organism. His ideas about the interdependence of various properties of a harmonious living being form a phenotypic counterpart of gene-pool coadaptation. The general notion may be extended to embrace all types of mutual adjustments between the various elements of a genetic system (Darlington's, 1956, *mutual selection*). Whenever a novel pressure of any origin is exerted in an interbreeding group, the various characteristics of the breeding structure of the population must undergo a change to regain balance. A simple example is provided by restrictions in population size imposed by domestication or other catastrophic changes in the environment. If the population is to survive, it must have or develop an increased tolerance to inbreeding and attain a reintegration of genetic structure. Indeed, no radical transformation of a population, whether occurring very slowly or because of a sudden genetic revolution, to use Mayr's (1954) term, can take place without coadaptation in this broad sense.

Selection imposed by man on laboratory or farm animals can be a strong disturbing pressure. Integrating processes in populations subjected to artificial selection must then, like coadaptation of the gene pool in the narrow sense, be continuous. In order to understand the forms they can take, and the mechanism underlying them, it is necessary to inquire into the relations between the constituent units of the gene pool on the one hand and the different parameters of the genetic system on the other. The next chapter is intended to provide a basis for such exploration.

2
Polygenic Inheritance

> This is an extremely
> intricate subject.

It has already been noted that the several entities to which the term *gene* was originally applied must be viewed today as being different from each other, depending on whether the unit of mutation, crossing over, or physiological function is considered. To make a distinction between these operationally defined factors in population genetics would be an exceedingly delicate task. The source of the difficulty is that all three aspects of the gene enter the description of evolutionary processes in populations. It may be worthwhile for purposes of emphasis to restate here the issues raised by this fact and already commented upon in the previous chapter.

The basic unit of Mendelian algebra, the tool that permits prediction and quantification of population properties, is the unit of segregation. This is ordinarily viewed as a particle transmitted from diploid parent to diploid offspring through a haploid gamete. It is capable of exact self-reproduction but occasionally fails in this enterprise or undergoes a change earlier (mutation unit). It is potentially independent of all other such particles, although it enters the gamete as part of a linked system (unit of crossing over). Substituting an alternative allelic form for a particle in a given genotype has some repercussions on the phenotypic level (functional unit).

The unit of segregation thus includes all three operational features of the gene. Vague as the concepts behind such a unit may be, it is still the most adequate one available for dealing with Mendelian populations. At least for the present we must then continue to refer to genes, loci, and alleles, even if we are not certain of the physical properties of the entities thus described. If it mitigates matters, it may be pointed out that such usage is consistent with Johannsen's intent, although this consoling fact may in a cynical way be tantamount to disavowal of a half-century of research since his day.

The allele, although it is the smallest and most permanent (in the sense of preserving its identity from generation to generation until a mutational event occurs) unit of evolutionary import, is by no means the only one that needs to be taken into consideration. Contiguous loci may form *blocks* of alleles which are of lesser permanency, since they are subject to change not only as a result of mutation of each of their components but also following crossing over between them. In terms of a few generations at a time, such blocks may act as single segregating units or as units of physiological function. Selection may operate directly to maintain the blocks intact or may promote various devices, including tighter linkage, inversions, and any other mechanisms for making crossing over non-random, for the same purpose.

Chromosomal segments stretching to include whole arms, entire chromosomes, groups of chromosomes, and indeed entire genomes may segregate as units and keep their identity for periods of variable duration. In fact, individuals, inbred lines, and total populations or gene pools may be viewed as complex evolutionary units. The contents of a gene pool are, of course, constantly being replaced, but just as each organism continuously renews its component cells without losing its individuality, so does a population retain its specificity throughout its lifetime. It is then a sort of river flowing in both space and time.

Within the scope of the discussion undertaken here, the allele, the block, and the population are of special significance. We have already seen how the first may be used as a unit in describing populations under selection. We have also referred casually to the problem of selection *between* populations. This leaves blocks, and in particular those described as *polygenic blocks*, to be brought under scrutiny.

8. Polygenic Balance

The traits familiar to students of elementary genetics are conditioned by genetic differences at one or two loci. Monogenic and digenic inheritance may be considered as limiting cases of multigenic inheritance, which are demonstrable in higher organisms only under special circumstances, such as a uniform genetic background. The majority of characters of significance in evolution and in selection practice, on the other hand, exhibit what may be described as *polygenic* inheritance.

In the early days of Mendelism, the term *multiple factors* was used to designate genes held responsible for the expression of continuously distributed characters dependent on differences at many loci. However, a number of features in the inheritance of many multigenic traits which escaped notice in the necessarily unsophisticated age of the multiple-factor theory have since come to light. Hence it may be desirable to differentiate between the earlier concept of multiple factors and that of polygenic inheritance.

The multiple-factor approach viewed the genotypes for a given quantitative character as being simply equal to the sum of the effects of a definite number of genetic differences. No coordinated genetic system was visualized. Each of the loci contributing to the total was thought to be potentially identifiable as to location and specific effect. It is possible that there are metric traits which are subject to this type of genetic control (particularly polyploids, in which duplicate genes may be common), but it is not likely that many of them are encountered in selection practice.

In contrast, polygenic inheritance is observed in many important economic characters which have a continuous or a discontinuous (*all-or-none* or *threshold* traits) distribution on a phenotypic scale of measurement. There is no general agreement about the precise nature of polygenes, the term often being applied in a sense diverse from that of Mather (1943), who introduced it into current literature. For the purposes of the discussion to follow, polygenic inheritance will be considered to exhibit a number of particular features. *It should be clearly understood that it is a matter of convenience to postulate the existence of these properties which, although probable on the basis of experimental evidence, have by no means been unequivocally demonstrated as generally present in the transmission of metric traits.* The main phenomena characteristic of polygenic inheritance are assumed to be:

1. Segregation occurs at an indefinitely large number of loci affecting the character.

2. The effects of allelic substitution at each locus are trivial compared to the total amount of observed variation in the character and may sometimes be comparable to the effects of isoallelic differences (i.e. they are detectable only under special circumstances).

3. The phenotypic effects of substitution at different loci are interchangeable, in the sense that identical phenotypes may be produced by a

large variety of genotypes, even in the absence of dominance, epistasis, and environmental differences.

4. The phenotypic expression of polygenic characters is subject to considerable modification by differences in the intangible environment to which the members of a given population are exposed.

5. Most populations carry great reserves of hereditary variability with respect to polygenically inherited traits; that is, they are genetically heterogeneous.

6. Polygenes tend to occur in balanced systems, the polygenic block being of particular significance in this connection.

7. Contrary to many interpretations of polygenic inheritance (including that in the original formulation of the concept), polygenes have pleiotropic effects and can act both as modifiers or suppressors of other genes and systems or as determinants of variation of traits for which no major gene differences are demonstrable.

Most of these points are sufficiently clear not to need amplification here. The concept of polygenic balance, however, may be elucidated further by illustration. Figure 2.1, which is designed to do so, is, together with much of the other material on polygenic theory, based on Mather's analysis of quantitative inheritance developed by him over the past decade and a half (a recent summary of his views appeared in 1954).[1]

A great variety of ways for the illustration of the basis of genetic balance is possible. The examples chosen for diagrammatic representation here are derived from a very simple model. They refer to a chromosome segment or polygenic block of four contiguous loci. At each locus, two alternative alleles, respectively designated by letters with and without subscripts, are found. A balanced genotype is one that produces an optimal phenotypic expression of whatever character is considered to be affected by the block pictured. Presumably the scale on which merit is to be judged is based on the contribution that the phenotypic property concerned makes to fitness. There are many implications in this definition, particularly where fitness may be determined arbitrarily by artificial selection, but we need not consider them at this point.

In the example it is assumed that genetic balance is attained under two stipulations: (a) heterozygosity at each locus (a type of relational balance) and (b) an internal balance within each block. The first provision then

---

[1] Mather's original theory proposed that polygenes differed from genes with major effects not only in some of the properties already described, but in their location on the chromosome. The view taken in the present volume does not acknowledge such differences in location to be necessary, since the same loci may have major effects on one trait and act as polygenes with respect to other characters, especially in different genetic backgrounds.

calls for each allele designated by a letter without a subscript to be balanced by one with a subscript on the homologous chromosome. The second condition demands that each of the blocks entering a diploid combination contain either all alleles denoted by subscripts or none.

In the upper left corner a diploid which is perfectly balanced both internally and relationally is portrayed. An example of unbalance of both

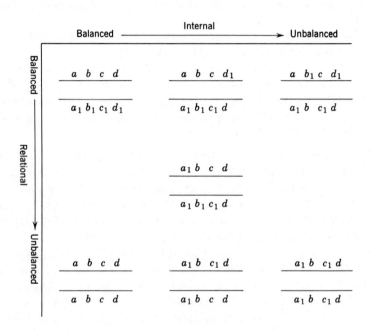

Figure 2.1. Examples of polygenic balance

See text for full explanation. Since a general model is being illustrated, capital and small letters are not used in allelic designations to avoid implications of dominance. Similarly, plus and minus signs might connote special quantitative relations such as intermediate or maximum optima and therefore are not employed. Mather (1943) presented a more complex theoretical example of balance involving both dominance and quantitative interactions.

types is shown at the lower right corner, and some of the number of possible intermediate conditions appear elsewhere in the figure.

Movement from a state of internal balance to that of unbalance and in the opposite direction can occur by means of crossing over. Once balanced blocks arise, they may be protected from disintegration by restrictions on further crossing over within them. As long as a block behaves as a unit, it may carry reserves of *potential* variability, which can be released by crossing over and made *free*. This process, of course, requires that homologous blocks containing different alleles be maintained in the population, perhaps as a result of relational coadaptation.

Relational balance is a property of the diploid organism, and thus its presence or absence in an individual is governed by chance at the time of union of gametes, unless preferential fertilization occurs. But selection can maintain the gene pool frequencies of internally balanced blocks at levels that will insure a high proportion of relationally balanced individuals in the population.

It should be understood that a vast number of complications, such as the presence of multiple alleles, variation in penetrance, the fact that each block must undoubtedly exhibit pleiotropy, if for no other reason than because of intercalation of loci affecting different traits, the complexity of fitness (the criterion of selection) as a character, and many others, make the diagram appear as a rather naive picture of the situation. Despite this limitation, the figure does show in a primitive fashion the basis of polygenic balance.

Polygenic inheritance must not be viewed as a mutually exclusive alternative to monogenic behavior. There are intermediate forms of conduct in the continuum between the two. It seems highly probable that in successful populations the possibility of passage from one extreme form of heredity to the other is kept open for many traits. If the genetic background consisting of modifiers of a given phenotypic expression is made uniform, a polygenic block may act as a single Mendelian unit. The breaking up of the block or the introduction of new modifiers may cause reversion to a complex pattern of segregation.

In some circumstances monogenic Mendelian behavior may be of advantage to the population. Thus a lethal genetic combination can be eliminated by selection more rapidly when it is conditioned by a difference at one locus than when conditioned by polygenes. On the other hand, in fluctuating environments the direction of selection for many quantitative traits may be drastically reversed every few generations. Should such characters behave as if dependent on single gene differences, selection pressures might drive a population so close to fixation that it could become extinct when reversal of the direction of the pressure occurred. Polygenically inherited traits protect the population against this danger by each of the features previously enumerated as being characteristic of them.

It is readily conceivable that the environment of a population may alter, or that the gene pool may change (for instance as a result of immigration) in such a way that, for a given character, the form of behavior which was originally advantageous becomes disadvantageous. A polygenic system may in consequence undergo modification and behave in a monogenic or digenic fashion. Reciprocally, a gene pool containing major gene differentials may accumulate so many modifying genes as to acquire a polygenic system. This process of course can be reversible. An example of change from polygenic to major gene behavior as a result of selection and modification of the breeding system is given by Dubinin's experiment on extra veinlets in Drosophila (summarized in Lerner's, 1954, book). Flux of this kind may account for discrepancies between the behavior of "good" genes in the laboratory and their likely comportment in the wild (see the discussion by Wallace and his collaborators, 1953).

Genetic differences at all loci, whether kept within a block or not, must have pleiotropic effects on the level of phenotypic observation (see Caspari, 1952, for a general review of this subject). Each block then affects more than one trait. The consequences of this fact are: first, that the polygenic balance is a compromise between possibly conflicting pressures on different traits, determined by the relative contribution that each makes to fitness; second, that gene interaction, as was astutely pointed out by Timofeeff-Ressovsky more than thirty years ago (Chetverikov, 1926), is a logically inescapable phenomenon, and third, as Darwin (1872) emphasized, that pressures applied to one character must of necessity have genetic effects on others.

9. Gene Interaction

The principle of internal balance suggests possible interdependence between either the immediate or the indirect products of genes at the different loci comprising a block.[2] Similarly, relational balance indicates that alleles at a given locus in a heterozygous state exhibit *interaction*, a term which has had for some time two different meanings. Thus, in considering the properties of a phenotype, it is often said, in a biological sense, that they are the result of interaction between genotype and environment. This formulation is usually interpreted to mean that both nature and nurture act in determining phenotypic differences between individuals. When the term "interaction" is used in the statistical sense, the above statement may or may not be true, depending on the character of the genetic and the environmental contributions to the phenotypic variance.

Environment has already been defined in section 2 so as to include all sources of phenotypic variation, except that deriving from genotypic

[2] Compare the biochemical evidence summarized by Demerec (1956) for *Salmonella typhimurium*.

differences between individuals. This definition is equivalent to the symbolic statement that

$$P = Ge + E$$

or in terms of variances,

$$\sigma_P^2 = \sigma_{Ge}^2 + \sigma_E^2 + 2r_{GeE}\sigma_{Ge}\sigma_E$$

A given genotype does not always produce a constant effect in every environment but may react differently under different external conditions. The variance generated by the differential responses of a genotype to the intangible elements in the presumably uniform environment to which a population is exposed is included in the σ_E^2 fraction of phenotypic variation. But if the milieu of a population consists of a set of different specifiable subenvironments, the right-hand part of the expression above may be found to be less than the actual phenotypic variance. The amount by which the two differ represents statistical interaction between genotype and environment. The expression for phenotypic variation then becomes

$$\sigma_P^2 = \sigma_{Ge}^2 + \sigma_E^2 + 2r_{GeE}\sigma_{Ge}\sigma_E + f(GeE)$$

in which (a) the meaning attached to E has become broadened to include tangible as well as intangible environment, and (b) the last factor is written as $f(GeE)$ in order to avoid any implications about the kind of interaction present.

The genotypic variance (σ_{Ge}^2), the environmental variance (σ_E^2), and the interaction term $f(GeE)$ can all be partitioned in diverse ways. To illustrate the compound nature of $f(GeE)$, a situation in which two sources of interaction are found may be examined. First, let there be a number of *locations* (e.g. farms where domestic animals are raised or bottles in which fruit flies are kept), and second, let the data on the population be gathered in several years. The behavior of three genotypes (A, B, and C), each grown in two different locations (X and Y) in two years (1 and 2), is schematized in figure 2.2. Four basic types of results with respect to the phenotypic performance may be obtained. In the upper left cell no interaction is demonstratable, since the order of merit of A, B, and C, as judged by the length of the blocks representing each, remains the same in both locations in both years. In the upper right cell the phenotypes corresponding to each genotype differ between locations but not between years, indicating genotype-location interaction. The remaining two cells can be readily interpreted in a similar manner.

In this example reversal of rank is used as an indication of statistical interaction. This, however, is not a necessary condition. Genotype A may be relatively less successful in one environment than in another but still outrank genotype B in both. This type of statistical interaction is of no consequence to a breeder wishing to chose the genotype best suited for each of several locations,[3] although it has some effect on the accuracy of the prediction of selection response within one location.

Interactions between parts of a genotype are also subject to two interpretations. Gene interaction in the strictly biological sense presumably

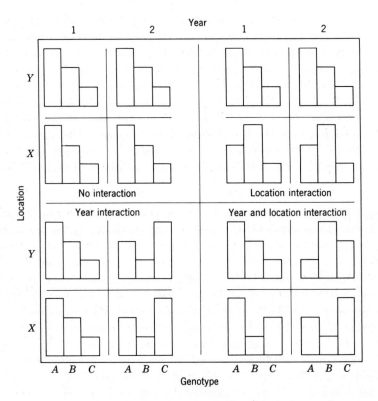

Figure 2.2.   Genotype-environment interaction (see text)

means that the genetic part of a given phenotype is determined by the products of many genes, the joint action of which contributes to its expression. The statistical meaning is more subtle. If a given allelic substitution produces a constant effect, irrespective of the allele at the same locus in the homologous chromosome, and independently of the

[3] Haldane (1946) may be consulted for a general examination of the problem of biological interaction between genotype and environment. Weber and Le Roy (1956) discuss the statistical aspects of the question. They fail, however, to distinguish interaction with reversal of rank (which may on occasion disappear when a transformed scale is adopted) from the potentially more important interaction with rank reversal.

rest of the genotype, no interaction in the statistical sense exists. When, however, the magnitude of the effect of substitution on the total genotype varies, depending on whether or not it is made in a homozygote, interaction due to *dominance* is present. Similarly, when the contribution of an allele is affected by the genetic contents of other loci, the interaction thus generated is said to be *epistatic*.

The variance traceable to the differences between the average values of the different alleles in all genetic combinations in which they appear is termed the *additive* portion of the total genotypic variance. The remainder forms the *non-additive* part which is due to interactions. The additive variance is often referred to as *genetic*, in contradistinction to *genotypic*, which includes both the additive and the non-additive fractions. *Additively genetic* may be preferred to *genetic*, in order to avoid confusion with the use of this adjective in the broad sense (e.g. as against non-genetic).

The interactions, as has been noted, can be due either to dominance, i.e. to variation produced by the fact that the value of an allele may depend on the identity of the other member of the allelic pair of a diploid, or to epistasis, i.e. to the joint variation of alleles at two or more loci. Epistatic interaction in turn can be of three kinds: (*a*) that between additive values of different loci, (*b*) that between their additive values and their dominance contributions to variance, and (*c*) that between their dominance contributions. Further subdivisions of variation caused by epistatic deviations from additively genetic values can be made according to the number of interacting loci. Such higher-order interactions, however, are of limited interest within the framework of our discussion. Indeed, for many of our purposes all epistatic interactions may be considered in a single category.

Thus, instead of writing

$$\sigma^2_{Ge} = \sigma^2_G + \sigma^2_D + \sigma^2_{GG} + \sigma^2_{GD} + \sigma^2_{DD}$$

where σ^2_G and σ^2_D stand respectively for additively genetic and for dominance variance, and the other terms for the different kinds of epistatic interaction, we may gather the latter under σ^2_I and write more simply

$$\sigma^2_{Ge} = \sigma^2_G + \sigma^2_D + \sigma^2_I$$

The term epistasis was originally used by Bateson to describe a specific kind of non-allelic biological interaction. It has now assumed a wider meaning to include all types of interdependence of gene effects, except that involving dominance (of which overdominance is, of course, a special case). But the respective usages of the term "epistatic interaction" in the biological and in the statistical senses are still unlike. In a way, the concepts behind the two are complementary since description of gene action in terms of one or the other alone does not furnish complete information about a given genetic situation.

For instance, if a 15:1 ratio is displayed by an F_2 generation of a diploid cross, it is assumed that the loci involved are *duplicate* in action. Similarly, a 9:7 ratio leads us to regard the loci in question as *complementary*. On the basis of the Batesonian approach, some idea of what the dominant alleles at the given locus actually do can be formed. In the 9:7 example, they probably produce different substances, both of which are needed for the phenotypic manifestation of some property. In the 15:1 example, identical substances, or substances interchangeable in effect, are presumably produced by the dominant alleles at both loci. However, non-statistical statements of this kind cannot tell us, in the absence of further information, what the effect of selection of a given intensity may be in a population segregating for these loci.

On the other hand, a description of interactions in statistical terms (boxes 2 and 3) can lead to predictions of population behavior under selection but tells us nothing at all about the physiology of action of the genes involved. Exactly the same proportions of additive variance and

---

BOX 2

Partitioning Two-Locus Interaction

The following may serve to illustrate the procedure of dividing genotypic variance into additive, dominance, and epistatic components. Two independent segregating loci are considered. The distribution of individuals in the population for the first locus is taken in the frequencies of

$$AA \quad - \quad 25 \text{ per cent}$$
$$Aa \quad - \quad 50 \text{ per cent}$$
$$aa \quad - \quad 25 \text{ per cent}$$

It is also assumed that the group investigated, rather than showing a Hardy-Weinberg equilibrium at the second locus, contains only two genotypes, Bb and bb, in equal proportions. The accompanying table gives the arbitrary values assigned to individuals of different genotypes.

Genotype for Locus $A - a$	Genotypic Value for Locus $A - a$	Additional Genotypic Effect		Total Genotypic Value	
		Bb	bb	Bb	bb
AA	1	3	-3	4	-2
Aa	1	2	-2	3	-1
aa	-3	1	-1	-2	-4

The computations to be made are summarized in the following table.

Geno-types	Fre-quency	Geno-typic Values	Addi-tive Values	Devia-tions	Computed Values Allowing for			
					Dominance		Epistasis	
					Values	Devia-tions	Values	Devia-tions
BbAA	1	4	4	0	3	1	5	−1
BbAa	2	3	2	1	3	0	2	1
Bbaa	1	−2	0	−2	−1	−1	−1	−1
bbAA	1	−2	0	−2	−1	−1	−1	−1
bbAa	2	−1	−2	1	−1	0	−2	1
bbaa	1	−4	−4	0	−5	1	−3	−1
Variance		7.5	6.0	1.5	7.0	0.5	6.5	1.0
Type of variance		Total	Additive	Non-additive	Total less epis-tasis	Epis-tatic	Total less domin-ance	Domin-ance

Thus of the total variance, 6.0/7.5, or 80 per cent, is additive, with dominance contributing 13.3 and epistasis 6.7 per cent.

In this table, the additive values are computed by summing the appropriate weighted average genotypic values of the individual alleles A (1), a (−1), B (3), and b (−1). To obtain computed values allowing for dominance, the $B − b$ additive values are combined with the $A − a$ genotypic values; the computed values allowing for epistasis are obtained from the combination of $B − b$ genotypic with $A − a$ additive values.

---BOX 3---

Examples of Gene Interaction

Figures 2.3 and 2.4 give examples of gene interaction. The first shows the genotypic values at two loci, X and Y, at each of which two alleles, 1 and 2, segregate. Five different models are examined: (a) fully additive gene action, (b) complete dominance at both loci, (c) overdominance (superiority of the heterozygote), (d) epistasis without dominance, (e) epistasis combined with dominance.

The relative proportions of variance contributed by the different types of interaction depend on allelic frequency. A locus at which dominance is present acts in a nearly fully additive manner when the dominant allele ·is rare. When the recessive is rare, and hence appears mainly in heterozygotes, most of the variance will, on the other hand, be of the dominance type. From Wright's (1935a) analysis it may be seen that if q is taken as the frequency of the recessive allele, the proportion of the total genotypic variance which is due to dominance is $(1 − q)/(1 + q)$.

Given the arbitrarily assumed allelic frequencies shown in the accompanying table, it is possible to compute in a manner somewhat similar to that indicated in box 2 the respective proportions of each type of variance. It should, of course, be understood that genotypic variation uncomplicated by environmental components is dealt with here.

Allelic Frequencies			Model		
	a	b	c	d	e
$X_1 = Y_2 = 0.5$					
% additive	100	67	31	94	16
% dominance	0	33	69	0	79
% epistatic	0	0	0	6	5
$X_1 = Y_2 = 0.25$					
% additive	100	77	68	96	40
% dominance	0	23	32	0	56
% epistatic	0	0	0	4	4
$X_1 = Y_2 = 0.75$					
% additive	100	77	27	96	53
% dominance	0	23	73	0	40
% epistatic	0	0	0	4	7

Figure 2.4 is taken from Kempthorne (1955a) who, following the principles discussed by Cockerham (1954), illustrated the actual computation technique to be used for partitioning the epistatic variance into its components. The model shown in the figure assumes three loci X, Y, and Z, with two alleles at each. The genotypic values of the carriers of the 27 different genetic constitutions are depicted graphically. The lower part of the figure shows the variance separated into its main parts with epistatic variance further subdivided.

The symbols should be clear, with the subscript G referring to the additively genetic fraction and D to the dominance fraction. The epistatic components of the first order (interactions between two loci) and those of the second order (interactions between three loci) are summed up in the bottom line.

of the different kinds of non-additive variance are to be found for completely different models of gene action, depending on the gene frequencies assumed. Examples of several situations of varying degrees of complexity are shown in figures 2.3 and 2.4. For the 9:7 ratio, Lush (1945) shows that, when all alleles are equally frequent, four-sevenths of the total genotypic variance is of the additive kind, two-sevenths is of the dominance kind, and one-seventh is epistatic. When the frequencies of the alleles in this example or in figure 2.3 are different, the physiology of gene action of course remains unaffected. Yet the assignment of the causes of variability to one or another type of interaction is no longer the same. In other words, specification of biological epistasis is appropriate to genetics on the individual level; that of statistical epistasis provides description on the level of populations.

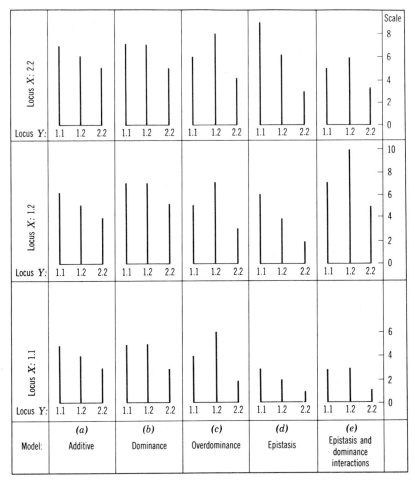

Figure 2.3. Genotype interactions (for explanation see box 3)

Horner, Comstock, and Robinson (1955) analyzed in statistical terms the various types of biologically specified epistatic interactions. They concluded that, for practical purposes, generalized statistical specifications of the genetic situation represented by the various types of F_2 ratios are of little use. Special limiting assumptions need to be made for the analysis of each situation in order to dispense with the otherwise too numerous variables in the general formulas.   Particularly serious difficulties may result from linkage.   Physiological evidence (Pontecorvo, 1955) now indicates that epistasis and dominance are probably not to be viewed as discrete phenomena.   They merge into each other, since the very distinction between alleles and contiguous non-alleles is becoming blurred.

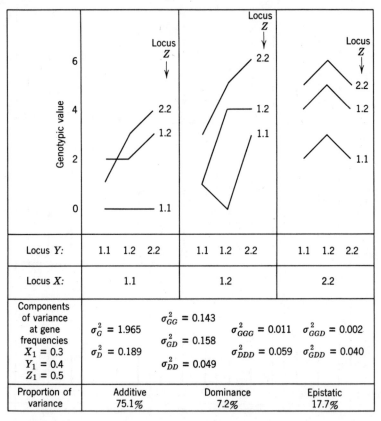

Locus Y:	1.1	1.2	2.2	1.1	1.2	2.2	1.1	1.2	2.2
Locus X:		1.1			1.2			2.2	

Components of variance at gene frequencies $X_1 = 0.3$ $Y_1 = 0.4$ $Z_1 = 0.5$	$\sigma_G^2 = 1.965$ $\sigma_D^2 = 0.189$	$\sigma_{GG}^2 = 0.143$ $\sigma_{GD}^2 = 0.158$ $\sigma_{DD}^2 = 0.049$	$\sigma_{GGG}^2 = 0.011$ $\sigma_{DDD}^2 = 0.059$	$\sigma_{GGD}^2 = 0.002$ $\sigma_{GDD}^2 = 0.040$
Proportion of variance	Additive 75.1%	Dominance 7.2%	Epistatic 17.7%	

Figure 2.4.   Partitioning epistatic variance (from Kempthorne, 1955a; for explanation see box 3)

This fact will no doubt eventually cause some difficulties for statisticians employing the currently accepted models.   In any case it should be understood that the discussion regarding the *fractionization of genotypic variance refers here to statistical phenomena and not necessarily to physiological phenomena.*

It follows that the degree of additiveness of the genetic portion of the variance in a metric trait is not a constant.   In a population with a low mean value for such a character, successive allelic substitutions at a series of loci may produce identical increments in all individuals. In a different population with a higher mean, the same substitutions may have effects with diminishing returns (Rasmusson, 1933). In individuals with a low expression of the character in question, the increases produced may be similar in magnitude to those in the first population. In individuals high on the scale, such substitution may remain without any effect whatsoever. In the first population, additively genetic behavior is observed; in the second, some of the variance has become non-additive. Changes in additivity of gene action in either direction appear to be not uncommon in isolates under prolonged selection and are one source of difficulty in prognoses of population behavior. Changes in environment of a population may also affect the proportion of the variability that is additive with respect to a given property. This fact is, of course, implied in the definition of additive variation as that between average values of alternate alleles at a locus.

10. Partitioning Phenotypic Variance

The partitioning of genotypic variance into its component parts has until now been discussed in purely theoretical terms. In particular, it was assumed that a limited number of identifiable loci are being dealt with and that genotypic values of each genetic combination present in a population are known. The total genotypic variance of any character determined by a series of such loci can then be calculated by summation of the variances contributed by each and of the joint contributions made by interactions between loci.

For polygenic characters, neither the number of loci[4] nor the magnitudes of the effects produced by allelic substitutions can be known. The only information usually available consists of individual phenotypic measurements for one or more generations and of the pedigree relationships between the members of the population. From these, means and statistics of higher degree can be computed for the whole group or for subgroups, ordered in whatever fashion we wish.

Such information may be still adequate for describing the total variation of a population with respect to a metric trait in terms of the fractions of

---

[4] Mather (1949a) suggested techniques for estimating the number of effective units segregating in a given cross. These methods are of greater utility for plant material than for handling data ordinarily available for animal populations. See also the method proposed by Dempster and Snyder (1950) and the discussion by Wright (1952), who had previously investigated this problem. Readers of this volume should take in their stride the fact that there are few matters in quantitative inheritance to which the last clause is inapplicable.

phenotypic variance noted in the previous section. In the situation where the population is exposed to a single uniform environment (one location and season of birth or hatch, identical diet for all members of the population, common housing, and so forth), no tangible environment-genotype interaction is, of course, present. The phenotypic variance then consists of the genotypic portion, subdivisible into an additively genetic part and a non-additive part containing the contributions of the different kinds of gene interactions, without reference, however, to individual locus effects. The environmental fraction may also be subdivided further into random and non-random portions. This subdivision depends on the fact that individuals, related to each other by descent more closely than would be members of a group randomly drawn from a population, often share a more similar environment. Thus, siblings have the source of their cytoplasm and of their embryonic nutrition in common, which is not true, let us say, of cousins. Hence, within any single general environment there are two types of variance produced by more or less intangible non-genetic differences between individuals: (*a*) those that are random for all members of the population and (*b*) those that are common to members of particular subgroups. The latter will be referred to henceforth as *C* effects.

Statistical techniques for the breakdown of the total phenotypic variance into its components have been developed. They lead to informative, albeit static, descriptions of variation in the population subject to analysis and make possible, on the basis of certain assumptions, inferences about the probable behavior of the population in subsequent generations, should it be subjected to, for instance, artificial selection of a specified kind.

No detailed discussion of the methods of subdivision of phenotypic variance will be undertaken here. They are described for different situations and different levels of refinement in many publications. A considerable degree of statistical sophistication is needed to follow the more advanced types of analyses, especially those used for plant material. As a small sample of the vast literature on theory and on directions for practical application, the works of Mather (1949*a*), Lowry (1955), and Robinson, Comstock, and Harvey (1955), and Kempthorne (1957) may be cited. The papers by King and Henderson (1954*a* and *b*) and by Jerome, Henderson, and King (1956) are of particular utility to those interested more specifically in the domestic fowl.[5]

Here a cursory examination of the ideas on which the principles of

---

[5] In the article by Jerome *et al.*, a misprint in the description of their notation may cause the reader concern. The error is easily corrected by reference to figure 2.9, which is equivalent to their table 8.

partitioning of variance are based will suffice. First of all, the biometric relations between relatives, such as parents and offspring, full-sibs, and half-sibs, must be considered. These are graphically illustrated in figures 2.5 and 2.6, the symbolism of which is explained in box 4. With an

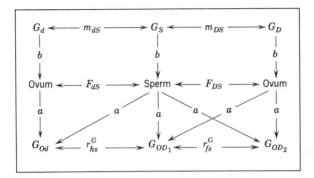

Figure 2.5. Relationship between parents and offspring (for explanation see box 4)

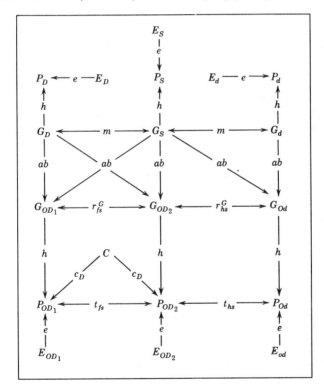

Figure 2.6. Relationship between sibs (for explanation see box 4)

BOX 4

Parent-Offspring and Sib Relationships

Figure 2.5 is a diagram of parent-offspring relationship based on Wright's (1921) technique of path coefficients. Li (1956) presented a thorough exposition of this method and summarized its various uses in genetics. Tukey (1954) may be consulted for a discussion of its efficiency relative to that of modern methods of regression analysis. In the diagram the arrows are directed from cause to effect. Double-headed arrows indicate correlations; G stands for the *additive genotype*, the subscripts indicating different individuals. Thus S symbolizes the sire; D and d, the two dams mated to him; OD_1 and OD_2, two of the offspring of the first; Od, one of the second. The paths designated b and a proceed respectively from parent to the gamete produced by it and from the gamete to the zygote. Under random mating the product ab has a numerical value of $1/2$. Three types of correlation are shown: (*a*) that between the genotypes of the mates, designated by m, (*b*) that between the uniting gametes (the *coefficient of inbreeding*) designated by F, and (*c*) that of *genetic relationship* between full- (r_{fs}^G) and half- (r_{hs}^G) sibs. When F is 0, r_{fs}^G is equal to $1/2$ and r_{hs}^G to $1/4$.

Figure 2.6 is an extension of figure 2.5. Here the phenotypic expression (P) of the individuals concerned is introduced by adding the environmental sources of variation (E and C) to the previous scheme, which referred to the genetic (G) values alone. The E fraction of environmental variance is the random one; C indicates the effects designated by this letter in the text. In the illustration C refers to a source of environmental variance common to full-sibs. Had a source common to half-sibs been pictured, c_S paths (not shown in the diagram) would lead to each P in the lower row.

Paths connecting G, C, and E to P have been given the respective designations of h, c, and e. These symbols refer to the ratios of the standard deviations of the causal variables to that of the dependent. If it is assumed that no gene-environment correlations or interactions are present, then

$$\sigma_P^2 = \sigma_G^2 + \sigma_E^2 + \sigma_C^2 \tag{1}$$

Dividing this expression by σ_P^2, we can write

$$\frac{\sigma_G^2}{\sigma_P^2} + \frac{\sigma_E^2}{\sigma_P^2} + \frac{\sigma_C^2}{\sigma_P^2} = 1 \tag{2}$$

or
$$h^2 + e^2 + c^2 = 1 \tag{3}$$

The method of path coefficients permits the computation of correlations between any variables connected by single- or double-headed arrows. The phenotypic correlation between full-sibs can be derived from the diagram given here as being,

$$t_{fs} = 2(ab)^2(1 + m)h^2 + c_D^2 \tag{4}$$

That for the half-sibs is

$$t_{hs} = (ab)^2(1 + m)h^2 \tag{5}$$

Under the assumption of random mating these expressions reduce to

$$t_{fs} = \frac{h^2}{2} + c_D^2 \quad \text{and} \quad t_{hs} = \frac{h^2}{4} \tag{6}$$

Finally, in the absence of C effects,

$$t_{fs} = \frac{h^2}{2} \tag{7}$$

It may be worthwhile to reproduce here part of a table adapted by Lerner (1950) from Wright (1921). It gives some general biometric relations between parent and offspring on the assumption of completely additive gene action.

Symbol	Definition	Value under Random Mating	Value under Inbreeding*
a	Path coefficient from gamete to zygote	$\sqrt{\tfrac{1}{2}}$	$\sqrt{\dfrac{1}{2(1 + F)}}$
b	Path coefficient from zygote to gamete	$\sqrt{\tfrac{1}{2}}$	$\sqrt{\dfrac{1 + F'}{2}}$
m	Correlation between genotypes of mates[†]	0	$\dfrac{2F}{\sqrt{(1 + F_S)(1 + F_D)}}$
F	Correlation between uniting gametes, inbreeding coefficient (see box 8)	0	b^2m
h^2	Heritability	h^2	$\dfrac{(1 + F)h^2}{1 + Fh^2}$
r_{fs}^{G}	Correlation between genotypes of full-sibs[†]	$\dfrac{1}{2}$	$\dfrac{1 + F' + 2F}{2(1 + F)}$
r_{SO}^{G} or r_{DO}^{G}	Correlation between phenotypes of parent and offspring[†]	$\dfrac{h^2}{2}$	$abhh'(1 + m)$

* In a population of inbred animals; not within inbred lines.

† The subscripts S and D refer to sire and dam respectively, O to the offspring. The prime superscript indicates the value of the constant in the previous (parental) generation. Thus when $F_S = F_D$, both are equal to F'.

empirical knowledge of the correlation between full-sibs or half-sibs, it is possible to estimate the value of the parameter designated as h^2. It is a measure of the variability of the character considered between individuals differing in their additively genetic values relative to the total variability between individuals. That is to say, h^2 is the proportion of the total phenotypic variation which is traceable to genetic differences in the population. It is known as the degree of *heritability*.

In the broad sense, heritability might include all the genotypic variance, be it of the additive, dominance, or epistatic kind. But for purposes of selection it is the amount of the additively genetic variance of a character rather than of the genotypic variance that is of particular significance. The additive variance is basically the property of the allele, whereas dominance and epistasis are properties of the genotype. Hence, since the selected parents contribute haploid genomes to the gene pool of the next generation, epistatic combinations, as well as those involving dominance relations, are in the course of reproduction broken up, to be reassembled in a different pattern in the population of genotypes in the next generation. Thus a parent superior to the mean of its generation only by virtue of possessing a particular genotype, and not because of its additive value does not contribute to progress under selection in the same way as does a parent contributing haploid gametes of high merit to any zygotes they may form. Hence, at least with respect to straightforward *mass* selection (that is to say, selection based on individual phenotypes), our interest is in heritability defined in the narrow sense, referring to additively genetic variance rather than to genotypic variance. In the notation of the previous section,

$$h^2 = \frac{\sigma_G^2}{\sigma_G^2 + \sigma_D^2 + \sigma_I^2 + \sigma_E^2}$$

It should be noted before proceeding further with a discussion of heritability that the assignment of variation to one or another fraction of the total often depends on the scale of measurement used. The scale, or rather scales, of primary biological action of allelic substitutions affecting a metric trait are, of course, not known. On the level of phenotypic measurement, any scale used, be it expressed in centimeters, in logarithms of inch measurements, in their square roots, or in more complex functions, is as arbitrary as any other. Hence, the best scale for practical purposes is one that is operationally the most efficient. Elimination of interaction by scale transformation, wherever this is possible, adds to selection efficiency by increasing the degree of heritability. Changes from the scale on which raw data have been expressed to another are therefore on occasion highly useful. A very simple example of elimination of dominance variance by scale transformation is shown in figure 2.7. It is usually considered worthwhile before undertaking extensive analyses to examine the raw data with a view to reducing interactions by transformations. Mather (1949a) devotes a chapter of his book on biometrical

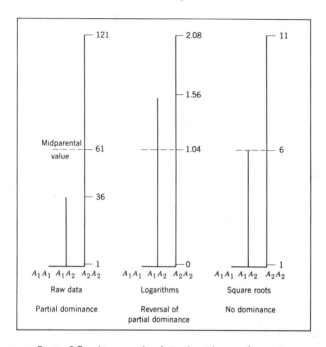

Figure 2.7. An example of simple scale transformation

Many interactions are so complex that no scale transformation can eliminate them entirely. Most threshold situations and the ordinary case of overdominance, when the heterozygote is superior to both homozygotes, cannot be easily made to behave in an additive fashion. In some other instances a simple transformation can accomplish this. Here the raw data on the left indicate partial dominance of the allele A_2. Conversion of the genotypic values into logarithms, as shown in the middle (adjusted to scale), leads to a reversal of the direction of dominance. Transformation to square roots, as on the right, makes the relation between the three genotypes completely additive.

genetics to a discussion of the problems encountered in such scaling tests, and Wright (1952) may be referred to for a broadly conceived discussion of the whole question of scales.

11. Heritability

Heritability can be estimated by a variety of methods. All of them, in one way or another, depend on the measurement of the degree of similarity between individuals related by lineal or collateral descent. Basically, relatives resemble each other because they have a greater number of particular alleles in common than do unrelated or less related individuals. Part of the phenotypic similarity between, let us say, sibs may also be attributed to the fact that their environments are more alike than those of non-sibs. If, however, the data are gathered in such a way as to randomize the environment of all members of the population, it is possible to estimate how much of the variation between phenotypes is due to differences between genotypes. The necessary conditions of independent environment of relatives may not always be met. In such animals as chickens, however, normally no difficulties should arise in measuring the degree of genotypic resemblance between paternal half-sibs, between sires and their offspring, and between other more distant kinds of relatives.

Techniques of estimation of heritability are discussed in many publications. The papers of Lush (1949) and of Le Roy and Lörtscher (1955) are particularly good sources to consult for the evaluation of the various

---

BOX 5

Estimation of Heritability

The technique of estimating the degree of heritability of a character from phenotypic correlations between sibs is based on an analysis of variance. The accompanying table shows a common design for data derived from polygamous matings of s sires with each of d dams producing n offspring apiece.

Source of Variation	Degrees of Freedom	Composition of Mean Square
Total	$sdn - 1$	–
Between sire families	$s - 1$	$Q + nD + dnS$
Within sire families	$s(dn - 1)$	–
Between dam families	$s(d - 1)$	$Q + nD$
Between full-sibs	$sd(n - 1)$	Q

The capital letters in the last column designate variance components: Q within groups of full-sibs, D between means of dam families, and S between means of sire families. On the assumption of additively genetic variance only, Q contains half the genetic variance and all the environmental one, D one-quarter of the genetic variance (and all the C type of maternal effect), and S the remaining quarter of the genetic variance.

Hence (assuming the absence of C effects), heritability estimates are provided by

$$h^2 = \frac{4D}{D + S + Q} = \frac{4S}{D + S + Q} = \frac{2(D + S)}{D + S + Q} \tag{1}$$

When maternal effects of the C kind are present, their magnitude can be estimated by the discrepancy between the h^2 values computed respectively from the D and from the S components. The expression in box 4 for t_{fs}, the intraclass correlation between full-sibs, is equivalent to

$$\frac{D + S}{D + S + Q}$$

while t_{hs} is equivalent to

$$\frac{S}{D + S + Q}$$

The estimates of h^2 thus derived include different fractions of dominance and epistatic variance. Figure 2.8 allows computation of the biases. An h^2 value estimated from $4D$ over the total variance includes all the additive variance, all the dominance variance, three-quarters of the additive by additive interaction, one-half of the additive by dominance interaction, and one-quarter of the dominance by dominance interaction (higher-order interactions may be comparatively negligible). Similarly an estimate based on $4S$ contains all the additive plus one-quarter of the first kind of epistatic interaction. It is clear that the estimate from the sire component is less sensitive to the presence of non-additive variance than that from the dam component. On the other hand, because it is usually based on a smaller number of degrees of freedom, it may not be as reliable.

This discussion does not take into account genetic variability that may be due to the sex chromosome. It is likely that in animals with many chromosomes polygenic variance due to this source forms a relatively small fraction of the total. When it is significant, it may be estimated under some circumstances by differences between the S and D components and by partitioning the variance of male offspring separately from the female.

Graybill, Martin, and Godfrey (1956) and Graybill and Robertson (1957) may be consulted for methods of determining confidence limits of heritability estimates. Other useful references on the sampling variance of h^2 are Osborne and Paterson (1952) and Smith (1957). Corrections for inbreeding in estimations of heritability are often used (see box 9). Within regularly inbred lines in which all parents are equally related to each other, and under completely additive gene action, it can be shown that the S and D components, rather than containing one-quarter of the additively genetic variance, each include

$$\frac{1 + F' - 2F}{4}\sigma_G^2$$

(see box 4 for the meaning of these symbols). However, as emphasized in box 9, such corrections are subject to the restriction that σ_G^2 and σ_E^2 are independent of each other, a condition that is not realistic.

methods. These include comparisons of phenotypic traits displayed by monozygotic as against dizygotic twins, calculations of parent-offspring regressions, correlations between full-sibs or half-sibs, and computations of differences between isogenic lines or lines selected in opposite directions. The latter procedure may not appear at first sight to depend on resemblance between relatives. In the final analysis, however, it involves the comparison of progeny with their ancestors, superior with respect to the character under selection in one selected line and inferior in the other.

Box 5 illustrates how heritability can be estimated from analyses of full-sib and half-sib performance. Figure 2.8 shows the composition of the

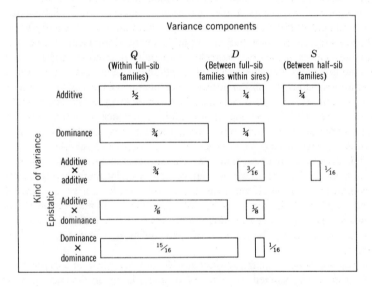

Figure 2.8. Variance components in heritability estimation

variance components thus obtained. A variant of the technique described in box 5 involves diallel matings and is noted in figure 2.9. Many formulas applicable to different mating systems (polygamy, monogamy, various degrees of inbreeding), to different types of characters (for instance, sex-limited), and to different bases of inheritance (e.g. sex-linked) are scattered throughout the literature. In particular, amendments to the fractions shown in figures 2.8 and 2:9 due to linkage have been investigated by Cockerham (1956).

The degree of heritability is of fundamental importance in the theory and practice of selection. It can be defined not only as the fraction of the total variance in the population which is due to additively genetic differences but also as the square of the correlation between genotype and phenotype (in unselected populations), or as the regression of genotype on phenotype. This is to say that h^2 can be used to measure changes in the average genotype of a population due to the removal from the population

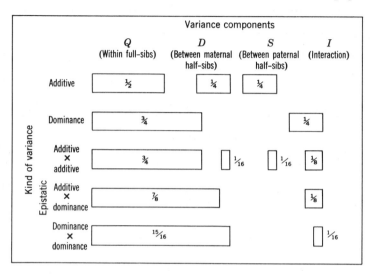

Fig. 2.9. Variance components in a diallel system

Polyallel crossing is a reciprocal polygamous system wherein several females produce separate families of offspring from individual matings to the same series of males. The *diallel* form of this system (though the term is often used as an equivalent to polyallel) refers to such a scheme in which two sires and two dams form a block of matings. The number of blocks in an experimental design is, of course, theoretically unlimited. The virtues of polyallelic mating for experimental purposes lie in the possibility of isolating interactions. In animals, however, the experimental techniques present difficulties, for instance in maintaining random environment for all offspring within a block. Recently, considerable advances in the theory of polyallel mating have been made (see e.g. Hayman, 1954, and Griffing, 1956). Heritability estimates can be readily obtained from variance analyses of data from polyallel matings. For a diallel design, see table 17 in Lerner, 1950; for a practical example, see Jerome, Henderson, and King, 1956. The present figure indicates the type of bias occurring when h^2 is computed in different ways from polyallel data. Thus the estimate $[2(D+S)]/(D+S+Q+I)$ includes all of the additive variance and one-quarter of the additive by additive interaction. The composition of other estimates can be similarly ascertained.

of particular phenotypic classes. Hence, the degree of heritability, in combination with the strength or intensity of selection, can be used in predicting the progress from selection. It may also be said that the *effective* h^2, i.e. the fraction of the superiority of the selected parents over the mean of their generation that is transmitted to their offspring, is a

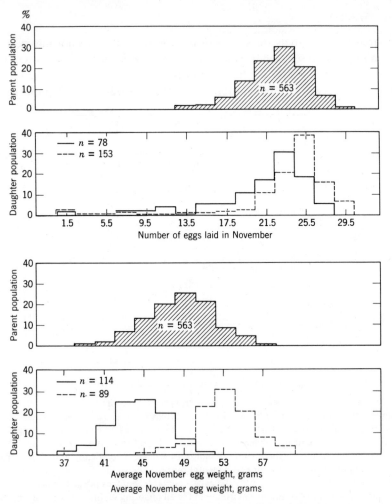

Figure 2.10. Selection progress as a function of heritability

The results of an experiment are shown here. Data from a population of 563 Leghorn pullets were obtained for (a) the number of eggs produced in November and (b) the average weight of these eggs. Selection of approximately equal intensity was then applied to form four groups of birds, of which one was selected for high egg number, one for low egg number, one for high egg weight, and one for low egg weight. The heritability of November egg number, as estimated from this population, is roughly 0.25; that of November egg weight is approximately 0.75. The contrasting distributions of the high and low lines for the two characters (the dashed lines represent offspring of the high selections, and the solid of the low) clearly illustrate the consequences of the difference between these values. In simple selection experiments, h^2 can often be estimated directly from the fraction of the difference between the mean of the selected animals and the mean of the parental generation formed by the gain obtained. Here h^2 values cannot be accurately computed in this manner·because the characters investigated are sex-limited.

measure of *accuracy of selection*. Figure 2.10 illustrates the contrast between a character of low heritability and one of high heritability so far as the change in the mean of the population which one generation of selection of a given selection intensity can produce.

The precision with which h^2 can be estimated might be expected to have considerable importance. In reality, most of the prediction expressions used in discriminating among the merits of different breeding schemes are not very sensitive to fluctuations in the degree of heritability in the narrow sense of the term. Hence minor discrepancies between the true value of h^2 and its estimates are not of great importance. Unfortunately the same cannot be said of the errors arising from the not infrequently made assumption that estimates of h^2 are entirely free of non-additive variance.

Since h^2 is a ratio, it is, in addition to sampling errors, subject to variation whenever either the numerator (additively genetic variance, which is itself a function of gene frequency) or the denominator (genotypic plus environmental variance) is altered. For example, under inbreeding it is to be expected that genetic variance will in the long run decrease to the point of disappearance. Clearly, h^2 values estimated from data gathered on inbred and non-inbred populations are not equivalent. Corrections to a non-random-bred basis are needed to make the two types of estimates comparable, although there are some complications in this seemingly simple matter (see box 5).

Similarly, environmental variance may increase or decrease for reasons extrinsic to selection. It is also very probable that this component of variation is not always independent of the amount and rate of inbreeding undergone by the population (see section 16). Whenever such relationship affects the accuracy of heritability estimates, disagreements will be found between gains expected and gains realized.

There are many gaps in our knowledge of the subject of heritability. They are due less to deficiencies in statistical methodology than to a lack of understanding of the fundamental ontogenic processes influencing the characters of interest to breeders or experimenters. The fact, then, that the heritability of a given trait may differ from one population to another, or vary in the same population at different times, should not occasion any surprise. Indeed, it should be clear that, *strictly speaking, any intra-generation estimate of heritability is valid only for the particular generation of the specific population from which the data used in arriving at it derive.* Some generalizations are, nevertheless, possible. Figure 2.11 shows the range of estimates of heritability of a number of economic traits of chickens made by different investigators applying a variety of statistical techniques to different populations. How much of the variability that is shown in it is due to real differences in the heritability of given traits, and

not merely to errors of sampling, is not easy to tell.   Few attempts have
been made to identify the actual amounts of non-additive variance by
which the estimates of heritability of economic characters are contaminated.
The reliance that can be placed on h^2 estimates is still not very high.

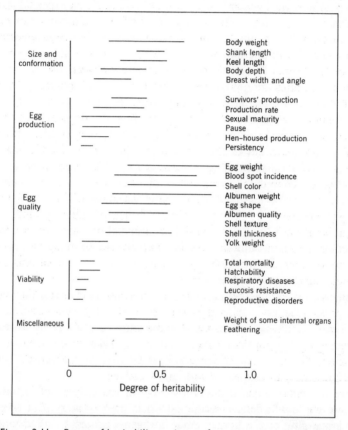

Figure 2.11.   Range of heritability estimates for economic traits of chickens

These data have been compiled from various publications accumulated since the
first estimate of h^2 for egg production of chickens was made by Munro (1936).   Spector
(1956) has a table which covers more or less the same material and also tables for other
species of farm animals.

Should a greater accumulation of concordant results became available, it
may be thought that derivation of consequences to breeding practice will
be facilitated.   Yet more than the fulfillment of this simple requirement
may be necessary to be able to predict changes in the heritability of a trait.
The range of h^2 values for many characters is of course not a happen-
stance.   It may be determined by the contribution of the trait to fitness

and by various other properties of a population. Because of this, selection pressure can itself cause modifications in the fraction of the genetic variation which is additive, although the mechanisms underlying such shifts are not known.

In a highly provocative and in many ways anticipatory article, which must, however, be interpreted with caution on several issues, Kislovsky (1937) pointed out that heritability of milk production in improved populations of cattle changed in the direction opposite to that expected from information on inbreeding. Similarly, Tantawy and Reeve (1956) found that effective heritability does not decrease under inbreeding of *Drosophila melanogaster* as rapidly as it should on the basis of simple theory, and Scossiroli (1957) noted increases in the heritability of bristle number in the same species as selected lines approached a plateau. Uncertainties of this kind limit the utility of even reliably determined values for the prediction of expressed selection responses.

12. Special Cases of Non-additive Gene Action

There are many circumstances in which dominance and epistatic interactions are responsible for errors of estimation of heritability and for failure to attain advances from selection. One theoretical model and three examples of observed situations in which such circumstances are of significance are discussed in this section.

The *theoretical* model is that constructed by Wright (1935a). It deals with deviation from an intermediate optimum and is based on the postulate that the genotypic value of a measurable character depends on how close it is to an optimum for some unobserved property. For instance, the number of eggs laid by a hen (the observed or secondary character) may well be a function of the genotype for the production of not too little and yet not too much of a particular hormone (the underlying or primary character). In analyzing such a relationship, Wright assumed that the amount by which the observed character falls below its maximum value is proportional to the square of the deviation of the underlying character from an optimum. Now it may be that the variation of the underlying trait is dependent entirely on additive gene differences (presence of environmental influences does not affect the point to be noted). But on the basis of the relationship postulated, the genetic variance of the observed character will not necessarily be of an additive type. When the mean and the optimum of the primary character are far apart, the genetic variability of the secondary character will be largely additive and the heritability on the observed level will be approximately the same as on the underlying scale.   As the mean of the underlying trait approaches the optimum, the proportion of epistatic variance in the observed character is found to increase.   When the mean and the optimum of the primary trait coincide, all the variance on the secondary level becomes non-additive, i.e. its heritability drops to the vanishing point.   Selection for the observed trait will under these circumstances lead to an asymptotic approach to a level below the maximum, whereas relaxation of selection results in loss of the amount hitherto gained.   Although this description of Wright's model may sound somewhat involved, it indicates the possible complexities of a situation that may be frequent in economically useful traits.   It is very likely that reproductive fitness actually behaves as the secondary character in this model.

The first example of *observed* non-additive behavior concerns characters in which inbreeding depression is manifested (it may be parenthetically noted that this effect is also a property of Wright's model).   Further consideration of inbreeding degeneration is undertaken in section 15.   Here it is sufficient to note that not only may heritability estimates from data on inbred populations be unrealistic guides for making comparisons between selection gains expected from different breeding schemes in non-inbred populations, but, more generally, unpredictable consequences regarding selection response often ensue from the imposition of consanguineous mating on normally outbred species.

The amounts respectively contributed by dominance and by epistasis to inbreeding depression and to heterosis are not known.   Although considerable theoretical investigation by Crow (1952), Horner, Comstock, and Robinson (1955), and others, as well as experimental work (e.g. Robinson and Comstock, 1955) on the subject has been carried out, it seems unlikely that a general answer to this question is possible.   As must be repeatedly stressed, the situation found in a given population at a specified time is a consequence of its genetic biography.   It is extremely likely that, even when statistical techniques can be made to take into account all the known complications, the experimental procedures that may be required for precise separation of the manifold sources of variability of a population will themselves affect the results obtained.   This uncertainty, or complementarity, may give rise to false conclusions about the properties of populations that have not been tampered with, if generalizations are to be made from information on populations subjected to artificial breeding systems.   At the risk of producing surfeit with this constant reminder, it may still be worth noting that many simplifying assumptions must be made in the interpretation of the different illustrative examples presented here.   Indeed, the various *statistical* models on which analyses of data have to be based are characterized by different *biological* restrictions.   One of them may disregard linkage, another multiple allelism, and a third some further complication, none of which disappear simply because it has been given a name. The difficulties of establishing the genetic basis of inbreeding degeneration and of heterosis trace, at least in part, to this unfortunate fact.

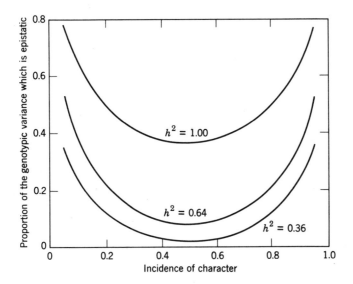

Figure 2.12. Epistatic variance of an all-or-none trait

This figure is reproduced from the theoretical study of selection for all-or-none characters by Dempster and Lerner (1950). It shows how the percentage of epistatic variance (which in this model is the complement of the additively genetic variance) changes with heritability and with the incidence of the character. When 50 per cent of the population exhibits a particular trait and heritability is relatively low, very little of the variance is epistatic. The disposable genotypic variation, i.e. its additive fraction, is high. As the incidence of the character moves in either direction, more and more of the variance becomes epistatic. Selection efficiency is thereby reduced. The curves for all heritability levels portrayed here are of the same general shape. The graph helps to explain the commonly noted phenomenon that natural or mass selection for or against threshold traits (e.g. disease resistance) is most effective at intermediate incidences and exceedingly inefficient at the extremes.

The next instance of non-additive behavior to be noted is that of polygenically inherited threshold (all-or-none) characters. The main difficulty in dealing with these traits lies in the fact that their heritability is a function of their level of incidence. Thus the validity of predictions of gains from an estimate of h^2 made in a given generation for the next generation is even more limited for threshold traits than it is for other characters. Figure 2.12 illustrates a single aspect of this situation, the complete statistical description of the problem being too complicated to discuss here. The papers of Lush, Lamoreux, and Hazel (1948), of Robertson and Lerner (1949), and of Crittenden, Bohren, and Anderson (1957a) may be consulted for techniques of h^2 determination of all-or-none characters.

The genetic basis of many traits with phenotypic expressions which are classifiable into discrete categories can be referred to a number of independently acting and identifiable loci. The interactions of the segregating alleles when multiple thresholds of this kind are present are often exceedingly complex and unpredictable from prior knowledge of the separate effects of substitution at each locus. Plumage or coat color pattern inheritance provide obvious examples. Constant revision of formal genetic schemes to account for the various patterns observed are apparently necessary. Probably the most thoroughly analyzed series of loci of this type is in guinea pigs (Wright, 1956). But for many characters no formal Mendelian schemes can be usefully invoked, even when variable penetrance and expressivity of single genes is postulated. Grüneberg's (1952) quasi-continuous variation falls into this class, as does the last kind of non-additive behavior to be dealt with here. This is essentially a combination of the immediately preceding types. Lerner (1954), in reviewing a number of instances falling into this category, coined the word *phenodeviant* to describe them.

Probably the earliest comprehensive analysis of phenodeviants (overlooked in Lerner's review) was that by Gordon, Spurway, and Street (1939) on *Drosophila subobscura*. Two years later, Gershenson (see Dubinin, 1948) suggested that phenodeviants are maintained in populations because of the adaptive properties of their heterozygous carriers. There have been several more recent reports of phenodeviants in chickens in which the basis of their inheritance was not recognized (Kushner and Kameneva, 1954; Fischer, 1956). Lerner interpreted the appearance of phenodeviants in inbred populations as a form of inbreeding degeneration, whereas Spurway (1955) proposed that the term should more generally cover abnormalities arising from the breakdown of developmental patterns occasioned by any drastic change in the mating system, i.e. hybridization as well as inbreeding.

It seems likely that phenodeviants (for example, crooked toes in chickens) are conditioned by small differences at a large number of loci, let us say n. When some fraction (m) of these is homozygous, the trait is phenotypically expressed. The alternative alleles at each locus are probably maintained in the population because of an advantage of multiple heterozygotes. In a sufficiently large interbreeding group, the number of homozygotes for m loci which might appear by chance in any generation could be very low when both m and n are large. Selection against the trait merely by culling the individuals exhibiting it would be virtually ineffective. Alleles for some phenodeviants are ubiquitous, so that whenever a population is inbred the frequency of the character in it rises sharply. The behavior of crosses between particular inbred lines is, however, completely unpredictable, since the incidence of expression in them will depend on whether or not the loci fixed in the two parental lines are the same or different.

The threshold of expression of these abnormalities varies with the environment. Fewer specific loci need to be in a homozygous state if an individual is to manifest the undesirable condition in poor environments rather than in good ones. It may also be argued that excessive homozygosity of a non-specific kind provides a poor inner environment. This fact may in itself lead to an increase in the incidence of phenodeviants under inbreeding. There is no doubt, however, that, as noted by Lerner, the frequency and the particular types of abnormality appearing in various inbred stocks depend on the allelic contents of the gene pool.

Selection against phenodeviants in populations that are experiencing reduction in size and are therefore subjected to inbreeding may have to be practiced if high levels of incidence are to be avoided. To be effective it has to be based on family testing. The rate at which the frequency of phenodeviants may be reduced by selection cannot be specified until precise information on the genetic background needed for their manifestation is obtained. The question whether this is a generally attainable goal must for the present remain conjectural.

The illustrations of non-additive behavior show the kind of difficulties that are still to be resolved, even with respect to the fundamental bases of selection. These difficulties, however, should not be a cause for discouragement since, little as we know today, we are still in possession of a vast array of facts denied to the empirically successful selectors of yesteryear. In particular, some of the mystery about the nature of hereditary variation and the basis of its preservation in Mendelian populations has been clarified.

3

Conservation
of Genetic Variance

There may truly be said to be a constant
struggle going on between, on the one
hand, the tendency to reversion to a less
perfect state, as well as an innate tendency to new variations, and, on the other
hand, the power of steady selection . . .

One of the fundamental contributions of population genetics to the
study of evolution was the discovery of the great amounts of genotypic
variability which underlie the relatively homogeneous phenotypic appearance of Mendelian populations. That considerable hereditary variability
might be expected behind the uniform facades of interbreeding groups was
deduced on theoretical grounds by the Russian zoologist Chetverikov
(1926), who also initiated the first experiments to test his hypothesis.
Since then much of the work on experimental population genetics, particularly in Drosophila, has been devoted to this issue (see Dobzhansky,
1951). Descriptive studies have also been made of the visible variation
of domestic animals kept under conditions in which apparently little or
no artificial selection had been consciously practiced.[1]

Cryptic genetic variability is experimentally revealed by (a) the appearance of monogenically determined traits immediately upon inbreeding,
(b) the variety of complex characters which manifest themselves only after

[1] Thus, attempts at a gene census of primitive flocks of poultry were undertaken by
Serebrovsky and his associates. It is a great pity that this series of investigations (e.g.
Serebrovsky, 1927 and 1935), having been reported in Russian, is undeservedly neglected
by students of both evolution and poultry genetics.

70

prolonged inbreeding (as in Dubinin's, 1948, study of extra veinlets in Drosophila), (c) the remarkable fact that artificial selection for modification of practically any arbitrarily chosen metric trait except fitness can, as a rule, be successful, and (d) the widespread and continued presence in natural populations of genetic systems modifying the expression of most, if not all, major mutants.

In addition to selection, which is to be considered in greater detail below, there are several ways by which genetic variability may be maintained in a population in equilibrium. Mutation may be a source of renewal of variation. The segregating alleles may be neutral in their effects on fitness. The population may be part of a geographic gradient or the mating system may be based on assortment of unlike parents. All these, together with such phenomena as meiotic drive (Sandler and Novitski, 1957), which results in unequal frequencies of the gametes produced by heterozygotes and which might be responsible for such abnormal segregation ratios as observed by Dunn (1957) in mice, could perpetuate a heterogeneous composition of the gene pool.

It is possible that each of these mechanisms plays a part under different circumstances. Yet none of them appears to be very probable for *metric traits in small populations, especially under directional selection and inbreeding.* Indeed, arguments may be raised even against selection as a major factor in preserving genetic variance. Thus it is possible to visualize a polygenic block (essentially a method of storing variation) arising by chance, but for it to be preserved in the face of pressures for disintegration, either it has to become rapidly fixed or be selected for. If it is fixed, it ceases to contribute to or to store genetic variance. The pressure required to keep it heterozygous in the population by selection may, on the other hand, be somewhat higher than is reasonable to expect (Wright, 1945), especially when more than a pair of neighboring loci enter a block. Possibly selection for tighter linkage resulting in non-randomness of crossing over along a chromosome, which does not present any theoretical difficulties (Kimura, 1956a), may be invoked to overcome this difficulty. Still whether selection in small populations can be powerful enough to account for the persistence of many unlike homologous polygenic blocks is a question which has not been settled.

With respect to single loci rather than blocks, a similar discrepancy may exist between the rate at which allelic fixation is expected on the basis of current models of balance between inbreeding and selection in populations of limited size and the number of loci at which continued segregation may be inferred to occur. The theoretical basis for maintaining more than one allele at a locus by selection is, as noted in the next section, rather simple. But for many such loci to exist, the total intensity of selection needed is far greater than appears possible. A simple illustration will serve to demonstrate this fact. In an ordinary monogenic situation in which the heterozygote is the only genotype producing offspring, selection intensity is 50 per cent. With every additional independent locus of the same kind, the number of prospective parents is halved. Thus, if heterozygosis were to be rigidly enforced at only seven loci, less than 1 per cent of the population (0.5^7) could be permitted to have offspring. None of the domestic animals has a high-enough reproductive rate to permit selection of such intensity. Lower selection rates would inevitably lead to fixation at all but a few loci. In the face of this fact there seems to be a great number of independently inherited traits conditioned by single genes, by several genes, or by polygenic systems that are manifested by parts of small herds or flocks or make an appearance upon inbreeding. For example, in the University of California flock of Leghorn chickens, sired over a period of 25 years by a maximum of 14 males per generation, maintenance of heterozygosity at a minimum of two independent blood group loci (Shultz and Briles, 1953) has been demonstrated. Furthermore, several suspected phenodeviants and other (possibly monogenic) traits have appeared in inbred lines derived from this population. These characters include nakedness, crooked toes, naillessness, kyphoscoliosis, a talpid-like lethal, pendulous crops, buff plumage, melanotic spots on the shanks, and a variety of others. Protective genes against many defects must be widely spread in poultry (Landauer, 1956). But unless protection is non-specific to a great extent, the possibility of selection for penetrance and expressivity of major mutants must depend on heterozygous reserves at many loci.

In other words, the explanations centering on selection which are currently invoked to explain maintenance of variability in small populations are not complete. It may be that factors as yet unknown enter the picture, or that the present interpretations of empirical evidence are in error, or that our models are not valid. As yet it cannot be decided which of these possibilities is the most probable one, since of the factors already known, many (e.g. pleiotropy) have not been fully explored. Thus, Kempthorne (1955b), who is not to be suspected of underestimating the power of statistics to solve genetical problems, has listed nine major questions that need to be solved before the statistical theory of quantitative inheritance can assume a definitive form. At the moment we must content ourselves with the models of current vintage, deficient though they may be. It is, of course, reasonable to anticipate that sooner or later they must undergo drastic revision or even complete repudiation, a not uncommon fate of models which are operationally useful or even indispensable while they last.

Since selection progress depends on the amount of genetic variability present in the population, conservation of variance in populations is of considerable significance to our main topic of discussion. The present chapter will therefore be devoted to an examination of various aspects of this question.

13. Population Equilibrium

Under the heading "Simple Mendelian Equilibrium," Wright (1931) observed that the "starting point for any discussion of the statistical situation in Mendelian populations is the rather obvious consideration that in an indefinitely large population the relative frequencies of allelomorphic genes remain constant if unaffected by disturbing factors such as mutation, migration or selection." The Hardy-Weinberg binomial and its extension for multiple alleles describe such an equilibrium. However, Wright's point of departure is only a theoretical concept or idealization, because no actual population is ever likely to be free from disturbing pressures (the effects of restricted population size are discussed in section 17).

Indeed, the constancy of population means and variances on the phenotypic level, and of allelic frequencies on the genetic one, is usually dependent on the balance between the disturbing factors rather than on their absence. This is a point of view on which Wright's whole conception of evolution rests and which he has emphasized repeatedly. A familiar example of the balance of two opposing forces is the equilibrium between selection and recurrent mutation pressure, which has already been noted. It is a great oversimplification of the probable state of things.

In fact it seems much more likely that nearly every population equilibrium is held at a particular configuration of allelic and genotypic frequencies (in Wright's term, an *adaptive peak*) by a complex interaction of opposing forces. When the impact of one of them is modified for some reason, either compensating adjustments occur in the responses of the population to the others, as has been suggested in the discussion of coadaptation, or the population moves from one equilibrium to another. Wright (1935b) has dealt with the nature of such changes in populations close to an equilibrium. It is entirely possible that the new adaptive peak consists of a radically different array of gene frequencies but preserves the identical means and variances for the metric properties that characterized the earlier equilibrium.

When one or another homozygote has an advantage over the heterozygote, the only stable equilibrium that can be reached is at the point of

┌─────────────────────────────── BOX 6 ───────────────────────────────┐

Selection Favoring Heterozygotes

Computation of changes in gene frequency when selection is directed against the recessive allele is illustrated in box 1. In that instance, as well as when the recessive is being selected for, the only stable equilibrium is at fixation. Thus if the expression for the rate of change in allelic frequency per generation,

$$\Delta q = \frac{sq(1 - q)^2}{1 - s(1 - q)^2} \tag{1}$$

is set equal to zero (so that q remains constant), it can be readily seen that, for values of s other than zero, the only roots of q are 0 or 1.

The equilibrium value of q, when the heterozygote is preferred to both homozygotes, can be determined in a similar fashion. As a starting point an appropriate table may be constructed as follows:

Genotype	AA	Aa	aa	Total
Initial frequency	q^2	$2q(1-q)$	$1-q^2$	1
Selective value	$1-s_A$	1	$1-s_a$	–
Parents selected	$q^2(1-s_A)$	$2q(1-q)$	$(1-q)^2(1-s_a)$	$1-s_A q^2-s_a(1-q)^2$

The change in q in successive generations is then

$$\Delta q = \frac{q(1 - q)[s_a(1 - q) - s_A q]}{1 - s_A q^2 - s_a(1 - q)^2}$$

When this expression is equated to zero, the equilibrium value of the frequency of A is

$$\hat{q}_A = \frac{s_a}{s_A + s_a} \tag{3}$$

and that of a is

$$(1 - \hat{q}_A) = \hat{q}_a = \frac{s_A}{s_A + s_a} \tag{4}$$

Li (1955b) may be consulted for a discussion of a variety of conditions under which stable or unstable allelic equilibria are attained.

└──┘

fixation of the preferred allele (see box 6). This is also true of selection against the heterozygote (Li, 1955a). Yet there are circumstances under which selection alone, without any other pressures affecting the situation, can maintain constant intermediate allelic frequencies. For example, Levene (1953) constructed a model in which the preservation of more than one allele in a population depends on the fact that the different homozygotes have ecological preferences for different environments, from which, however, they need to emerge for mating.

Dempster (1955a) presented another model in which a regular cyclic alternation of the direction of selection in favor of one or the other allele can keep both in a population. Although within a given generation the heterozygote has a lower fitness than one of the homozygotes, its average fitness for a cycle of two generations exceeds that of both homozygotes. The consequences of this situation, when viewed in terms of cycles instead of generations, correspond to the general type of heterozygous advantage considered later. Reversal of selective advantage from one to another homozygote within a single life cycle may operate in a similar way.

Generally speaking, it is the superiority of the heterozygotes which appears to be of greatest importance in the conservation of genetic variability of populations. Heterozygous advantage is usually referred to as being due to *super-* or *overdominance*. *Real* overdominance found at single loci is often distinguished from *pseudo*-overdominance, where the superiority of the heterozygotes is based on chromosome segments or blocks. In some species, inversions are known to protect such segments from disintegration.[2] Experimentally, it is virtually impossible to establish whether a given instance of apparently real overdominance is due to action at a single locus or at two or more contiguous loci possibly containing pseudoalleles. It is likewise difficult to ascertain whether pseudo-overdominance of a chromosome segment is based on the heterozygote advantage of one or more specific loci within it, or on interaction between them. Under the simplest assumptions of random mating and constant genotypic selective value, theoretical considerations examined by Kimura (1956b) suggest that epistasis alone cannot maintain alternative alleles in a population.

---

[2] See in particular the reviews of Dobzhansky (1951, 1955) dealing with his monumental work on *Drosophila pseudoobscura*. Investigations have also been conducted on other species, e.g. in several genera of grasshoppers (White, 1951, 1957) and in *D. subobscura*, most recently by J. Maynard Smith and his associates (see Hollingsworth and Smith, 1955). Haldane (1957a) concluded on theoretical grounds that maintenance of inversions in populations must be based on cumulative heterosis, i.e. epistatic interactions between heterozygotes, such as has been found by Shultz and Briles (1953) for two of the blood group loci in chickens.

The existence in a given population of multiple genetic variants in frequencies greater than can be accounted for by recurrent mutation pressure is a variety of the phenomenon designated by Huxley (1955) as *morphism*. This term is an abbreviation of *polymorphism* known to Darwin, but first defined in this sense by Ford (1945). When morphism is found in a population not in equilibrium, it may be of the *transient* kind,

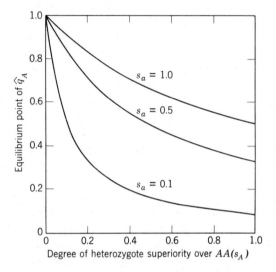

Figure 3.1. Equilibrium values of q_A when selection favors the heterozygote

The relative reproductive values of the three genotypes are taken to be

$$AA - 1 - s_A$$
$$Aa - 1$$
$$aa - 1 - s_a$$

The curves show the equilibrium points of q_A for three arbitrarily selected values of s_a and for the whole range of s_A from zero to unity. The derivation of the expression for the equilibrium

$$\hat{q}_A = \frac{s_a}{s_A + s_a}$$

is given in box 6.

i.e. one of the morphs is on the way to extinction. An equilibrium situation in which the different morphs are maintained in the population by overdominance represents a case of *balanced* morphism. Other causes of morphism (i.e. the alternatives to selection already noted in the introduction to this chapter), such as the neutrality of morphs in their effect on fitness, linkage, and non-random segregation, have been reviewed, together with those already mentioned, by Cain and Sheppard (1950). The conditions governing equilibrium values under balanced morphism are set out in box 6, which gives the elementary mathematical treatment of this problem. Figures 3.1 and 3.2 illustrate some aspects of it.

In the first of these diagrams, the three curves show equilibrium values for alleles that are at a disadvantage when homozygous. In the top curve the *aa* genotype is assumed to be lethal. The abcissa indicates the superiority of the heterozygote over the other homozygote. When the selective values of *AA* and *Aa* are equal ($s_A = 0$), the wild allele (*A*) proceeds to fixation. At the other extreme of the upper curve, *AA* is also

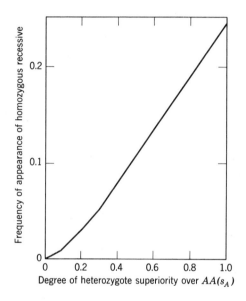

Figure 3.2. Incidence of recessive lethals maintained in a population by heterozygote superiority

The scale of the abcissa is the same as in figure 3.1. The ordinate shows the values of $(1 - q_A)^2$ at equilibrium.

taken to be lethal ($s_A = 1$). The equilibrium value of q_A will then be 0.5, as in figure 1.7.

The two lower curves can be interpreted in a similar fashion. The *aa* genotype is not lethal in these examples but is at a constant disadvantage *vis a vis* the heterozygote (with the values of s_a equaling 0.5 and 0.1 respectively). When $s_A = s_a$, the point of equilibrium for both alleles is 0.5 (see also box 7).

That overdominance can prevent an allele which is lethal when homozygous from becoming extinct is clearly shown by the upper curve in the

---
BOX 7

Symbolization of Dominance

The effects on a metric character of allelic substitution at a locus may be independent of those on fitness. A convenient system of notation is the following:

Genotype	Frequency	Fitness	Metric value
AA	x	$1 - s_A$	$X + 2d$
Aa	y	1	$X + d + h$
aa	z	$1 - s_a$	X

Where the character considered is fitness itself, only one of the last two columns is needed. The following table compares several systems of symbols in current usage with particular reference to overdominance in fitness. To avoid confusion some of the letters used in the original sources cited have been changed here.

	Reference				
	Wright (1931)	Wright (1931)	Fisher, Immer, and Tedin (1932)	Hull (1945)	Haldane (1958)
Reproductive rate or metric value					
$\quad AA$	$1 - s_A$	1	$X + 2d$	$X + 2d$	1
$\quad Aa$	1	$1 - ls$	$X + d + h$	$X + d + kd$	$1 - m$
$\quad aa$	$1 - s_a$	$1 - s$	X	X	$1 - t$
$AA - aa$	$s_a - s_A$	s	$2d$	$2d$	t
$Aa - \dfrac{A + Aaa}{2}$	$\dfrac{s_A + s_a}{2}$	$\dfrac{2 - (2l + 1)s}{2}$	h	kd	$1 - m - \dfrac{t}{2}$
Complete dominance	$s_A = 0$	$l = 0$	$h = d$	$k = 1$	$m = 0$
Overdominance	$s_A > 0$ $s_a > 0$	$l < 0$	$h > d$	$k > 1$	$m < 0$ $t \geq 0$
Equilibrium under over- dominance $(\hat{q}_A)$	$\dfrac{s_a}{s_A + s_a}$	$\dfrac{1 - l}{1 - 2l}$	$\dfrac{d + h}{2h}$	$\dfrac{1 + k}{2k}$	$\dfrac{t - m}{t - 2m}$

For a simple illustration, assume the following genotypic values:

$$AA = 1.0$$
$$Aa = 1.6$$
$$aa = 0.8$$

The various constants in the different notations will be:

$s_A = 0.6$	$l = -3.0$	$d = 0.1$	$d = 0.1$	$m = -0.6$
$s_a = 0.8$	$s = 0.2$	$h = 0.7$	$k = 7.0$	$t = 0.2$

The equilibrium value of $\hat{q}_A = 0.57$.

figure under discussion. Another way of illustrating this unhappy outlook for some breeders is presented in figure 3.2. The abcissa here is the same as in the previous graph. The ordinate represents the equilibrium value of $(1 - \hat{q}_A)^2$, which is the frequency of incidence of the lethal genotype. All other things being equal, 25 per cent of the population falls into this category when only heterozygotes are permitted to reproduce themselves. This proportion recurs in every generation, whenever AA, even though surviving, is not bred from.

Directional artificial selection is obviously a force endeavoring to move a population not previously subjected to it from an equilibrium composition. It will be shown later that populations can be forced into reproductive difficulties when artificial selection for a specific metric trait is carried too far. Here an example in which a new equilibrium has been reached under continued selection pressure will be shown. Figure 3.3 deals with a trait, the inheritance of which has not been analyzed completely. Yet the situation is clearly one of morphism, even if its exact genetic basis can only be guessed. The data on which this chart are based were obtained by Taylor (1946 and unpublished) and have been summarized in graphic form by Lerner (1954). They derive from a selection experiment conducted in a flock of chickens of mixed origin. In 1940 this population, previously used for studies of plumage color inheritance, exhibited a variable number of comb blades. Selection was then applied to increase the incidence of the multiple combs.

The blocks indicate the relative proportions of each type of comb observed in successive generations. In 1941 quadruplex combs made their first appearance in the flock, followed by quintuplex combs in 1944. At the other extreme, no single-comb birds occurred in the population after 1942, and a year later the last of the duplex combs was seen. Selection for the extreme forms was continued. Yet the figure shows that during the last three years the population remained in equilibrium. The genetic mechanism for this apparently balanced morphism has not been investigated.   It is by no means certain that the extreme expression represents the homozygous form.   However, the flock was an inbred one and was characterized by low reproductive rate.   Hence, not only quintuplex

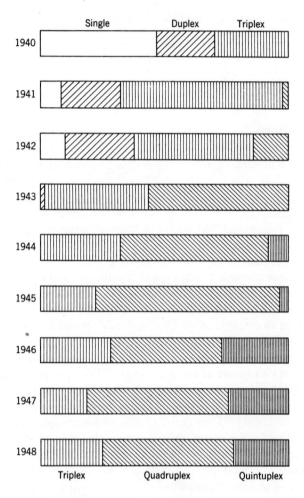

Figure 3.3.   Selection for the number of comb blades in chickens (from Taylor, 1946, and Lerner, 1954; see text)

but quadruplex individuals were used as parents.   If most of the progeny in the last three generations were produced by these birds, rather than by the extreme quintuplex class, overdominance may not be an unreasonable explanation for the results observed.

14. Fitness of Intermediates

The example illustrated in figure 3.3 started as an experiment on directed selection. In the last few generations it seems likely that, although artificial selection of the directed type was still being attempted, natural selection of the stabilizing kind gained the upper hand. Haldane (1954), in suggesting a formula for describing natural selection for a metric trait (x), pointed out that it is likely that "almost all natural selection for a quantitative character is of this type. Even when the mean of x is appreciably higher in the parents of the next generation it is probable that selection occurs against very high values of x. This seems to be so in a good many cases of artificial selection. The individuals showing the selected character with the highest intensity are often weak or sterile. If this is so, natural selection, even when it is altering the genetic composition of a population, is probably usually weeding out homozygotes at a number of loci."

Stabilizing selection thence seems to be of considerable importance in that it may interfere with directed selection.[3] Indeed, in many instances the fitness of phenotypic intermediates is greater than that of the extreme types, which is another way of saying that the individuals close to the average for a metric trait are favored by natural selection over those far removed from the mean value of the population.

Figure 3.4 (based on the experiment reported by Lerner and Gunns, 1952) shows the relationship between the egg weight typical for a bird and two partial indexes of its reproductive fitness: percentage hatchability and the relative number of chickens each bird produced in a given period of time. The latter measure includes the ability of the bird herself to survive the test period, her egg production, and the fertility and hatchability of the eggs laid. The arrows indicate the egg weight at which fitness, as measured here, is at its maximum and the mean egg weight of the population. It is obvious that the array with the highest fitness is in the intermediate range of egg weights. It is also somewhat below the mean. The discrepancy between optimum and mean is accounted for by the fact that the average egg weight is sustained in this flock at an artificially high level by intermittent directional selection (see Lerner, 1951).

The analysis of Lerner and Gunns, as well as that of Rendel (1943), who had earlier conducted a similar investigation on the eggs of ducks,

---

[3] Waddington (1953*b*) prefers to designate stabilizing selection by the epithet *normalizing*. In his terminology, stabilizing refers to selection for buffered developmental patterns, a process that can account for the phenotypic uniformity of populations but not for their genetic variability. See also the discussion by Haldane (1957*b*).

suggests that the superiority of intermediates, at least in these examples, is not entirely phenotypic but is based in great part on genotypic differences in fitness. The question, however, arises whether the reproductively superior genotypes are more fit only because they correspond to inter-mediate phenotypes or because, as is at least hinted at in Haldane's statement, they are heterozygotes.

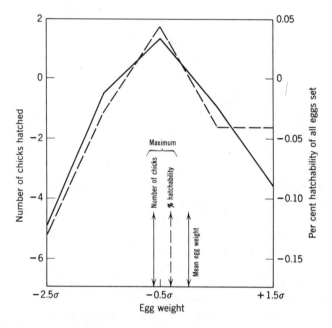

Figure 3.4.   Relation between egg weight and fitness in chickens

A group of 154 mass-mated Leghorn pullets was characterized for egg size by weighing five consecutive eggs.   The birds are classified on the chart in arrays based on standard deviations above and below the population mean for this trait.   The solid line repre-sents an index of fitness; in this instance it is the average number of chicks hatched per pullet in each array.   The left-hand scale for this trait is calibrated in deviations from the mean.   The dashed line shows percentage of hatchability for each array in terms of deviations from the mean (right-hand scale).   Further explanation is provided in the text.   The data are from Lerner and Gunns (1952).

It is not an easy matter to establish unequivocally which of these possibilities applies to a given character of a certain population living in a particular environment.   The two situations represent two kinds of stabilizing selection (I and II in figure 1.1) which, as has been shown by Robertson (1956), should on theoretical grounds lead to different conse-quences.

He found that the so-called homeostatic model, in which the extremes have a low fitness not because they are extremes but because they are homozygotes, can preserve genetic variability in a population. This was the model, proposed by Lerner (1954), in which population properties were viewed as a by-product of properties of individuals. Lerner's reasoning was based on the idea that a population can benefit from the conservation of genetic variability which is consequent on a reproductive advantage of heterozygous individuals. Genetic reserves maintained in this manner would endow the interbreeding group with protection against

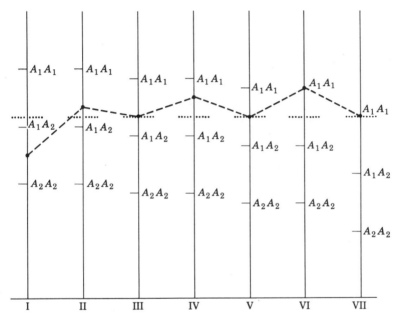

Figure 3.5. Model of allelic fixation when selection favors an intermediate phenotype (from Robertson, 1956; see text for explanation)

stresses of fluctuating environment, that is, with homeostatic ability. Populations with this capacity would be expected to have an increased probability of survival as compared with those lacking it.

The other model of stabilizing selection is based on the assumption that the superiority of the individual in the central arrays is due to the intermediate character of their phenotype. Robertson established that fixation is inevitable under this condition. Figure 3.5 illustrates the process described by him, which for each locus goes through seven stages. It is postulated that it is locus A which originally has the major effect on the character in question. The intermediate phenotype selected for is shown by the dotted line. The average values for the three genotypes (A_1A_1, A_1A_2, A_2A_2) are also indicated on the vertical scales. The dashed line connects the means of the populations at the different stages. Because the rate of change in allelic frequency on this model is dependent on the square of the effect of allelic substitution (i.e. on the magnitude of the difference between the values of the two homozygotes), it is locus A that will be the first to be affected by selection.

Stage I corresponds to the initial population. As a result of the selective advantage of intermediate phenotypes, locus A reaches an equilibrium (stage II), such as to have the new population mean exceed the desired value (dotted line) by the same amount by which the latter exceeds the heterozygote. At this stage, loci which previously had only modifying effects come into play to bring the mean of the population closer to the value selected for. This process will reduce the value of all three genotypes, as is shown in stage III. In consequence, locus A will be thrown off its stage II equilibrium. Selection then proceeds to establish a new one at a higher frequency of A_1A_1 (stage IV). Once more selection directed at the loci with minor effects brings together the value selected for and the mean (stage V). Eventually when the value of A_1A_1 and the mean are the same, the frequency of A_1 becomes irreversibly fixed at unity (stage VI). The final stage (VII) involves the last reduction in the average values of the three genotypes (or, more correctly, A_1A_1 alone, since it is now the only one in the population) to coincide with the values selected for. The whole process will now be repeated with respect to the locus which, after the fixation of A, has become the major differential. In this manner all loci contributing to the differences in the trait concerned will, one by one, become fixed.

In the same paper, Robertson also presented a formal proof of the fact that the mating together of extremes will maintain genetic variability as shown in example III of figure 1.1 (see also Moree, 1953). Negative assortment is occasionally practiced with respect to morphological traits. In nature at least one instance involving a major allelic difference, that in the moth *Panaxia*, has been demonstrated (Sheppard, 1952). But for continuously distributed traits this mating system is not a common one. When combined with a selective disadvantage of intermediates, it leads to stabilizing or to disruptive selection (examples III and IV in figure 1.1).

Robertson's model shows that maintenance of genetic variance for metric traits is not likely to be accounted for by superiority of intermediate types *per se*. At the same time, when the higher fitness of the average individuals is a consequence of their heterozygous constitution, genetic variance will be preserved. Other models of heterozygote advantage that are not based on the superior fitness of intermediates do not necessarily permit perpetuation of heterogeneity in the contents of the gene pool. One of these, for example, is the epistatic model constructed by Rendel (1953), in which in spite of heterosis displayed by individuals produced by a first cross of non-interbreeding populations, loci responsible for the hybrid vigor displayed tend toward fixation in subsequent generations. More generally, heterosis observed in crosses between populations may have a basis independent of selection or coadaptation (Dobzhansky, 1952). As demonstrated in a number of experiments, this type of hybrid vigor is transient (Vetukhiv, 1953; Brncic, 1954; Dobzhansky, 1955). It is not a dead-end phenomenon only to the degree that subsequent to the original cross a new coadapted gene pool incorporating material from both parental populations may eventually evolve as, for instance, happened in the experiments of Buzzati-Traverso (1955).

All in all, it may be seen that for Mendelian populations in equilibrium, which in order to survive must retain a fund of genetic variation, Herbert Spencer's winged phrase "survival of the fittest" becomes more modestly "survival of the mediocre," unless "fitness" is given the technical meaning defined in section 3, which is unlikely to have been what Spencer meant. Indeed, Darwin (1872) in accepting survival of the fittest as a synonym for natural selection has, in common with many a lesser man, regrettably helped to confuse laymen and biologists alike by failing to distinguish between the specialized meaning of a word and its current dictionary sense.

15. Inbreeding

Selection advances in an isolated population, when it is viewed as a closed system which lacks sources of variation provided by mutation or immigration, are made at the cost of additive genetic variance (see Mather, 1949b, for a discussion of the *balance sheet* of hereditary variation). Changes in the mean of a trait under selection are theoretically accompanied by reduction of variability. But the immediate effect may be so small as to be undetectable, especially for characters of low heritability.[4] The total potentialities for advance are nonetheless circumscribed by the original amount of genetic variation. Some of the loss in the initially free variation is compensated for when crossing over releases potential variability possibly locked in heterozygous polygenic blocks. But once

[4] Morley (1955a) may be consulted for a tabulation of the relative amounts of reduction in genetic variance expected because of selection for continuously distributed traits. The reduction of additive variation, when the incidence of all-or-none traits approaches extreme values, has already been noted in section 12.

homozygosity is achieved at a locus, it can no longer contribute to selection progress until a mutation or an introduction of new alleles from outside the population occurs. Hence, any pressure that tends to bring about allelic fixation limits further selection gains.

The most important cause of decay in genetic variation within unselected populations is consanguineous mating or inbreeding. Its effect is to diminish the genetic variance contributed by all segregating loci, not just by those toward which selection is directed. The total usable genetic variability and the effective degree of heritability are thereby reduced. An additional damping effect on the gains may arise because of inbreeding depression. This follows because, as a rule, the metabolic efficiency of

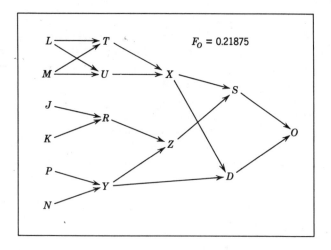

Figure 3.6. A pedigree showing irregular inbreeding (see box 8)

inbred animals is relatively low. Hence, should the genotypic values of inbred offspring be below their estimated genetic values, advances in the phenotypic mean of an economically useful trait might fall short of expectation on the basis of a given selection intensity and observed heritability.

The increase in homozygosity occasioned by fixation is best measured by the inbreeding coefficient F. This constant can be defined as the correlation between the genetic values of the uniting gametes or as the probability that two alleles entering the zygote are derived from a common ancestral allele (boxes 4 and 8). It was first suggested as a measure of the amount of inbreeding by Wright (1921), who in a series of further publications amplified and generalized its significance (his 1951 review includes a bibliography of his writings on the subject). Other useful measures of inbreeding that have been proposed are either identical with

F (Bernstein's, 1930, α), or are related to it in a fairly simple way (Fisher's, 1950, λ). Instructions for computing the F values from pedigrees have been given by many investigators. It may suffice to note here a short-cut method described by Cruden (1949), which is particularly useful for irregular systems of mating. Box 8 demonstrates the application of Wright's original path-coefficient technique of computing F to the pedigree in figure 3.6.

When a population is subjected to inbreeding, it undergoes a fractionization into a series of non-interbreeding groups or inbred lines. Within each additively genetic variation decreases, while between lines it increases. If no lines are discarded (which in practice is not possible), the

---

BOX 8

The Inbreeding Coefficient

The inbreeding coefficient F devised by Wright (1921, 1923, 1951) has been defined in a variety of ways (see discussion by Kempthorne, 1957). It can assume any value from zero to one; F may be considered as expressing the probability that the two alleles at a locus which enter the zygote are derived from a common ancestral allele, or as measuring the proportionate decline in the average number of heterozygous loci carried by a randomly chosen individual in the population. The value of F can be estimated for any individual on the assumption that no selection of heterozygotes occurred in the course of inbreeding. With very close inbreeding, the discrepancy between the computed F and the most probable actual level of heterozygosity due to such selection is not a serious one. When, however, inbreeding is mild and prolonged, it is probable that the computed F is an overestimate. For theoretical discussions of the relationship between the rate at which homozygosis is attained and the extent of heterozygote advantage, the papers of Hayman and Mather (1953) and of Reeve (1955) may be consulted. For an experimental demonstration of the degree of discordance between computed F values and homozygosity, as judged by the success of skin grafts within inbred lines of chickens, see Cock and Clough (1956).

Figure 3.6 extends the pedigree shown in figure 1.2 (taken from Lerner, 1950). It can serve to illustrate Wright's (1923) method of computing the value of the coefficient of inbreeding (references to extensions and simplifications of this technique are given in the text).

The general expression is

$$F = \sum(\tfrac{1}{2}^{n_{SA}+n_{DA}+1})(1 + F_A) \qquad (1)$$

where n_{SA} is the number of paths from an ancestor, found in the pedigree of both parents of the individual in question, to the sire; n_{DA} is similarly the number of paths from the dam to the common ancestor; and F_A is the inbreeding coefficient of the latter. The value of F for any individual is then obtained by summation of the contributions of each common ancestor corrected for its own inbreeding.

In the pedigree, S and D are non-inbred relatives originating from the same sire, X, who is himself a product of brother by sister mating; the maternal granddam, Y, is also the granddam of the sire. The following table shows how the value of $F_O = 0.21875$ is arrived at.

Individual Con- sidered	Common Ancestor	Paths to Sire	Paths to Dam	$n_{SA} + n_{DA} + 1$	Uncorrected Contribution to F	F_A	Contribution to F Corrected by $(1 + F_A)$
	L	LT	LU	3	0.125	0	0.125
X	M	MT	MU	3	0.125	0	0.125
						$F_X = 0.25$	
	X	XS	XD	3	0.125	0.25	0.15625
O	Y	YZS	YD	4	0.0625	0	0.06250
						$F_O = 0.21875$	

The measure of genetic relationship between individuals in a population is closely related to F. Its general form (for the relationship between S and D, with A indicating a common ancestor) is

$$r_{SD}^G = \frac{\sum(\tfrac{1}{2}n_{SA}+n_{DA})(1 + F_A)}{\sqrt{(1 + F_S)(1 + F_D)}} \qquad (2)$$

The common ancestors of S and D are the inbred X and the non-inbred Y. The paths between S and D on the one hand and X and Y on the other are readily counted from the pedigree. The values of F_S and of F_D are zero.
Hence,

$$r_{SD}^G = (\tfrac{1}{2})^2(1.25) + (\tfrac{1}{2})^3 = 0.4375 \qquad (3)$$

a value closer to that for full-sibs (0.50) than for half-sibs (0.25).

Under random mating the approximate relationship between the average F of a population and the average r^G is

$$\bar{F} = \frac{r^G}{2 - r^G} \qquad (4)$$

The extent of formation of partially inbred lines within a population may be judged by a comparison between the $\bar{F}$ expected from this relationship and that actually observed (see Lush, 1946).

original allelic frequency (q) remains constant, while, on the assumption of complete additivity of gene action, the genetic variance of the population rises to a limit of double the amount originally present.   Within each line, however, there is a tendency toward fixation of one or another of the segregating alleles, accompanied, of course, by a decrease in the variance. Thus, for example, if the original value of q_{A_1} were 0.3, of q_{A_2} 0.6, and of q_{A_3} 0.1, it is to be expected that when complete homozygosity is attained (in the absence of selection), 30 per cent of the inbred lines will be of the genotype A_1A_1, 60 per cent of the genotype A_2A_2, and the remaining 10 of the constitution A_3A_3.   That is to say, unselected inbred lines are equivalent to random choices from the original gene pool which have been made diploid.   The relative proportions in which genetic variance is distributed under inbreeding between and within lines are shown in box 9.

BOX 9

The Effect of Inbreeding on Variance

The following is a corrected version of table 10 from Lerner (1950), valid when the genetic variance (σ_G^2) is completely additive.   Another important assumption is that inbreeding has no consequences to the amount of environmental variance.   As noted in section 16 and in box 5, this is not a realistic postulate.   Hence, the formulas given below must be used with caution.   Since corrections for inbreeding for variance components in use in heritability determinations (e.g. those given by Hazel and Terrill, 1945) suffer from the same handicap, this admonition also applies to them.   Robertson (1952) may be consulted for a theoretical discussion of the effects of inbreeding on variance due to recessive alleles.

Variance	Under Random Mating	Under Inbreeding		
		Between Inbred Lines	Within Inbred Lines	Total
Environmental	σ_E^2	0	σ_E^2	σ_E^2
Genetic	σ_G^2	$2F\sigma_G^2$	$(1-F)\sigma_G^2$	$(1+F)\sigma_G^2$
Phenotypic	$\sigma_G^2 + \sigma_E^2$	$2F\sigma_G^2$	$(1-F)\sigma_G^2 + \sigma_E^2$	$(1+F)\sigma_G^2 + \sigma_E^2$
Heritability	h^2	1	$\dfrac{(1-F)h^2}{1-Fh^2}$	$\dfrac{(1+F)h^2}{1+Fh^2}$

A population in which inbreeding is inevitable simply because the number of individuals it contains is limited and sooner or later relatives have to be mated to each other, is equivalent to an inbred line.   Loss of genetic variability will occur here at a rate which is a function of the size of the population (see section 17).   If many such populations are considered, the total allelic frequency will remain the same as in the original indefinitely large population.   For each individual interbreeding group,

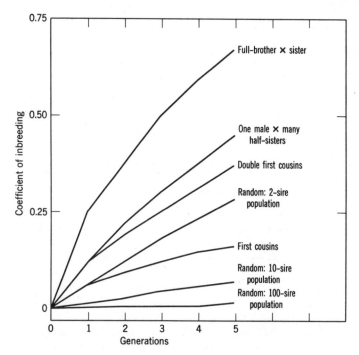

Figure 3.7.   Increase in homozygosity under inbreeding

This diagram, as practically every other on the subject to be found in the literature of the last 35 years, derives from Wright's (1921) classical study which contains much similar information in an extended form.   All the inbreeding systems in this figure lead to an eventual coefficient of inbreeding of 1.00.   There are milder inbreeding schemes which in theory have lower limits of F.   Thus, continued mating between second cousins will not lead to an F value of over 0.02.   Such schemes can be carried on indefinitely only in very large populations, since in populations of restricted size relatives closer than second cousins will eventually have to be mated together.

however, fixation at different loci will take place in an unpredictable pattern unless selection is practiced.

Figure 3.7 illustrates the increase in homozygosity expected under different inbreeding schemes.   Several examples of random mating in which inbreeding is due to a limited number of males siring each successive generation are also shown.   In these examples it is assumed that heterozygotes do not enjoy a selective advantage over homozygotes.

Figure 3.8 shows the increase in the inbreeding coefficient in the flock of Leghorn chickens selected for egg production which is described in detail in section 31.   In this population a maximum of 12 to 14 sires was selected every year, with up to 10 dams mated to each.   The theoretical expected increase in F per generation under random mating is

$$\varDelta F = \frac{1}{8S} + \frac{1}{8D}$$

where S and D are the respective numbers of sires and dams producing offspring.   In populations with equal numbers of sires and dams, this

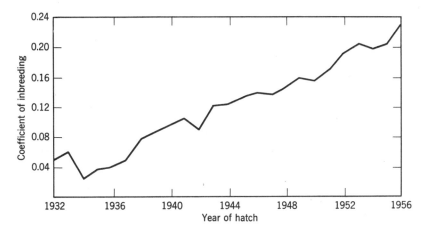

Figure 3.8.   Rise in inbreeding in a flock of chickens

The population referred to here is described in section 31.   The inbreeding coefficient is computed on the basis of the birds hatched in 1925.   Introduction of breeding stock from outside sources accounts for the drops in F value noted in 1934 and 1941.   After 1941 no further immigration occurred.   The slight increase in steepness of the curve after 1950 is due to the shortening of the intergeneration interval as a consequence of an increased use of young birds as parents.

expression reduces itself to $1/2N$.   It is possible to minimize $\varDelta F$ in a population by negative *genetic assortment*, i.e. by mating together individuals with a lower relationship to each other than that expected on the average between mates chosen at random.   The degree of inbreeding is also affected by *somatic assortment*, in which mates resemble each other more (*positive assortment*) or less (*negative assortment*) than they would had they been coupled by chance.   Wright (1921) may be consulted for the genetic consequences of various mating schemes of this sort.   Selection may either reduce the rate of inbreeding (when heterozygotes are preferred) or accelerate it, if it leads to a high proportion of ancestor

elimination by family selection (see section 17).   In the example shown in
figure 3.8 (representing 25 years but only 15 generations of breeding), the
pulls in opposite directions were apparently equal: the expected ΔF and
the actual are not greatly different.

   We may conclude the present section with a few illustrations of inbreeding degeneration.   This is a subject that has been much discussed
and written about since before Darwin.   Its genetic basis is not completely

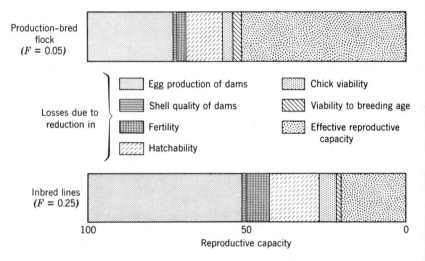

Figure 3.9.   Effect of inbreeding on reproductive fitness of chickens

   This diagram is based on the analysis by Düzgüneş (1950) of the causes of reduction
from the potentially possible average fitness of a production-bred flock of chickens
($F = 0.05$) and of mildly inbred lines extracted from it ($F = 0.25$).   The reproductive
capacity on the abcissa refers to the relative proportion of offspring per dam surviving
to 9 months of age.   The length of the hatching season was kept constant (28 days)
so that each dam had a potential reproductive capacity of 28 offspring, equivalent to
100 per cent.   If only 14 birds were alive at 9 months of age, relative fitness would be
50 per cent.   The first six blocks indicate the proportionate reduction from the maximum at different stages of the reproductive cycle.   The last block shows the proportion
of offspring alive at 9 months of age.

clear.   The   consequences   of   inbreeding   in   normally   cross-fertilized
organisms   are   usually   attributed   to   fixation   of   alleles   with   undesirable
recessive effects.   The role of homozygosity *per se* in this connection has
not been definitely established, although overdominance has been credited
with producing heterosis, when this phenomenon is measured by the
excess of a trait in a cross over its value in a population in equilibrium
(Crow, 1952).

   Countless observations documenting the effects of inbreeding on various traits in different species have been made. In general, the closer the character is related to fitness, the more it is subject to inbreeding depression. Indeed, not only inbreeding degeneration but the extent of heterosis, the relative amount of additively genetic variance, the stability of gains obtained from selection are all connected to fitness, an issue to be explored in some detail in the following section.

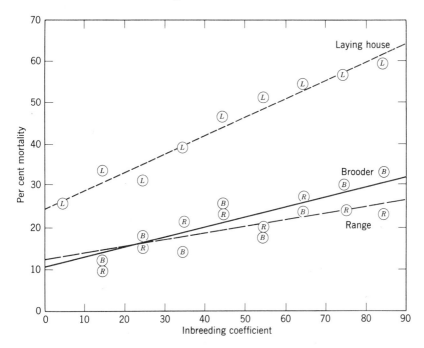

Figure 3.10. Effects of inbreeding on viability of chickens

Unweighted linear regressions from a series of 25 inbred lines of White Leghorns of mortality in three stages of life (chicks in the brooder; growing birds on range; and adults in the laying house) on inbreeding. The data are from McLaury and Nordskog (1956).

Here, in order to indicate the degree to which the traits of the domestic fowl commonly subjected to selection are affected by inbreeding, three graphic illustrations are given (figures 3.9, 3.10, and 3.11). The first shows the loss of fitness under consanguineous mating, empirically observed by Düzgüneş (1950). It may be seen that an increase of F from 0.05 to 0.25 reduces fitness by more than half. Nearly all the components of fitness (in particular the fecundity of the dams and the hatchability of the embryos) show a decline. In this illustration, viability from time of hatch to breeding age appears to be independent of the degree of inbreeding. whereas in figure 3.10, derived from a different source, a positive regression of mortality rate on the coefficient of inbreeding can be observed. Finally, figure 3.11 is an extrapolation of the analysis of Tebb (1957), which shows the expected loss in egg production occasioned by inbreeding due to small flock size.

Jull's (1952) book has extensive literature references to inbreeding effects in poultry. The publications of Shoffner (1948) and of Blow and Glazener (1953) may be particularly noted with regard to the consequences of

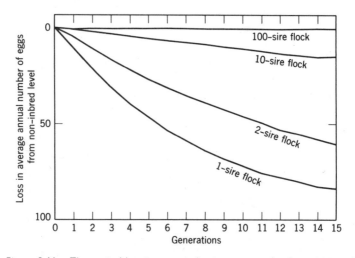

Figure 3.11.   Theoretical loss in egg production as a result of restriction of flock size

These curves are based on Tebb's (1957) estimate of a linear intrageneration regression of annual egg production on the coefficient of inbreeding of -1.0 egg per each 0.01 increase in F. This value was computed from data on the flock dealt with in section 31. It is assumed here that the inbreeding coefficient in populations of different sizes increases at the rate of $1/8S$ (where S is the effective number of sires) per generation. The relation between actual and effective numbers of parents is considered in section 17.

inbreeding to economically useful traits. Shultz (1953a) has a thorough analysis of inbreeding carried on simultaneously with directional selection. Most of these studies are in reasonable agreement with each other. Nonetheless, many significant problems connected with the subject are still inadequately explored. For instance, the linearity of inbreeding degeneration of egg production in the various regions of F values has not been fully established, although figure 3.11 assumes without justification that the relationship is indeed a linear one. Another problem requiring illumination is the relation between rate of inbreeding per generation and the extent of inbreeding decline, a question that may be complicated by differential effects of consanguineous mating on the various components of a trait under observation (e.g. the C effects). With selection favoring heterozygotes, it may be expected that the regressions of various traits will differ both in linearity and magnitude, depending on whether a given F is attained in a few or many generations (see Hayman and Mather, 1953, for a discussion of the interference by the selective advantage of heterozygotes with the process of allelic fixation under different schemes of inbreeding). But adequate information on this matter is still lacking.

16. Overdominance

Superiority of heterozygotes perpetuates the heterogeneity of the gene pool and thereby provides the population with insurance against constant threats to its adapted structure. The sources of danger may lie in changes in the extrinsic environment or in new mutations which contribute to the inner environment of their carriers. But overdominance is of no aid to directional selection within a population. After a locus, block, or chromosome segment, having a heterozygous advantage with respect to a selected trait, attains an equilibrium frequency (box 6), further selection pressure in favor of heterozygotes will act in a stabilizing fashion depicted in example II of figure 1.1 and not directionally. Should the segregating unit have additive effects on the desired character, but be overdominant as far as fitness is concerned, natural selection will counteract artificial selection once the equilibrium frequency is reached. The gains obtained will then be subject to dissipation, as soon as artificial selection is suspended. Continued selection will produce progress, but the increments realized per generation will be lower than those expected. Eventually, the advance may stop entirely, or at best will be attained in a closed genetic system[5] at the cost of lowered fitness. Behavior of this kind may be especially frequent under pseudo-overdominance. One or another component of a reasonably long section of a chromosome, maintained as a unit in a population because of its high contribution to fitness, would be likely to have some effect on a metrical trait under selection pressure and thus put natural selection in opposition to artificial selection.

Overdominance then, although a boon to a natural population needing a fluid genetic composition to meet the challenges of a variable environment, can be a vexation when artificial directional selection is attempted.

[5] Release of new variability by crossing over, mutation, or migration may lead to a new coadapted gene pool and realization of increases sought in the mean of the population for some character. In discussing the model referred to in figure 3.12, Lerner (1954) gives a theoretical illustration of this possibility for a simple case of crossing over between two closely linked loci.

This may be expected to be particularly true in improved populations in which additive variance with respect to the selected trait has either been exhausted or is due to the very loci or blocks which are overdominant in their action on fitness.

A model illustrating this phenomenon has been constructed by Lerner (1954). Its essential features are shown in figure 3.12. The assumption in it is that the variability of a metric trait is additively determined by a

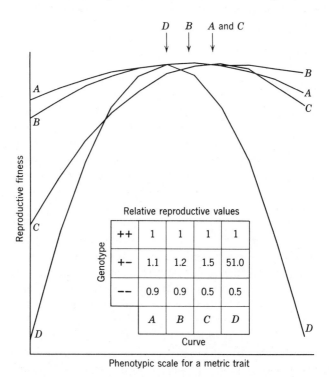

Figure 3.12.   A model of genetic homeostasis (see text for explanation)

segregating unit, the alternative forms of which are designated as $+$ and $-$. At the same time, the three genotypes, $++$, $+-$, and $--$ have a differential effect on reproductive fitness. Four cases differing in the degree of overdominance are considered.   The arrows indicate the means of the metric trait at equilibrium frequencies of the allele or block for the reproductive rates given in the inset.

Under natural selection, the mean of the population will oscillate within the limits of sampling error around the respective means in the examples labeled A, B, C, and D.   Should artificial selection be applied in either direction to the metric character, the mean will move along the appropriate curve and the average fitness of the population will be reduced. The four instances show great variation in the sensitivity of fitness to selection pressure. When overdominance for reproductive capacity is only slight (*A* and *B*), the curves are flat-topped, and the mean for the metric trait can change considerably without having the population suffer much loss of fitness. When, on the other hand, the advantage of the heterozygote is overwhelming (*D*), the population is doomed to extinction should directional selection be enforced. Removal of the disturbing pressure by suspending selection will in all cases cause the population to revert to its original mean. Robertson (1956) has generalized these examples and has derived a constant that measures the *homeostatic strength* of a character. This is a parameter which quantifies the decline in fitness under selection, as well as the rate of the reversion of the metric trait to the equilibrium state after selection has been suspended.

It should be noted that the abcissa of figure 3.12 can be calibrated, either in terms of metric values of the phenotypic trait selected or in terms of allelic frequency. Under the assumption of additiveness of gene action (for the metric trait), the two scales coincide.

According to this model, traits *A* and *B* are of trivial significance in determining reproductive capacity. They may be referred to as characters *peripheral* to fitness. Trait *C* is of somewhat greater importance and may be described as a *minor* fitness component. Trait *D* is a character having a *major* effect on fitness, with an intermediate optimum.

These traits may also be considered on the individual level rather than on the population level. Indeed, Robertson (1955*a*) presented a strikingly similar model (the terms peripheral, minor, and major fitness components were originally used by him) in analyzing certain aspects of artificial selection response. Figure 3.13 is adapted from his paper, with the distinguishing letters for the different curves paralleling those in the previous graph. Curves *A*, *B*, and *C* are virtually identical with their analogues in figure 3.12. Curve *E*, contrary to the earlier example of *D*, represents a major fitness component with the optimum closer to the maximum than to the mean. Curve *F* stands for fitness itself. These curves are not related to allelic frequency as are their antecedents. Yet they reflect the close connection between individual and population properties, which are undoubtedly significant in evolutionary phenomena. This point merits a slight digression.

Lerner (1950) applied the term genetic homeostasis to the tendency of a population to maintain a genetic composition leading to an optimum balance, a definition which appears to be equivalent to the *genetic inertia* of Darlington and Mather (1949). In a more extensive treatment of the subject, Lerner (1954) dealt nearly exclusively with overdominance in the wide sense, comprising both the real and the pseudo varieties, as the mechanism of such self-equilibration. The concept of genetic homeostasis, however, can be much broader, covering the full range of devices

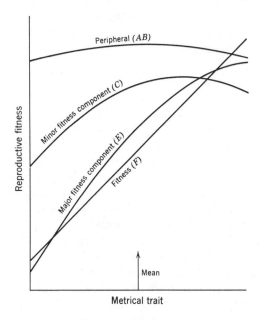

Figure 3.13. The relation between metrical traits and fitness (from Robertson, 1955a)

Curve AB: Optimum and mean coincide; variance mostly additive; no effects of inbreeding.
Curve C: Optimum above mean; more non-additive variance; slight deterioration under inbreeding.
Curve E: Optimum approaches extreme; little additive variance; considerable inbreeding depression.
Curve F: Optimum at maximum: no additive variance at equilibrium; severe inbreeding degeneration.

The connection between this and the previous figure is discussed in the text.   See also Clarke and Smith (1955) and Michie and McLaren (1955) for other views regarding the basis of contributions that different traits make to fitness.

for autoregulation of populations, including processes of coadaptation. Although few of them have been investigated experimentally, many have been conceptually visualized.

The interregulation of dominance and mutation rate discussed by Berg (1941; see also the bibliography of her papers in the compilation of Hers-

kowitz, 1952) is one example. The variability of mutation rate in laboratory and wild populations of Drosophila (Ives, 1950), if it has an adaptive
basis, is another. The relationship between the size of a population and
its breeding structure, including possibly recombination rate, could
similarly be an aspect of genetic homeostasis. In particular, populations
that can pursue a chain of regulatory adjustments in the face of externally
imposed changes of their genetic system survive, and those unable to do
so perish. The development of tolerance to inbreeding in laboratory
animals is a simple example of this process (see box 23 in chapter 6).
When incest is forced on a normally outbreeding population, only lines
capable of conversion to the new conditions remain in existence. Extreme examples of this situation are found in plants that change from
cross- to self-fertilization. Thus the cultivated tomato is known to have
passed, in the absence of specific pollinating insects, from facultative
cross-fertilization to obligate selfing (Rick, 1950). The first form of
reproduction kept the genetic variation of partial isolates renewed; the
second resulted in a closed system. It seems highly probable that various
adaptive changes in the physiology of individuals and of populations
must have followed in the wake of the alteration of the mating system of
this plant.

The simplest type of population self-regulation may lie in the dependence of selection coefficients on allelic frequencies. When an allele is
rare, it may not be discriminated against, but as its frequency rises, its
selective advantage may increase. This process may be viewed, as noted
by Dempster (1955a), as a form of genotype-environment interaction,
since the frequency of other genotypes in a population is a characteristic
of the environment of individuals of a given genetic constitution. A
particularly striking illustration of this phenomenon is provided by
multiple alleles involved in self-sterility (Lewis, 1948, lists a variety of
instances). In this breeding system preservation of a large number of
alleles must be of adaptive significance to the population and not to the
individual, since a diploid individual can contain at the most only two
alternative forms at a locus. Yet, the mechanics of reaching an optimum
distribution of allelic frequencies are based on variation in individual
fitness. An individual carrying rare alleles will have more descendants
than one carrying common ones, because fewer of its gametes will enter
into lethal homozygous combinations. Such reproductive advantage will,
of course, tend to increase the frequencies of the rare alleles and reduce
those of the common ones, until an equilibrium is established.

The term genetic homeostasis was intended to convey an analogy with
the phenomenon of homeostasis on the level of individual organisms,
particularly in connection with the suggestion that at least with respect to

maintenance of heterozygosity this property of populations is a by-product of homeostasis of individuals. Regrettably, confusion has arisen in the literature between the genetic homeostasis of populations (for which Lewontin's, 1956, term *collective* homeostasis might have served better) and the genotypically controlled developmental homeostasis of individuals, first studied in relation to heterozygosity by Dobzhansky and Wallace (1953).

The *evolutionary* implications of both phenomena deal with the maintenance of a steady state with respect to fitness. Other properties of individuals (e.g. the devices for temperature control of homoiothermic animals) or of populations (for instance, selection coefficients) may show fluctuation or remain invariable, depending on what best serves the end of maintaining the constancy of reproductive behavior.

Lerner (1954) has discussed the evidence for the hypothesis that control of homeostatic devices may be vested to a considerable degree in heterozygosity.[6] Should selection for developmental homeostasis be responsible for the preservation of genotypic variability, genetic homeostasis follows as a consequence. Differential reproduction of individuals can thus promote both a high degree of individual homeostasis and heterozygote superiority. Selection between populations could similarly favor survival of groups possessed of collective homeostasis. The causal relations between homeostasis and heterozygosity in cross-fertilized organisms are probably of a circular nature, each being both cause and effect of the other.

This general concept may be restated by saying that heterozygotes are better buffered, i.e. are less responsive to environmental stresses than homozygotes, as far as traits directly related to fitness are concerned. In the course of their ontogeny they exhibit *canalized* development (Waddington, 1942), tending not to stray from the paths that lead to the assumption of normal adult form. The flexibility and stability aspects of developmental homeostasis as related to buffering are schematically shown in figure 3.14.

For major characters contributing to fitness nearly proportionally to their metric magnitude (as in case *E* of figure 3.13), environmental variance of heterozygotes must on the homeostatic hypothesis be lower than that of homozygotes. The evidence supporting this notion is plentiful (see Lerner, 1954; Yoon, 1955; Bader, 1956; McLaren and Michie, 1956; Clough and Cock, 1957), although it is by no means certain that the high phenotypic variability of inbreds is always due to homozygosity and not to their lowered means. In some instances the situation seems clear-cut.

---

[6] The claim that heterozygosity is the factor *uniquely* responsible for homeostasis has been attributed to Lerner by a number of writers, in spite of his explicit statements to the contrary (*inter alia* on pp. 16, 69, 71 and 78 of his book).

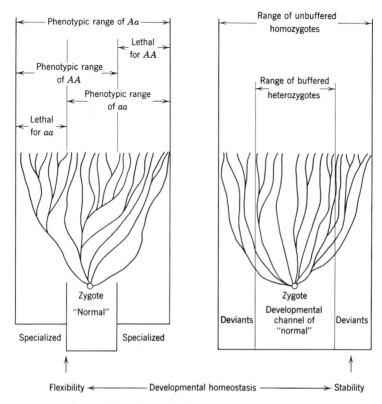

Figure 3.14. A model of developmental homeostasis

This diagram, although resembling figure 6 of Lerner (1954), is interpreted here in a somewhat different way. Pathways of development from the zygote to the stage at which phenotpyic observations are made are represented by the branching curves. In the left graph it is assumed that each of the two homozygotes is capable of survival only when the pathways stay within the central "normal" channel or within one, but not the other, specialized channel. The heterozygote, however, can survive throughout the total array of developmental possibilities portrayed. It is therefore flexible and may show a wider range of phenotypic expression. The right side shows the buffered behavior of heterozygotes which, despite various pressures, can stay within a narrow range of phenotypic expression. Homozygotes, being poorly buffered, may produce deviant forms when straying from the central developmental channel. They thus lack stability and have a higher environmental variance than do heterozygotes. The two parts of the diagram thus represent the genetic plasticity of heterozygotes, which can vary when this is necessary for survival or remain constant when such behavior bestows higher fitness on them. There are considerable difficulties in designing and interpreting experimental studies on the circumstances favoring respectively stability and flexibility. Indeed, threshold models can be readily constructed which assume that stability is more desirable in the heterozygotes but in which greater observed environmental variance in the heterozygotes than in homozygotes may be observed! See Thoday (1953) for a discussion of flexibility and stability of fitness components. Lewontin's (1956) paper and a subsequent exchange of remarks between him and Dempster (1956) should also be noted.

101

Thus, in the following figures from the University of California flock of chickens bred for egg production, environmental variance may be seen to have risen concurrently with the average inbreeding coefficient, although the mean egg number also increased under selection.

Year of Hatch	1933–1940	1941–1948
Average F	0.059	0.125
Average egg production of survivors	232.7	247.3
Genetic variance	649	595
Environmental variance	1514	2710

However, data for the same period on average hen-housed production do not show this relationship.

Should major buffering effects hinge on heterozygosity at a few loci, they may be instrumental in lowering the efficiency of selection. It is possible that minor additively genetic differences between individuals will be completely obscured by potent buffering forces. Many different genotypes will then have identical phenotypic expressions or be *equifinal* in their development. This fact (as pointed out by Comstock, 1955, in a different connection) has the same consequences as the absence of genetic variance—advances under mass selection will not be possible.

Although the importance of pseudo-overdominance is well established, unequivocal evidence for overdominance pure and simple is very difficult to obtain (see Donald, 1955, for a discussion of the subject with particular reference to livestock). Pontecorvo (1955) noted the paucity of well-established cases in which physiological information on allelic action is available, and Hexter (1955) reviewed a number of possible instances in Drosophila; in only a few did overdominance provide the simplest explanation for the observations made. However, the experimental techniques needed for statistical demonstration of overdominance, in even the most favorable material, are laborious and may, as has been suggested earlier, change the initial genetic system in such a way as to conceal the fact that in the pre-experimental population the phenomenon was present.

There are good reasons to believe with Emerson (1952) and Haldane (1955 and earlier) that there is a biochemical basis for overdominance. One reason suggested is that the physiological versatility of a locus carrying two different alleles is greater than that of a locus carrying a double dose of a single allele. This hypothesis, originally proposed in broad terms by East (1936), may also be described as one involving complementary dominance or availability of alternative genetic pathways (Lewis, 1954). Another possibility lies in the capacity of the heterozygote for manufacturing a product different from those elaborated by each allele in the absence of the other (Cohen, 1956, has added another instance of this kind to those listed by Haldane, 1955).

Unfortunately, domestic animals are exceedingly unsatisfactory material for investigating the fundamental nature of heterosis. Even in the field of immunology, where it has been possible to establish a biochemical basis for the selective advantage of heterozygotes at certain loci in humans (Allison, 1955), data from chickens have so far permitted only very broad conclusions to be made. The work on blood group inheritance in the fowl by Briles and his associates (Shultz and Briles, 1953; Briles, Johnson, and Garber, 1953; Briles and Krueger, 1955; Briles, 1956) includes both inferential and direct evidence for the superiority of heterozygotes in fitness and in a series of economic traits. But not even a hint on the exact physiology of the hybrid advantage demonstrated has so far been offered.

Data from inbreeding experiments initiated by Pease (1948) strongly suggest that heterozygote advantages are to be found not only with respect to blood group differences (Gilmour, 1954) but also at several loci involved in plumage color determination (Cock, 1956). There are other less clear-cut instances which will emerge from later discussion. They involve polygenic traits and therefore are hopelessly far from anything resembling undisputed proof for overdominance.

Finally, overdominance and heterosis must not be viewed as properties that have arisen fortuitously. When they exist within Mendelian populations, they do so by virtue of prior selection. It is not known exactly how they originate and whether they have come into being wherever they exist in the same way. It is, however, known that overdominance can be experimentally produced as a result of selection (Dobzhansky and Levene, 1951). It may also be argued (see discussion by Wallace, 1956) that, since mutants, because of their initial rarity, are subject to selection in a heterozygous state, overdominant effects on fitness must be a phenomenon more common than has been suspected or than is usually asserted on the basis of information from physiological genetics. In any case, in spite of the great extent of work that has been done, knowledge of the physiology of heterosis, in contrast to that of its formal genetic aspects, is in its infancy. Gowen (1952) may be consulted for a series of articles dealing with the subject and Mayr (1955) for a summary of current evidence on the relationship between heterozygosity and fitness.

17. Population Size and the Effects of Chance

The conditions specified in section 13 for allelic frequency equilibria in the absence of disturbing forces included indefinitely large population size. In practice, Mendelian populations are limited in the number of individuals they contain. Under artificial selection, a considerable fraction of the population is prevented from reproducing itself. Population size is then not specified by the total number of individuals in the flock or herd but depends on the number of selected parents.

The *effective* size of a population is, however, different from the actual number of parents selected when the variation in the number of offspring per parent exceeds that expected on the basis of the Poisson distribution, i.e. when the parents do not have equal probabilities of contributing the mean number of offspring to the next generation. The actual and the effective sizes are related by an expression that takes into account the standard deviation of the mean number of offspring (Wright, 1940). Crow and Morton (1955) have made an extensive study of the interdependence of these two parameters. They concluded that only under unusual circumstances can the effective size be expected to drop below three-quarters of the actual or census size. It seems likely that under artificial selection the discrepancy between the effective and actual number of parents may be greater, especially when genotypic selection leads to the culling of complete families of grandchildren. Thus, ten sires might be selected in every generation to reproduce the population, but all ten may be sons of one couple.

In each generation selected parents are the product of a two-by-two union of a sample of gametes from the gene pool of the previous generation. When the number of parents is N, the gametic sample size from which they originated is $2N$. Even in the absence of any selection, allelic frequencies of the sample will not be exactly those of the gene pool, because they are subject to sampling variation. But, as the population size is significantly reduced, the amplitude of the sampling effect is increased. Indeed, since the direction of the change in every generation is independent of what happened in the previous generation, allelic frequencies will in a certain proportion of cases move farther and farther away from the equilibrium values.

The evolutionary significance of *random drift*, which can in the extreme lead to fixation in the face of selective forces tending to maintain equilibrium values, has long been a subject of acrimonious debate, which at times assumed the magnitude of a *guerre des savants*. A historical review of the controversy has been given by Kimura (1955*b*) in presenting a general mathematical treatment of the subject. For experimental evidence on laboratory mutants of *Drosophila melanogaster* the studies of Buri (1956) and of Kerr and Wright (1954, the last of a series of three papers) may be consulted. An investigation of drift of naturally occurring inversions of *D. pseudoobscura* maintained in population cages was reported by Dobzhansky and Pavlovsky (1957).

The important point with respect to selection is the effect of reduction in population size on the rate of fixation of alleles and thus on the decay of genetic variability. In a very general way, we can see that the eventual distribution of allelic frequencies in a series of populations starting from a given value of q will depend on the effective population size (figure 3.15). Different loci within a single population will also show this distribution. In very large populations the distribution will be leptokurtic; in populations of medium size the range will be spread out; in small populations the eventual distributions will tend to be concentrated at the two extremes. Most populations of domestic animals can probably be regarded as being

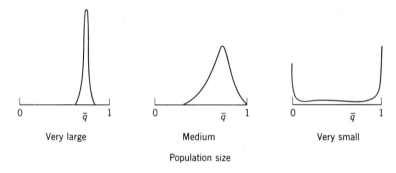

| Very large | Medium | Very small |

Population size

Figure 3.15.   The effect of population size on the distribution of allelic frequencies

From Wright (1932).   Random mating and absence of disturbing factors are assumed.

of medium size. However, alleles, the frequency of which is closer to zero or unity than is shown in the figure, run the risks of either extinction or fixation.

Sampling errors of allelic frequencies under Mendelian inheritance are functions not only of population size but also of the value of q. The former enters the expression for sampling variance in the form of the increase of the inbreeding coefficient per generation (ΔF), the latter in the form of the binomial variance component, $q(1 - q)$. In a randomly mated population of infinite size, ΔF is, of course, zero. When populations are of finite size, the relationship between mates must perforce assume significant values, thus producing an increase in F. When mating is at random, ΔF can be taken to be equal to the reciprocal of the sum of eight times the number of effective sires plus eight times the number of effective dams (section 15). When the number of sires and dams are equal, this expression, as has already been noted, reduces itself to $1/2N$.

The amplitude of chance fluctuations in allelic frequency then depends on the sampling variance,

$$\frac{q(1 - q)}{2N}$$

Here N is the effective number of parents, which, practically, is equal to the census number of parents when all parents have an equal probability of producing a given number of offspring.

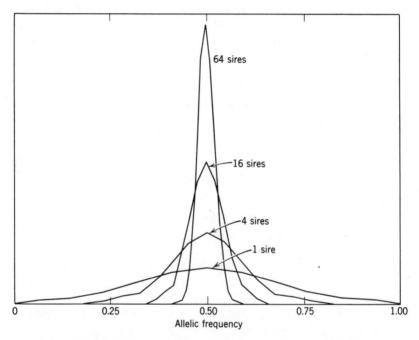

Figure 3.16.   Distribution of allelic frequencies in polygamous populations

   The curves portray the distributions of allelic frequencies initially at 0.5 after one generation of reproduction in populations with different effective numbers of sires.

   Box 10 demonstrates how this expression can be used in determining the effects of population size on allelic frequency.   Figure 3.16 illustrates the distribution of frequencies, initially at 0.5, after one generation of reproduction from a limited number of parents.   It is assumed in this instance that many dams are mated to each sire.   Under this mating scheme the value of $1/8S$ (where S is the effective number of sires) is the only one that needs to be taken into account, since one over eight times the number of dams will be a relatively small number.
   Lush (1946) has discussed in detail the consequences of restricted

---

BOX 10

Sampling Variance of Allelic Frequencies

The general expression for the sampling variance of allelic frequencies is $Fq(1 - q)$ (see Li, 1955a). In a randomly mated population of size N,

$$\frac{q(1 - q)}{2N}$$

can be used to determine the distribution of allelic frequencies after one generation of reproduction of a population having a given value of q. For the simplest situation we may assume that at each locus alternative alleles are found in the frequency of 0.5 (other frequencies between 0 and 1 produce asymmetrical distributions). From this formula the standard deviation is seen to be $1/\sqrt{8N}$. From tables of areas under the normal curve, it is known that the proportion of the population expected to fall within one standard deviation on each side of the mean is approximately 68.4 per cent. This is equivalent to saying that 34.13 per cent or 3413 loci out of 10,000 starting at $q = 0.5$ will in the next generation have a frequency above 0.5 but below 0.5 plus one standard deviation. In a similar manner, the proportion of loci expected to fall in the area between one and two standard deviations above (or below) the mean can be obtained. The accompanying table shows the distributions for three arbitrarily chosen values of N. It can also be taken to show the distribution after one generation of frequencies at a single locus with an initial q of 0.5 in 10,000 populations.

Range of Allele Frequencies		Number of Loci per 10,000	Population Size		
			8	128	2048
Below Mean	below 2σ	227	below 0.25	below 0.44	below 0.47
	2σ–σ	1,360	0.25–0.375	0.44–0.47	0.47–0.48
	σ–0	3,413	0.375–0.50	0.47–0.50	0.48–0.50
Above Mean	0–σ	3,413	0.50–0.625	0.50–0.53	0.50–0.52
	σ–2σ	1,360	0.625–0.75	0.53–0.56	0.52–0.53
	above 2σ	227	above 0.75	above 0.56	above 0.53

It may be seen that in a population produced by eight parents, approximately 2 per cent of loci are expected to drop from a frequency of 0.50 to less than half that figure. On the other hand, in a population of 2048, no allele approaches the point at which it is in peril of extinction.

population size on breeding practice. In surveying the selection and mating patterns in a number of livestock breeds, he arrived at the conclusion that the variation of allelic frequencies in them was greater than was expected on the basis of the number of parents selected. Should this finding also apply to flocks of domestic fowl, it is likely, in the light of the study of Crow and Morton, that the breeder's intent and not natural selection among the potential parents is the agent responsible for such enhancement of the effects of restricted population size on the gene pool.

The role that chance plays, whenever reduction in size occurs as a unique event (in Wright's sense, see section 7) in the life of a population, is also of great significance. Thus in the formation of inbred lines the particular array of alleles which are fixed in one and eliminated in another population is determined fortuitously. But sudden isolation of small groups and colonizations of islands or other detached habitats by a few individuals have decidedly more dramatic consequences than slight shifts in allelic frequencies (Mayr, 1954). A reintegrated gene pool must be arrived at. What happens depends not on population size alone but on the interaction between drift and selection, as has been experimentally shown by Dobzhansky and Pavlovsky (1957). The principle of co-adaptation must be of more than minor importance in such situations.

The present and preceding chapters have set out the general premises on which the modern theory of selection rests. We may now turn to the more direct questions of what selection is expected to accomplish on the phenotypic level, and what, as judged from empirical evidence, it actually succeeds in doing.

4

Response to Selection Pressure

The results of the various, unknown, or but dimly understood laws of variation are infinitely complex and diversified.

The purposes of artificial selection for a metric trait are: (*a*) to modify its mean (directional selection); (*b*) to reduce its variability (stabilizing selection); (*c*) to extend its range in one direction (directional selection to produce a record performance). It is the first of these goals that has particular economic significance, although the other two may not be uncommon.

There are useful characters, the pecuniary value of which depends on their phenotypic uniformity in a population (e.g. color of eggs). Therefore reduction of variation by selection is sometimes attempted. In view of the information available on the phenotypic variability of heterozygotes, this aim may be served better by controlling the mating system. Stabilizing selection may reduce genetic variation but, in accordance with the discussion in section 16, it is likely to affect environmental variance only when heterozygotes have a reproductive advantage (type II in figure 1.1). Indeed, an attempt by Falconer and Robertson (1956) to change environmental variance in mice by low-intensity stabilizing selection of type III failed. On the other hand, crosses between genetically isolated populations not only may exhibit heterosis but are characterized by a minimum of both genotypic and environmental variance.

Directional selection aimed at producing individuals with an unprece-dented extreme phenotypic expression was very common before the operations entering breeding practice were rationalized.   In some classes of livestock, and doubtlessly in sport circles, a breeder may still be econo-mically justified in bending his efforts to such an end.   In poultry where breeding flocks number hundreds and thousands of birds, rather than dozens or scores, neither the monetary worth nor the publicity value of outstanding individuals is currently very high.   At any rate, there is little that selection theory can offer a breeder to help him satisfy an ambition to produce a single champion performer.   Counsel to practice somatic assortment by mating the best to the best would be as useful as carrying coals to Newcastle, especially if the method of ascertainment of what is the best is left unspecified.

Directional selection designed to shift the population mean, and only incidentally to extend the range of a character, may offhand be expected to call for the application of sufficiently powerful pressure to make the population move to a new stable equilibrium or adaptive peak.   If no such peak is attained, advances would be procured presumably only at the cost of losses in some property not subjected to selection.   Furthermore, continuous selection might be needed to prevent reversion of the population to the original state.

In reality, the situation is not always as difficult to handle as these suppositions imply.   First of all, new adaptive peaks are very likely attained not as a result of extremely intense pressures which do violence to the population but in consequence of prolonged but moderate ones which permit gradual coadaptation of the gene pool. Secondly, if selection is directed toward minor components of fitness, or traits peripheral to it, the population may be moved a considerable distance from the equilibrium value without any dire effects.   This situation is represented by the flat-topped curves in figures 3.12 and 3.13.

It may also happen that the initial population is not in equilibrium, in which case artificial selection may act synergistically with natural selection in seeking an adaptive peak.   Hybrid origin, or changes in environment coincidental with the initiation of artificial selection, which may bring into play segregating alleles of previously neutral or trivial effect on the charac-ter selected, provide appropriate circumstances for this.   In general, when free additively genetic variability is available, selection should be effective in producing changes in the population in the direction sought without generating any serious complications.

In the first chapter the effect of selection on gene frequency was dis-cussed.   The formulas given and the curves depicted help to visualize the nature of the selection process. But for metric traits inherited poly-genically, they are insufficient to allow prediction of gains. The degree of heritability of the selected character and the details of the breeding struc-ture of the population, including reproductive rate, age of parents, distribution of individuals in families, and the mating system need to be known for this purpose. As shall be presently noted, the accuracy of prediction of selection response on the basis of such information is reasonably high in the early generations of selection programs for various characters. However, after a population has been under fairly intense pressure for a number of generations, it is not uncommon that response to further selection becomes erratic. Gradual decay of additive genetic variability and the consequent increase in the importance of complex non-additive interactions may in part explain this fact. Even when the exhaustion of additive variance cannot be demonstrated, it is likely that factors to which the early selection responses are not sensitive may gradually assume significance as determinants of the course taken by a selected population.

The significant influences include the force of genetic homeostasis, which is only now beginning to be explored. Also important are factors on which information is currently not available: the number and size of the effective units of segregation, their linkage relationships, the means by which they are protected from disintegration, the magnitude of their individual effects, the nature of their interaction with each other and with environmental sources of variation, and so forth. If (and this is highly problematic) prediction of selection advances can be made to take these factors into account, the observed variability of response may be found to fall within specifiable limits of sampling error. Unfortunately, unless they are very narrow, the breeder who deals with individual flocks or herds, and not with populations of populations, will still lack assurance regarding the results he personally can expect over a long period of selection.

In the following section the elements of selection response, knowledge of which appears to be necessary and sufficient for making short-term predictions of fair precision, will be reviewed. Only the simplest form of selection—that based on individual phenotypes (mass selection)—is to be considered at this point of the discussion. The possible reasons for the breakdown of prediction accuracy will then be recapitulated. Following this theoretical section, a generalized representation of selection progress together with some concrete empirical examples will be introduced. The final section of the present chapter will be devoted to correlated responses, i.e. the changes occurring in characters which themselves are not criteria of selection.

18. Gains under Selection

In figure 1.4 and those immediately following it, the changes in allelic frequency under selection were shown as functions of the selective advantage of the desired genotype and of the reproductive potential of the population. The latter is in a sense a measure of the amount of selection possible. More generally the amount of selection applied can be expressed in terms of *selection intensity*, the percentage of the population permitted to reproduce itself. For directional selection, intensity (v) can be measured by the proportion of the area of the normal curve formed by the truncated tail of the frequency distribution.

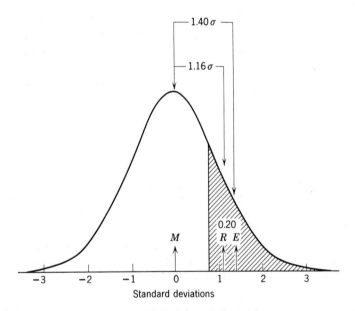

Figure 4.1. The selection differential

The shaded area represents the 20 per cent of the population which are extreme for a metric trait. The arrow labeled M indicates the mean of the population; that labeled E indicates the mean of the selected group (1.40σ). Should there be differential reproduction among the parents so that the more extreme deviates contribute fewer progeny to the next generation than the less extreme ones, the effective superiority of the selected parents over the mean of their generation would not be as high. It may be computed by weighting the contribution of each parent to the mean selection differential by the number of offspring it produces. In the example shown it is assumed that this factor reduces the expected selection differential from 1.40σ to 1.16σ, indicated by the arrow labeled R, and equivalent to a selection intensity of 30 per cent. For the relationship between the selection differential and selection intensity see box 11.

In figure 4.1 this tail (shaded area) represents 20 per cent of the population under selection for a positive value of a metrical character. The abcissa in this figure is given in standard deviations. The relationship between v and the mean value of the individuals falling within the selected group measured in standard deviations ($\bar{\imath}$) is a constant one, as long as the distribution is normal. Selection intensity can then be translated into values of $\bar{\imath}$, which is equal to the average superiority of the selected individuals above the mean of the population of their origin. It is known as the *selection differential* and can be expressed, as is noted in box 11, either in standard deviations or in absolute units of measurement (i). The nature of the interrelationship between v and $\bar{\imath}$ is also demonstrated in the same box. Figure 4.1 explains the important distinction between the *expected* and the *realized* selection differentials.

BOX 11

The Selection Differential

The proportion of the population which is selected for reproduction can be readily transformed into a selection differential on the assumption that the expected number of offspring contributed by each parent chosen is a constant. The value of every individual in the population for any trait considered, X, can be expressed as a deviation from the population mean, either in absolute terms, $X - \bar{X}$, or in terms of standard deviations, $(X - \bar{X})/\sigma_X$. Under directional selection, a certain proportion of the population, v, is usually chosen for reproduction from the extreme of the frequency distribution for X. The height of the ordinate at the point of truncation of the distribution curve which separates the selected group from the discarded may be designated as z. A property of the normal curve is that the mean of all the individual values of $(X - \bar{X})/\sigma_X$ in the truncated tail is z/v. This is the selection differential expressed in standard deviations, $\bar{\imath}$. To convert it into the original units in which X is expressed, it suffices to multiply $\bar{\imath}$ by σ_X (that is, $i = \bar{\imath}\sigma_X$). Tables of areas and ordinates of the normal curve may be consulted for the values of z corresponding to different intensities of selection, v. Part II of Pearson's (1931) tables includes a direct tabulation of z/v.

When the population size is small, the selection differential obtained in this fashion will be an overestimate because of the discontinuity of the frequency distribution. For $N \leq 50$, more exact values of i may be obtained by computing the average deviation of the parents chosen from the mean (table XX in Fisher and Yates, 1953, gives the values of the individual deviations). The accompanying table shows the expected selection differentials corresponding to various intensities in populations of different size. When N is above 50, the assumption that the population is infinite in size is accurate for most purposes.

| Population | Selection Differential | | |
Selected, v	$N = 10$	$N = 50$	$N = \infty$
0.005	–	–	2.90
0.01	–	–	2.67
0.02	–	2.25	2.42
0.03	–	–	2.27
0.04	–	2.05	2.15
0.05	–	–	2.06
0.1	1.54	1.70	1.75
0.2	1.27	1.37	1.40
0.3	1.07	1.14	1.16
0.4	0.90	0.95	0.97
0.5	0.74	0.79	0.80
0.6	0.60	0.63	0.64
0.7	0.46	0.49	0.50
0.8	0.32	0.34	0.35
0.9	0.17	0.19	0.19
1.0	0	0	0

The selection differential is related to the selection coefficient s (box 1). When the effect of the average allelic substitution d is small, s is independent of gene frequency and is equal to id/σ_X. The appendix of Falconer's (1955) report contains a discussion (derived from Haldane's 1931 treatment) of the relation between the intensity of selection, the magnitude of d, and allelic frequency.

These measures of the amount of selection are not practicable for natural selection which usually involves differential reproduction of all the arrays, rather than truncation such as is shown in figure 1.1. Other methods for expressing the intensity of natural selection must then be used. Haldane (1954), for instance, suggested that such a measure may be couched in terms of the logarithm of the ratio of fitness of the optimum genotype to that of the population as a whole. For artificial selection, this statistic does not appear to have any advantages over the selection differential. For mating systems for which the numbers of male and female parents selected are not identical, the selection differential can be computed by averaging the i values for the two sexes. Figure 4.2 shows the selection differentials corresponding to varying degrees of selection intensity for sires and dams.

Given the superiority of selected parents over the mean of their generation and the heritability of the trait in question, the expected gain from a generation of selection can be computed. In fact, for mass selection the gain simply equals the product of heritability (h^2) and the selection differential expressed in actual units (i). A formal demonstration of this relationship is developed in box 12. Since heritability is the ratio of the genetic to the phenotypic variance, and i equals $\bar{i}\sigma_P$ (see

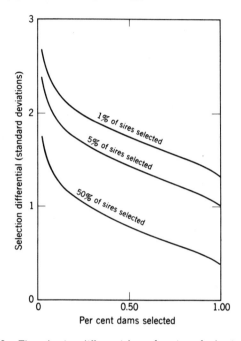

Figure 4.2. The selection differential as a function of selection intensity

box 11), the formulas for the expected change in the population mean ($\bar{G}$) per generation of selection, which may be symbolized by $\Delta\bar{G}_g$, can take on a variety of forms:

$$\Delta\bar{G}_g = h^2 i = h^2 \bar{i}\sigma_P = \frac{\sigma_G^2 \bar{i}}{\sigma_P}, \text{ etc.}$$

Heritability is also the regression of the genotype on the phenotype ($b_{G \cdot P}$) or the square of the correlation between the genotype and the phenotype (r_{GP}^2). The expected gain may therefore also be written as

$$\Delta\bar{G}_g = b_{G \cdot P}\bar{i}\sigma_P = r_{GP}\sigma_G\bar{i}$$

Indeed, the subscript P here need not stand for the phenotype corresponding to G, but may represent any criterion of selection. The general formulation that the expected gain is the product of accuracy by the amount of selection can then be made.

---BOX 12---

Prediction of Gains under Mass Selection

The demonstration that the gain expected per generation of mass selection is equal to the product of the degree of heritability by the selection differential can be made in a variety of ways. Probably the simplest and the most direct one is that developed by Robertson (1955b).

We may designate the phenotypic value of an individual for the trait selected as P, and the mean of the population as $\bar{P}$. The latter is by definition equal to the average genetic value of the population, $\bar{G}$. The variance of individual P values is σ_P^2, but if P were to be used as an estimate of an individual's true genetic value G, the error variance around G would be entirely environmental and equal to $\sigma_P^2 - \sigma_G^2$.

A given G can be estimated either from the mean of the population of its origin, $\bar{G}$ or $\bar{P}$, with a variance of σ_G^2, or directly from P, with an error variance of $\sigma_P^2 - \sigma_G^2$. For the best estimate, the two sources of information can be combined by weighting them proportionally to the reciprocal of the variances. On this basis, the most accurate prediction of the value of G is

$$\hat{G} = \left[\frac{\bar{P}}{\sigma_G^2} + \frac{P}{\sigma_P^2 - \sigma_G^2}\right] \Big/ \left[\frac{1}{\sigma_G^2} + \frac{1}{\sigma_P^2 - \sigma_G^2}\right] \tag{1}$$

which is readily reduced to

$$\hat{G} = \bar{P} + \frac{\sigma_G^2}{\sigma_P^2}(P - \bar{P}) \tag{2}$$

or

$$\hat{G} = \bar{P} + h^2(P - \bar{P}) \tag{3}$$

The average G value of selected individuals is, by definition of additive genetic action, also the average G for the next generation. Hence the gain expected from mass selection is the difference between this expression (averaged over all selected individuals) and $\bar{P}$, or

$$\Delta\bar{G}_g = h^2(P - \bar{P}) \tag{4}$$

where the subscript g refers to a generation and the term in brackets represents the average superiority of the selected group over the mean of their generation. Thus,

$$\Delta\bar{G}_g = h^2 i \tag{5}$$

Robertson has also shown how the same reasoning may be used to derive expected gains from more complex schemes than mass selection. Another form of derivation is to be used for didactic reasons when family selection is dealt with in box 16.

Operational considerations may require that the gain from selection be measured not per generation but per unit of time. If it is agreed that the best selection scheme is the one producing the most rapid changes in the required trait, this fact is obvious. Its significance is particularly high for comparisons between alternate schemes of selection in which the average interval between generations is not the same. For instance, progeny testing may on occasion increase the accuracy of selection or the effective heritability over that obtained under mass selection. Yet the use of this technique must perforce lengthen the period of time elapsing between successive generations. Because of this fact it cannot be decided solely from a comparison of the respective values of ΔG_g for mass and for progeny-test selection which of the two is the more efficient.

Dickerson and Hazel (1944) have thoroughly explored this problem. They demonstrated that by including the average age (A) of the parents in a given breeding scheme as the denominator in the prediction equation for $\Delta \bar{G}$, the latter is converted to an estimate of the gain expected per unit of time. If the unit chosen is a year (y), then

$$\Delta \bar{G}_y = \frac{ih^2}{A}$$

Dempster and Lerner (1947) applied this principle to selection for annual egg production in poultry. They compared the expectations of progress from a number of selection schemes differing in the age distribution of breeding birds. These schemes varied not only in the use of progeny testing but also in the amount of phenotypic information available on the birds selected. Selection may be based on egg production records for only a part of the laying year, a practice which permits the mating of birds one year old or younger (pullets). In contrast, if the full annual record is used as the criterion of selection, birds mated for the first time must be at least two years old (hens). Similarly, selection of males may be based on the performance of their dams or on part records of their sisters, in which case cockerels (males under a year of age) can be chosen for mating. If the full annual record of sisters is the basis of selection, sires which are at least two years old (cocks) have to be used.

Figure 4.3 illustrates the theoretical conclusions reached by Dempster and Lerner. Under two types of breeding plans, one based on the use of cockerel sires only and the other in which 20 per cent of males selected by a progeny test are cocks (i.e. older birds), the expected gains can be seen to depend on the proportions of the dams of different ages in the breeding flock. When the minimum age of the females to be used as parents is taken as two years, the effects of the age structure of the flock on the advances expected is small.   But lowering the minimum age to one year increases the expected gains per year by some 50 per cent.

Another determinant of the expected gain is the amount of inbreeding degeneration that may occur in populations of limited size.   In considering this factor, the premises for the prediction equation are somewhat

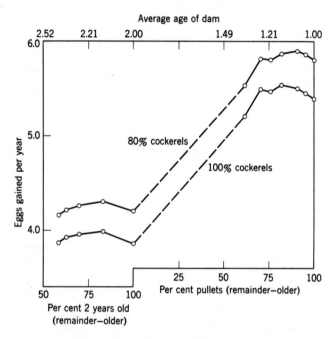

Figure 4.3.   Gains expected from selection for egg production in relation to the age structure of the breeding flock

This diagram is based on the analysis of Dempster and Lerner (1947).   It shows the expected gains from selection for annual egg production on the basis of different mating plans.   When 20 per cent of the selected sires are progeny-tested, the expected advances are somewhat higher in all schemes considered than when only untested cockerels are used.   When only birds 2 years old or older are mated, the maximum gains are obtained when the average age of the female parents is 2.21 years.   When pullets (1-year-old birds) are used for reproduction, the gains expected are not very sensitive to changes in the proportions of younger and older birds, so long as at least 70 per cent of the breeding birds are pullets.

changed, since non-additive genetic variation now becomes important. If inbreeding decline in a character under selection is linear with increases in F, a correction may be added to the prediction equation, a procedure originally suggested by Comstock and Winters (1944).   The correction is the product of the linear regression of the trait on the inbreeding coefficient

($b_{P.F}$) and the expected increase in the latter (ΔF). Here, instead of designating the expected gains as $\Delta \bar{G}$, the symbol $\Delta \bar{P}$ should be used. The former indicates that we are dealing with the additively genetic value of the population which is not affected by inbreeding degeneration. The latter refers to the phenotypic value. The prediction equation then becomes

$$\Delta \bar{P}_y = ih^2 + b_{P.F}\Delta F$$

in which $b_{P.F}$ is expected to be negative for positive values of ΔF. It is exceedingly unlikely that the same regression coefficient will be valid when ΔF is highly negative. Indeed, for many characters of economic importance, the accuracy of the correction term is highly suspect since evidence for the linearity of inbreeding degeneration, especially in the lower ranges of F, is nebulous (see e.g. Stephenson, Wyatt, and Nordskog, 1953, for relevant information on egg production in poultry). Hence, it is not certain whether the corrected prediction equation is an improvement on the original. Similarly, inbreeding affects the magnitude of h^2 itself (box 9). Yet it is also dubious whether taking this fact into account in prediction equations increases their accuracy.

Asymmetry of response to pressures applied in opposite directions assumes significance in agricultural practice under a number of circumstances. Changes in market preference, or attempts to create a demand for a new product, may cause reversals in the scale of desirability. A specific instance is provided by the domestic turkey. For many years selection was practiced for increases in body weight. But when an attempt to have turkeys compete with chickens for the housewife's favor was initiated, a variety of small birds was developed. Another example refers to egg size of chickens. This trait, having a very high heritability, is readily increased beyond the economically optimum weight. As a result it is often necessary to reverse the direction of selection or to shift to a stabilizing form of selection.

Asymmetrical response specifically means that, for the same amount of selection pressure, greater advances may be obtained in one direction than in the other. This is equivalent to saying that effective heritability (i.e. the actual fraction of the selection differential transmitted to the next generation) depends on the direction of selection pressure. Estimates of heritability based on data from experiments in which selection toward increasing the metric value of a trait was applied would not then be valid for prediction of the rate of response in the opposite direction. The degree of heritability assessed in the manner described in box 5 may be expected to be close to the average of the effective heritabilities for selection in the plus and minus directions, without being accurate for either.

Figure 4.4 illustrates asymmetrical response to selection for six-week body weight of chickens. Six generations of selection resulted in approximate doubling of body weight in the high line, whereas the low line remained at its original level. Though environmental fluctuations between generations interfere with a full interpretation of these data, it seems

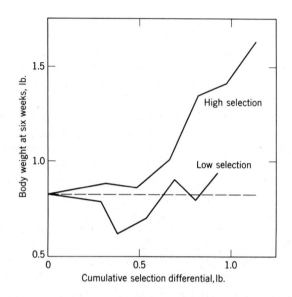

Figure 4.4.   Asymmetry of selection response

The data for this graph, as well as for figures 4.18 and 7.16, have been supplied by Dr. G. F. Godfrey, late of the Oklahoma Agricultural Experimental Station. They derive from an experiment by Godfrey and Goodman, the results of which have not yet been published. The method of plotting cumulative selection response against the cumulative selection differential was introduced by Falconer (1954a) at the suggestion of Dr. B. Woolf. It is probably the most informative graphic technique for depicting the course of selection experiments, although in the absence of unselected controls intergeneration environmental variability may make interpretation uncertain. Unfortunately, with multiple criteria of selection, and the use of various types of auxiliary information, the selection differential is sometimes difficult to compute. Thus, of the poultry selection experiments illustrated in this book, only one other lends itself to this manner of representation (figure 4.15). For a further example of asymmetrical response to selection, see figure 7.13.

clear that the amount of response to selection pressure differs in the two lines. Falconer (1954a, 1955) may be consulted for a thorough investigation of the theoretical basis of asymmetrical response and for a report on a series of selection experiments with mice in which this phenomenon was marked.

The factors that may be held responsible for asymmetrical response include both fundamental biological causes and artefacts of the experimental situation. Among the latter, the use of improper scales of measurement is the most obvious. Thus it can happen that the asymmetry may disappear when suitable scale transformation is made. Initially unequal frequencies of the plus and minus alleles may be another reason for asymmetry. More general causes for the phenomenon may be found in inbreeding effects. Intrapopulation selection of the traits subject to inbreeding decline may be expected to be more effective in the negative direction than in the positive. Directional dominance, especially combined with unequal allelic frequencies and greater opposition of natural selection to one than to the other direction of artificial selection, is also a possible cause of asymmetry. The way in which these factors may operate is shown by curves C and D in figure 3.12, from which it may be deduced that selection toward the equilibrium values would meet with much greater success than selection away from them.

All these sources of asymmetry may increase in significance when a character approaches what has often been called the "physiological limit." In genetic terms such a limit is simply the potential expression of a given trait that can be developed by the current gene pool in the given environment. There is, for example, a temperature above which chickens cannot survive for more than a short time. Yet it is entirely possible that mutations may eventually arise which will lead to the production of a genotype extending this physiological limit. There are, no doubt, some reasonably permanent minimum requirements for all forms of life. It seems improbable that a breed of chickens capable of living without food could be produced, no matter how many hitherto unknown mutations are invoked. But the "physiological limits" ordinarily referred to do not deal with such extreme notions. The term is applied more often to specific maxima or minima (e.g. body size), which are transcended by other often related species. It is most frequently encountered in the description of selection experiments in which a plateaued trait responds to reversed selection. Presumably in such cases genetic variation is present if there is a response to selection, but it can be utilized in only one direction.

Yet another cause for asymmetry of response to selection may arise from interactions between different alleles and between the genotype and the environment. Such complications may be consequences of the compound nature of the trait in question. Indeed, the most exhaustively studied example of differential response to selection in opposite directions, that relating to body weight of mice, has been interpreted by Falconer (1955) as being due to a combination of two types of maternal effects on the body weight of the young.

To conclude the enumeration of the factors entering response to selection, it should be noted that so far the relative efficiency of selection plans has been assumed to be entirely specified by the $\Delta \bar{G}_y$ expected from them. Although in comparing the merits of different breeding schemes (chapter 5) the same postulate will be adopted, it must be understood that it has severe limitations not only from the standpoint of long-range objectives but also in application to single generations. Should the assumption that the best breeding plan is the one with the maximum expected $\Delta \bar{G}_y$ be taken literally, the selection scheme with the highest possible value of i would always be preferred. Thus, were it feasible to reproduce the whole Mendelian population from a single couple, such drastic selection might be adjudged to be optimum. In reality, this is far from being the case.

The specific objections toward overly intense selection are manifold. The loss in the plasticity of the population which would result from the fixation of alleles determining highly heritable traits under intense selection had already been mentioned. In artificial selection practice there are other factors of even greater weight, although attainment of genetic constancy of useful traits without loss of reproductive capacity would, were it possible, be a desideratum of high order if animals were to be kept in a completely controllable environment.

Haldane (1932) pointed out that selection of exceedingly high intensity would result in the propagation, not of the best genotype for the desired expression of a trait but of one with the most variable response to a given environment. A single individual chosen for reproduction out of a thousand or a million would be more likely to have a high E component than a high G component the lower the heritability of the trait. Under such intense directional selection, unbuffered individuals with a predisposition to vary with the environment would be preferred to buffered ones. If genotype-environment interaction of the kind that makes a poorer genotype more variable than a better one were present, too intense selection could result in genetic regression instead of improvement.

The effects of inbreeding also become more pronounced under intense selection, because the size of the breeding population is greatly reduced. Chance loss of desirable alleles is thus encouraged. Furthermore, non-additively acting alleles tested in only a few genetic backgrounds are subject to elimination, even if they have superior value in a majority of the possible genotypes. In fine, no opportunity for recombination or, more generally speaking, coadaptation is provided by selection of too high an intensity, which thereby limits the full potentialities of the initial gene pool for progress in the desired direction.

Unfortunately, as yet not enough information on the subject is available to allow construction of prediction equations which could take these considerations into account. The deficiency in current selection theory makes it necessary to follow rules of thumb in deciding on the selection intensity to be used in any given situation.

Before bringing this section to an end, a resume of the factors that may inhibit or prevent expected selection progress should be offered. It seems impossible to predict the point in the biography of a population under selection at which any of them becomes of significance. Neither can the ultimate ceiling, which a selected trait can reach but not exceed, be known. It may also happen that a population, after remaining refractory to selection for a period of time, renews response without any tangible change of circumstances. The specific causes for discrepancies between expected and realized population behavior are exceedingly difficult to establish in any specific instances. Most of the explanations suggested, nevertheless, have partisans among the workers in the field. The following are some of the causes of resistance of populations to selection pressure that have been suggested by various investigators. These causes are not mutually exclusive. In fact, they overlap each other and sometimes represent different aspects of a single phenomenon.

1. CHANGE OF ENVIRONMENT. It is conceivable that deterioration of environment may occur either independently of the selection practiced or because of it. Building up the concentration or the virulence of pathogenic organisms in the immediate milieu of a population may be a common example of this factor.

2. CONVERSION OF ADDITIVE TO NON-ADDITIVE VARIANCE. This is a form of the broad case of exhaustion of utilizable genetic variance. In the simplest instance, a recomputation of the degree of heritability would prevent overestimates of expected gains. However, sometimes biases in assessing additively genetic variation (from parent-offspring regressions or correlations between full sibs as shown in figure 2.8) may be difficult to determine. More generally, only non-additive variation may be present in the population with respect to a trait under previously prolonged selection. A common type may be that represented in Wright's (1935a) model (section 12). Inbreeding degeneration may also be included under this heading.

3. GENOTYPE-ENVIRONMENT INTERACTION. Both the above factors may contribute to this category. The most important kind of interaction adversely affecting gains involves successive generations. Selection within a given generation may be directed to alleles favorable in its own particular environment but of no effect or harmful in that of the next generation. Another kind of interaction that could be placed in this category is between genotype and maternal environment (which may itself be in part genetically determined).

4. RECURRENT MUTATION IN THE DIRECTION OPPOSITE TO THAT OF SELEC-
TION.   Although there is no evidence for the significance of this factor in
multigenic situations, it would be virtually impossible to obtain conclusive
proof or disproof of its operation in larger animals.

5. MULTIPLICITY OF OBJECTIVES.   Reduction of effective selection intensity because of selection for many traits at once is common.   Negative
correlations, either initially present or induced by selection, between the

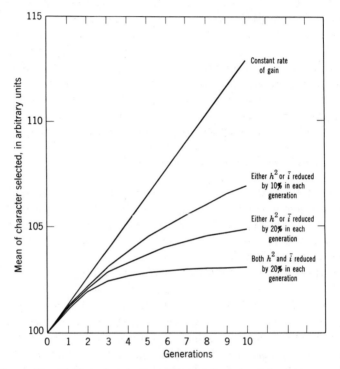

Figure 4.5.   The gains expected when heritability or intensity decline under
selection

components of a phenotype treated as a single character may also occur.
This factor may be of significance not only under natural selection but in
commercial practice.

6. ABSENCE OF EFFECTIVE PRESSURE.   A variety of reasons for lack of
pressure is possible.   Among them, in addition to multiplicity of objectives, are genotype-environment interactions (e.g. lack of exposure of the
selected parents to a disease adversely affecting the offspring) and negative
correlations between genotype and environment, such as may occur in
some maternal effects.

7. ANTAGONISM BETWEEN NATURAL AND ARTIFICIAL SELECTION. In a sense, this is equivalent to multiple objectives, with the trait under artificial selection forming one goal of selection and fitness another.

The intervention of one or more of these factors produces a decrease in selection response either directly (reduction in effective heritability) or by lowering selection intensity. Figure 4.5 illustrates how a constant decline in h^2 or in i changes the shape of the curve of expected response to selection. But in most situations the interference of the disturbing influences does not manifest itself with the regularity portrayed here.

In general, when invoking one or another of the possible causes for lack of selection response, it should be recalled that they must account not only for the cessation of gains but sometimes also for their resumption. Several of, if not all, the possibilities are ambivalent in this sense and hence are probably preferable to the others as working hypotheses. Numbers 3 and 7 are particularly attractive in this connection: the first because of the usual impossibility of controlling precisely the environments of successive generations, the second because coadaptation and homeostasis provide a general pattern of interpretation rather than *ad hoc* explanations for particular experiments. In the introduction to chapter 5 we shall return to the issue of how closely the basic prediction equations developed to date correspond to observation.

19. Types of Selection Response

Robertson's model represented in figure 3.13 sets out the relationship between different metric traits and fitness. It is very probable that all the types of interdependence discussed by him have counterparts among useful traits under selection in commercial breeding practice. However, there is not always sufficient information to locate even approximately a given character on the scale graduated in terms of magnitude of its relation to fitness, even though there is no shortage of empirical examples of various types of selection response in the literature. Unfortunately, very few of them provide data adequate for an exhaustive analysis of the diverse elements entering selection response. In fact, most of the available illustrations have to be discussed nearly exclusively in terms of advances made per generation or per unit of time, without reference to other factors of significance.

In this section a broad generalization of empirically observed patterns of response to selection pressure will be discussed. It will be followed by three examples illustrating different degrees of success in reaching the objectives of selection. A fourth example dealing with selection for increased length of shank of Leghorn pullets is to be taken up more fully in the succeeding section.

Figure 4.6 is an idealized representation of changes that might be expected in the mean of a metric character under selection, concurrently with the changes in the average fitness of the population (both on an arbitrary scale of measurement), which, it is assumed, is not being subjected to direct artificial selection. The abcissa can be calibrated in units of time; the letters appearing between the vertical bars on the chart indicate successive phases of selection progress. The curves are, of course, not intended to show precise quantitative relationships but merely gross trends.

The interpretation of the changes assumed to occur is as follows:

Phase	Metric Trait	Fitness
A. Preselection	Remains constant	Remains constant
B. Selection	Steady response	Remains constant
C. Selection	Attenuated response	Declines
D. Selection	Remains constant	Declines
E. Selection	Declines	Rises
F. Selection	Renewed response	Declines
G. Selection	Remains constant	Remains constant
H. Selection suspended	Declines	Rises
I. Post selection	Constant at a new level	Trend toward full recovery

In the early stages of selection, the effect of the shift in the mean of the metric trait on fitness is negligible, but in phase C the population begins to resist change. Artificial selection pressure continues to be effective but only at the cost of loss of fitness. By the time stage D is reached, selection intensity is sufficient only to keep the character at the level attained, but not to produce further gains. In the next stage, E, natural selection becomes more powerful than artificial selection; fitness begins to rise, whereas the mean of the metric trait moves in the direction contrary to that of artificial selection. However, by then new genetic combinations have had time to be formed. Stage F thus witnesses renewed response to selection with only a slight decrease in fitness. In stage G an equilibrium between artificial and natural selection pressures is attained, both fitness and the selected character remaining at a constant level. Suspension of artificial selection causes some decline in the latter but permits fitness to rise. A coadapted gene pool, differing from the original one, has how gradually come into existence, and the population finds itself at a new adaptive peak represented by stage I.

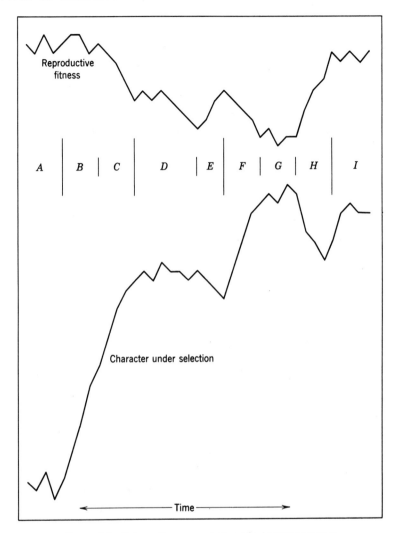

Figure 4.6. Schematic representation of selection progress

See text for explanation of letters between the vertical bars. The diagram may be taken as a very modest attempt to present an archetype of selection progress for a metric trait. Empirical examples can fit short sections of the lower curve shown here by a proper choice of starting point. The scale on which reproductive fitness is portrayed may need transformation for a point-to-point correspondence between the two curves. The effect of suspending selection shown here (partial regression of the selected trait) is, however, only one of the possible kinds in the continuum between preservation of all gains attained without further selection and complete reversion to the initial state. Furthermore, selection in only one direction is represented. If an actual instance of successful selection fits some part of the curve, it seems improbable that the results of selection for the same trait in the opposite direction would always fit the same stretch of the curve.

Obviously it has been assumed in this sequence of events that much of the variance of the selected trait is initially additive, although that of fitness is not. However, neither the proportions of additively genetic variance of the two properties nor the interrelation between them is static, as it might be assumed from the classification of characters shown in figure 3.13. Indeed, the important aspect of the concept underlying figure 4.6 is capacity for change under selection, not only of the metric character but of the regression of fitness on this trait. Under artificial

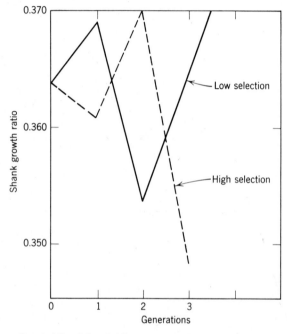

Figure 4.7.   Selection for the shank growth ratio (see text)

selection an arbitrarily chosen character which might have been initially peripheral to fitness can be turned into a major fitness component. Its response to selection would be accordingly modified, but the process may be a reversible one when the balance of natural and artificial selection pressures is changed. It must, however, be emphasized that reversibility is likely to be only apparent, i.e. on the level of phenotypic observations: the mean of a trait may return to the initial value, but the genetic constellations producing this value will have changed, and the exact composition of the gene pool will differ strongly from what it was at the point of departure.

The claim made in the caption to figure 4.6 that this diagram is intended as an archetype for curves for selection response is, of course, an exaggeration, simply because the fluidity of the reaction system involved in a prolonged selection experiment is not susceptible to two-dimensional representation.   At the same time, most short-term selection experiments, such as those shown in figures 4.7 and 4.8, can be loosely fitted into one or another of its phases.   The illustrations immediately following do not deal with the effect of artificial selection on fitness.   In other respects they might be found to correspond to some stage represented in figure 4.6, even if it is not clearly identifiable.

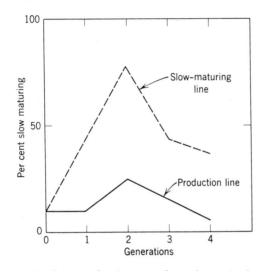

Figure 4.8.   Selection for slow rate of sexual maturity (see text)

Figure 4.7 describes three generations of an attempt to modify by selection the shank growth ratio[1] of a flock of chickens of crossbred origin.   Since there seems to be no systematic relation between the direction of the pressure applied and that of the response, the attempt has apparently failed.   The simplest explanation of the lack of success is that, as it rarely happens for multigenic traits, no genetic variation in the character selected was present in the initial population.   That the simplest possible explanation is also the correct one cannot, of course, be taken for granted.   Other information available suggests that the shank growth ratio is a species-specific trait and does not possess variability which

[1] The shank growth ratio is the exponent in the allometric growth equation $y = bx^\alpha$, where y is the length of shank, x is the body weight, and b is a constant.   The exponent α measures the growth rate of the shank relative to that of the body as a whole.   It has been used as an index of conformation.

could readily be transformed into changes of the mean. The situation in figure 4.7 corresponds more or less to stage *D* in the previous diagram during which selection is ineffective. The correspondence, however, is superficial: the shank growth ratio remains unchanged upon removal of selection pressure; the trait in figure 4.6 would in this phase be expected to exhibit at least a partial recession to a lower level.

Figure 4.8 shows a slightly more successful undertaking. From a flock of birds under selection for high egg production (designated as the "Production Line"), a population characterized by slow sexual maturity was extracted. Although capable of being represented by a continuous distribution, sexual maturity is treated in this graph as an all-or-none trait. The fact that a varying proportion of individuals in the two lines failed to reach sexual maturity within the period of time they were kept under observation makes the frequency distributions skewed to different degrees. The percentage of slow-maturing birds is therefore a more informative statistic than the average age at maturity, at least for the limited purpose of demonstrating the type of selection response obtained.

If the difference between the selected line and its population of origin were real, the advance made by the end of the fourth generation would apparently have been gained entirely from the first selection. The parallel course of the two curves following generation 1 is clearly due to environmental differences between years of hatch. In the absence of further information, especially with reference to the effects of suspending selection, it is not possible to interpret these results with any assurance. It is conceivable that a major gene differential is responsible for them, although various more or less unlikely assumptions about allelic frequency, the character's susceptibility to environmental effects, and its relation to fitness would have to be made to permit such a simple interpretation. Any number of synthetic explanations on a polygenic basis could be easily manufactured, but they would not serve any useful purpose. Similarly an attempt to locate the initial population on the curve in figure 4.6 would not be especially fruitful, because the direction of selection and the probable relationship between sexual maturity and fitness do not have a counterpart in the stages represented there. Suffice it to say that, empirically speaking, the example presented is intermediate between total failure of selection as pictured in the previous figure and complete success as portrayed in the next.

Figure 4.9 plots the incidence of a phenodeviant (see section 12) trait, crooked toes, in three lines of Leghorns. The character is of the all-or-none type, although the severity of its expression may vary. In the production-bred flock spontaneous incidence of the trait at a very low level had been observed for several generations before the selected line was inaugurated. It may be seen that seven generations of selection and inbreeding (due to the small size of the breeding population) were sufficient to fix the trait. Selection in the reverse direction, initiated midway, was not as fully successful, but the possibility of eventual elimination of all crooked-toe alleles in this line is not entirely excluded, although there are several difficulties in attaining this goal. In particular the threshold of manifestation of the crooked-toe character varies with changes in the

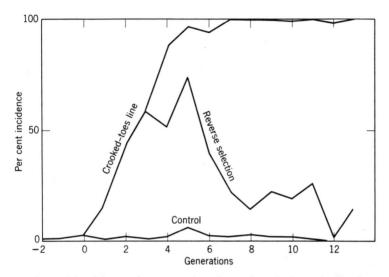

Figure 4.9. Selection for increased incidence of crooked toes (see text)

environment, and it is known that the low point in generation 12 was not due to effective selection but to changed incubation conditions. Therefore it is possible that from generation 9 onward the reverse selection line had reached a plateau in the incidence of the defect. Coadaptation to permit further gains is unlikely to occur in time for the line to benefit from it, because by the thirteenth generation the F value has reached 0.76. The level of homozygosity attained is probably too high to allow ready evolution of a reintegrated gene pool, and the probable rate of polygenic mutation may be inadequate to redress this situation.

This experiment shows that the total objectives of selection even in a complex polygenically conditioned trait may be sometimes attained. No doubt the outcome was greatly facilitated by cooperation between selection and inbreeding. The behavior of the reverse selection line supports this idea, for which additional evidence, which need not be discussed here, is also available (see Lerner, 1954). At any rate, the shape of the curve for the crooked-toe line clearly parallels figure 4.6 from stage *A* through stage *D*.   An example which extends more or less to stage *G* is provided by the next experiment to be considered.

20. A Detailed Case History

This section deals with an experiment on selection for increased shank length of Leghorn pullets carried on for 18 years (box 13).   There are several features of this project which call for comment before discussion of the graphic material is undertaken.

The trait selected for was measured only in mature females (about $8\frac{1}{2}$ months of age).   The primary criterion of selection was the individual phenotype, although some attention was paid to full sisters.   Only the family average was considered in the selection of males.   The number of dams mated in the different lines included in the experiment ranged from 15 to 33, and of the sires from 2 to 4 per generation, with 3 being the usual number.   The control line was an exception.   It was a flock selected for egg production and propagated by approximately 12 sires mated to a total of about 120 dams per year (see section 31).   There is adequate evidence for maintaining that selection for egg production in this population had little directional effects on the mean shank length (although some stabilizing effect is possible).

The experimental lines included the control (*P*), the selected line originating from it (*S*), a line extracted from *S* in which selection was suspended (*SS*), and two lines (*RS*−1 and *RS*−2, averaged under the designation *RS*) which originated from *SS* and in which selection had been resumed.   The suspension of selection in the *SS* line was not accomplished by mating a completely random sample of birds but by choosing as parents individuals with an average expected selection differential of zero.   The procedure followed was to prepare a list of all females in the population arranged in a random order.   The average for the first *n* birds was then computed (*n* being the number desired for inclusion in the mating pens).   If, for example, the average yielded a positive selection differential, the first bird on the list with a shank length above the mean was crossed off, and the first pullet whose shank length was below the mean in the series beginning with the (*n* + 1)st bird was added to the list. This process was repeated until the averages of the selected group and that of its generation coincided.

The alternative method of suspending selection would be to choose for mating a group of birds at random.   In such a procedure there is no assurance that the expected selection differential will be zero, which was

---

BOX 13

Numbers of Birds in the Shank Length Experiment

In order to give some indication of the scope of the experiment on which figures 4.10 to 4.17 are based, the following table, listing the number of pullets measured in each line, is presented. It should be noted that only part of the production flock, comparable in date of hatch and in housing arrangements to the birds in the selected line, was measured.

Year of Hatch	Line				
	Production Control, P	Selected, S	Selection Suspended, SS	Reselected 1 RS — 1	Reselected 2 RS — 2
1938	368				
1939	274	84			
1940	137	89			
1941	346	106			
1942	260	119			
1943	543	191			
1944	184	75			
1945	382	61			
1946	309	88			
1947	377	59			
1948	471	53			
1949	473	92			
1950	526	80			
1951	308	51	40		
1952	400	30	88		
1953	536	24	76		
1954	662	25	72		
1955	446	60	89	79	75
1956	640	59	167	39	76

Many details of this experiment which have been previously reported are not discussed here.   The following sources may be consulted for them: Lerner (1944) and Lerner and Gunns (1944) for embryonic and post-embryonic growth patterns of the selected and control populations; Lerner (1946) for correlated response in body size, egg weight, and sexual maturity; Lerner and Dempster (1951a) for heritability estimates in different generations and the computation of extent of antagonism between natural and artificial selection.

an important desideratum in the experiment described here.   Should any association exist between family size and the trait under observation, random choice of parents may result in automatic selection in either the positive or negative direction, depending on the sign of the association (for an example of such an effect, see Gyles et al., 1955).

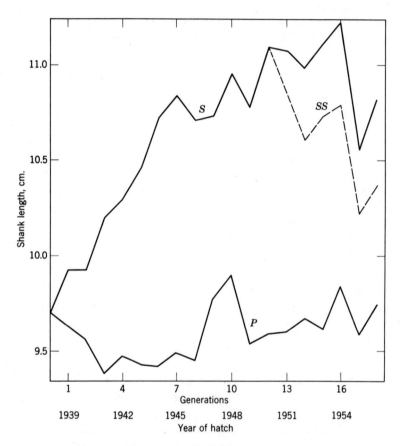

Figure 4.10.   Selection for increased shank length (see text)

The heritability of shank length had been reported by Lerner and Dempster (1951a).   Because of the small number of birds in the population studied, the individual values computed for each generation fluctuate widely.   The best overall estimate appears to be about 0.25.   The interesting observation of Lerner and Dempster that inbreeding did not seem to have affected the h^2 has no simple explanation.   Somewhat puzzling also is the fact that h^2 rose upon suspension of selection.   Thus in the 1955 population the heritability estimate from intrasire daughter-dam regressions for the S line was 0.27, and for the SS line 0.50.   The extent of bias induced by inclusion of non-additive fractions of variability in these and other values is not easily measured.   The fact that estimates from half-sibs, as a rule, are not smaller than those made from full-sibs suggests that such bias is not severe.   The small number in each line and the lack of replicates, of course, limit the degree of confidence in the results.   This is a lamentable and only seldom remediable aspect of experiments with large animals.

Figure 4.10 shows the general progress of selection.   The early drop in the control line is explained by the fact that the removal in 1939 of the foundation birds for the S line lowered the frequency of plus alleles in the P pool.   Over a period of years the control line gradually returned to the approximate shank length of 1938.   The occasional marked fluctuations occurring simultaneously in all the lines (as in 1948 and 1954) are probably of environmental origin, although no fully satisfactory explanation for them is available.

The first seven generations of selection were highly effective.   Several generations at a plateaued level then follow (a fact more clearly seen in figure 4.15), succeeded by a brief resumption of advance.   The total gain over the control population was of the order of six genetic standard deviations (taken at about 0.25 cm. from the figures given by Lerner and Dempster, 1951a).   The changes noted in the 1955 and 1956 generations cannot be adequately interpreted without data for several further generations.   Suspension of selection in 1950 had a clearly retrogressive effect on shank length, but whether the downward trend was arrested in the SS line is not obvious from this diagram.   There are some indications in the charts to follow that this may indeed have been the case.

Figure 4.11 portrays the frequency distributions of shank lengths in several selected generations.   Although the mean shank length was obviously displaced from the control value after two generations of selection, the ranges of the two distributions at that point were identical. In the seventh generation the selected group can be seen to have transcended the original limits of shank length, but up to and including the eighteenth generation no further extension of range occurred.   The lower limit of expression in the selected line, however, remained unchanged between the seventh and the last generation portrayed.   Shank length frequency distributions of the various lines in the eighteenth generation are shown in figure 4.12.   The distribution of the SS line is, generally speaking, intermediate between the control and the selected populations. The group reselected is in turn intermediate between the S and the SS lines.

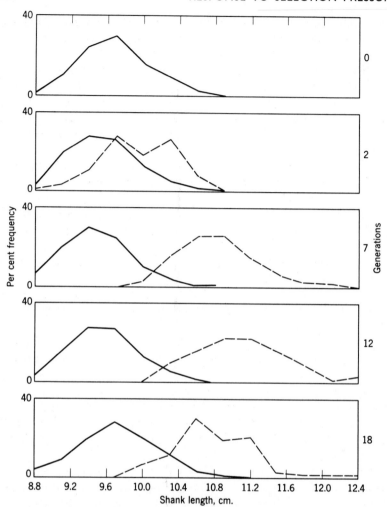

Figure 4.11.   Frequency distributions in the shank length experiment

The solid line shows the distribution of shank lengths of the control flock, the dashed line that of the selected population in several generations of selection.

Figure 4.13 shows the rise in the inbreeding coefficient in the course of selection and the concurrent changes in the relative hatchability of fertile eggs.   The F values were computed on the basis of the 1935 population of the P line which in that year itself had an inbreeding coefficient of 0.087 calculated on the basis of the flock hatched ten years earlier.   In the selected line, hatchability shows an apparent non-linear decrease concurrently with the increases in F.   In the last two generations the decrease in hatchability may have been arrested. This may be interpreted as evidence that the inbreeding crisis has been overcome, i.e. that the population has "learned" how to exist under this form of mating, or more likely that a genotype-environment interaction is present. The latter possibility arises from improved incubation equipment and better low-temperature storage facilities for eggs being saved for hatching, which were available for the last two generations. The control line, following these changes in management, showed an increase in the hatchability of fertile eggs from 70 to 75 per cent to approximately 90 per cent. It is possible that the S line

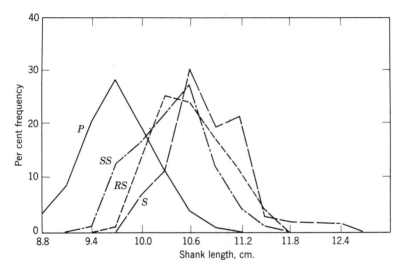

Figure 4.12. Shank length frequency distribution in the eighteenth generation
of selection

responded to the improvement by a relatively greater rise in its hatchability than the production-bred flock. At any rate, the highly significant fact about data of figure 4.13 is that hatchability showed an immediate improvement as soon as artificial selection for shank length was suspended, *although the inbreeding coefficient continued to rise*, whereas resumed selection produced an instantaneous decline in hatchability.

Obviously, natural selection for increased fitness, of which hatchability is a major component, still has considerable opportunity for exercising its effect despite an F value approaching 60 per cent. Future generations of the SS line could provide an answer to the question whether its gene pool can in spite of a heavy loss in genetic variance recover a fully balanced composition at a new level of shank length, as in stage I of the original model in figure 4.6.

Figure 4.14 shows the increasing discrepancy between the selection differential expected on the assumption that all selected birds have equal fitness and the selection differential actually realized.   If the two were equal, all points portrayed would fall on the diagonal straight line with a

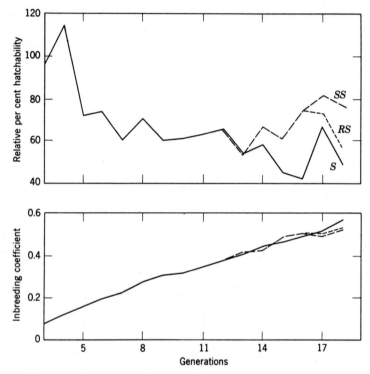

Figure 4.13.   Inbreeding and hatchability under selection for shank length

Relative percentage hatchability is computed by dividing the actual percentage of fertile eggs which hatched in the course of a standard hatching season by the analogous figure for the control (production-bred) flock.   The symbols *SS*, *RS*, and *S* stand, as in the earlier charts, respectively for selection-suspended, selection-resumed, and the original selected lines.   The scale of the graph does not permit clear distinction between the inbreeding coefficients of the three lines; they are obviously not significantly different from each other in any generation.   The data for the two *RS* lines in this diagram are given in the form of unweighted averages.

slope of unity.   When the longer-shanked pullets do not leave as many offspring as the shorter-shanked ones, the points tend to fall at an increasing distance below the diagonal.   In the early generations of selection, the difference between the expected and the realized differentials was negligible.   As it increased, selection progress was accordingly inhibited.   In fact,

Lerner and Dempster (1951a) demonstrated that this attrition of artificial by natural selection can account for about two-thirds of the decrease in the rate of gain observed past the seventh generation (see figure 4.10).

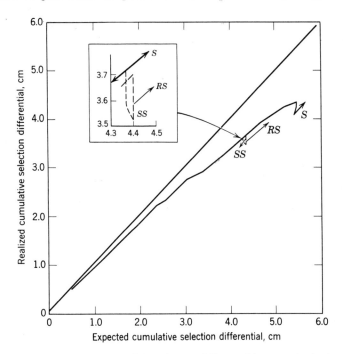

Figure 4.14.   Attenuation of the selection differential by natural selection
(see text)

The following table summarizes by five-year periods this effect in the *S* line.

Year of Hatch	Average Expected Selection Differential, cm.	Average Realized Selection Differential, cm.	Ratio of Realized to Expected Selection Differential
1940–1944	0.41	0.38	0.93
1945–1949	0.37	0.29	0.78
1950–1954	0.32	0.20	0.63

As soon as selection was suspended, the discrepancy no longer increased, a fact shown by the loop formed by the points for the *SS* line in the inset of the figure. The effects of resumption of selection (*RS*) cannot be assessed from the only two points as yet available.

The next figure (4.15) enlarges on the difference between the expected and the realized selection differentials.   It is basically a restatement of the situation in figure 4.10, in a form that permits an inspection of the relation between selection pressure and selection gain.   The retrogression of the *SS* line and the renewed advances of the *RS* line are clearly shown, together with the successive changes in the nature of the responses of the *S* line.

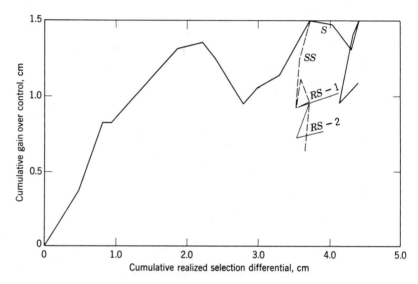

Figure 4.15.   Gains in shank length as a function of the realized selection
differential

The abcissa is equivalent to the ordinate in figure 4.14, the scale, however, being different to permit greater detail.   The ordinate represents cumulative gains based on the control values in each generation, rather than on the average shank length of the flock before selection.   Unless there is genotype-environment interaction, this method of plotting gains is free from intergeneration differences in environment.   The designation of lines is the same as in the previous graphs.

In figure 4.16 the crucial evidence on the relation between selection for shank length and fitness is given.   The method for computing the latter value needs explanation.   All eggs produced by the dams mated in each line and in the control population in the course of a four-week hatching period were incubated.   Whenever the reproductive capacity of a line dropped to a very low level, it was necessary to prolong the hatching season in order to preserve the population from possible extinction.   The birds produced in the extended part of the hatching period were not included in the computation of the fitness index.   All pullet chicks

hatched were reared without culling until maturity. The index of absolute fitness can then be defined as the number of female offspring per dam
mated, which were produced within a four-week hatching period and
which survived to December 31 of the year of their hatch (approximately
nine months of age). The average relative fitness of each line (the ordinate
in figure 4.16) is the absolute fitness index divided by that of the control

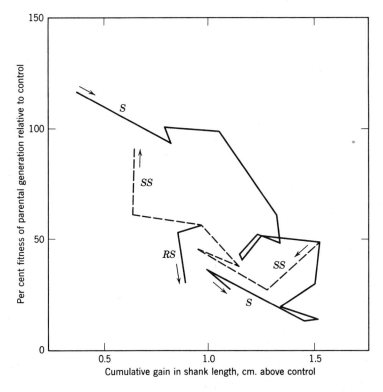

Figure 4.16.   Fitness and gains under selection for shank length (see text)

population (the fitness of which was measured in the same way) and
expressed in percentage terms.

The abcissa in figure 4.16 is equivalent to the ordinate in figure 4.15.
It may be seen that in the early generations of selection advances were
being obtained at no cost in fitness. The gains beyond 1 cm. are, however, associated with considerable losses in reproductive capacity. The
loop in the S curve corresponds to the first plateau. Further advances
and the second plateau are clearly shown, together with the unexplained
retrogression in shank length in the next to the last generation, a point

already commented upon.   The gradual recovery of fitness of the *SS* line concurrently with the reversion in mean shank length can also be readily noted.   The data for the two *RS* lines are pooled in this graph.

The last diagram to be presented in this series may serve as a bridge to section 21.   It shows that the suspension of selection for shank length carries in its wake not only changes in shank length itself and in fitness but correlated ones in other characters as well.   In figure 4.17 the character considered is body weight.   The *SS* line shows a drop in the average for this trait as shank length decreased.   Resumption of selection results in a reversal of this trend.   No interpretation of the curves shown in this graph will be made here; the next section, which examines the general phenomenon of correlated response, serves this purpose adequately.

Several highly probable conclusions are rendered manifest by the series of figures on the shank length experiment.   No computation of the expected ΔG was made here because of the complications arising from the use of criteria of selection auxiliary to the phenotype of the female parents. Nonetheless it seems reasonably clear that the gains in the early generations were in a general way consistent with expectation on the basis of the simple postulates set out in section 18.

The results obtained in the later generations suggest that in them opposition of natural selection to artificial selection arose.   This was a dynamic response by the population to the pressure applied and not the consequence of a purely static relationship between the character selected for and fitness.   The behavior of the line in which selection was suspended indicates that a gradual coadaptation of the contents of the gene pool occurred.   The results from lines in which selection was resumed have not been carried on long enough to make a significant contribution to the data but, in general, fit these notions.

Other possible explanations for the plateaus observed have been discussed in section 18.   Although none of them can be ruled out entirely, a fairly good case can be made against the idea that any single one was of major significance in this experiment.   No indications of exhaustion of additively genetic variance are present, since the heritability estimates remained high.   Neither can it be said that additive variance was transformed into the non-additive type.   There is no evidence for systematic changes in environment.   *Ad hoc* kinds of genotype-environment interaction would have to be assumed to explain the comportment of all lines. Polygenic mutations opposing selection seem improbable, especially if renewed response after a plateau can be obtained. Multiplicity of objectives as a major factor (excepting the opposition of artificial and natural selection) fails for the same reason.   Finally, lack of selection pressure as a causative agent in preventing realization of gains can be disproved rather readily.   It must nevertheless be borne in mind that one-third of the amount by which in some stages of selection realization fell

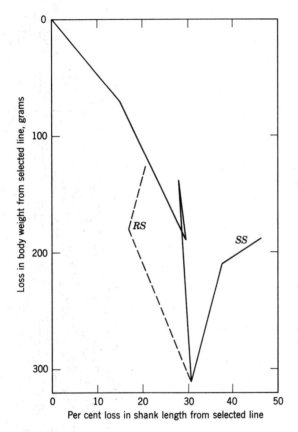

Figure 4.17.   Correlated response to suspension of selection for shank length

The ordinate represents the difference in gains between the average body weight at the time the shanks were measured (at about $8\frac{1}{4}$ months of age) of the S population and the SS (solid line) or RS (dashed line) groups.   The abcissa is based on the proportion of the gain attained by the S line, which was subsequently lost.   For any generation the value of y (difference in body weight) for a line is given by

$$\bar{Y}_S - \bar{Y}_{SS} \quad \text{or} \quad \bar{Y}_S - \bar{Y}_{RS}$$

The value of x (loss in shank length) is computed from

$$\frac{\bar{X}_{SS} - \bar{X}_P}{\bar{X}_S - \bar{X}_P}\,100 \quad \text{or} \quad \frac{\bar{X}_{RS} - \bar{X}_P}{\bar{X}_S - \bar{X}_P}\,100$$

where X_P is the mean shank length of the control in the particular generation. The data for the RS lines are pooled.

short of expectation has still not been accounted for. Hence, although the factors just listed are not likely to have been of major effect, some of them may still have played a minor but significant role.

Most readers will, of course, be aware by now that it is not that the shank length experiment happens to fit the general course of events shown in figure 4.6, but rather that the graph has been constructed on the basis of experimental results. A great many selection experiments with poultry and with other animals have been carried out. References to a number of these have already been given, and those to others will be found in succeeding chapters. It would be idle to claim that all of them fit a single pattern of response. Robertson's (1955a) analysis, especially if considered from the dynamic point of view, incorporating the notion that selection itself modifies the relationship between a selected trait and fitness, should be enough to disabuse anyone of the idea that selection results may be easily generalized.

The case history presented in this section then, although useful in assessing how much is known about selection, may be even more valuable in showing how incomplete our understanding of the underlying processes is. Above all, its moral lies in the demonstration of the fluidity of inter-relations between the various elements of coadaptation over a long pull in the integration of the contents of a gene pool.

21. Correlated Response

So far, with one exception, only the changes in fitness that are coincident to selection for metric traits have been discussed. The problem of cor-relative modification of unselected traits may now be considered from a broader point of view. Darwin (1872, 1875) has repeatedly insisted that living beings are in a state of such precarious balance that whenever "one part is modified through continued selection, either by man or under nature, other parts of the organization will be unavoidably modified." Among the more recent students of evolution, Chetverikov (1926, see end of section 28) and Schmalhausen (1949) have been equally emphatic in stressing the importance of the constitutional unity of organisms. This property inevitably causes changes in characters not directly selected for when traits under selection are shifted from equilibrium values.

Indeed, the very notions of homeostatic regulation and of coadaptation of the gene pool imply the existence of correlated changes in allelic fre-quencies. When these do not lead to genotypes equifinal with the original phenotypic "norm," the correlated frequency changes must also have counterparts on the level of phenotypic expression.

In recent years two different approaches to the theory underlying correlated responses have been developed. One, on a purely qualitative basis, derives from Mather's theory of polygenic inheritance (Wigan and Mather, 1942; Mather and Harrison, 1949). If metric traits are conditioned by polygenic systems organized in blocks, it is to be expected that polygenes concerned in the variability of one trait are intermingled along the chromosome with those determining variability of another. Selection directed toward increasing frequencies of certain blocks will then also affect the frequencies of alleles linked to them, thus generating correlated response. The other treatment of the question is a quantitative one and is rooted in the theory of genetic correlation developed by Smith (1936) and by Hazel (1943) from the respective fundamental formulations of biometrical genetics of Fisher and of Wright. The exposition of the subject here combines features of both approaches.

There is no lack of empirical evidence of changes in some metric traits of populations following selection directed to others. Haskell (1954) reviewed a number of instances without, however, considering the quantitative aspects of the problem. A further example dealing with reciprocal correlated response to selection for body weight on the one hand, and tail length in mice on the other, has been comprehensively analyzed by Falconer (1954b), using appropriate biometrical methods. In general, the literature on livestock, including poultry, abounds in data bearing on correlated response, but most of them have not been examined critically. For instance, Lerner (1946) presented material referring to correlated changes in the shank length experiment discussed in the preceding section in terms of phenotypic correlations. These, however, as noted in box 14, are inadequate for purposes of prediction of population behavior, which needs to take into account also the genetic correlations. One aspect of correlated response, the behavior of correlated traits upon suspension of selection, based on the shank length experiment, is exemplified in figure 4.17. Another example on poultry material is given by figure 4.18.

Correlated response may be either obligate or facultative. The first type is particularly important when the response takes the form of decreased fitness. This consequence of selection obtains when (a) selection for a character, which initially may not be a major component of fitness, is continued for a long time; (b) when a major fitness component which is subjected to selection has an intermediate optimum; (c) when selection is directed to a metric trait in the direction opposite to the sign of the correlation between it and fitness. In selection for a character not a major component of fitness, inbreeding may in part be responsible for the reduction in fitness, but this is not always the case, as has been shown in figures 4.13 and 4.16.

That the correlated response of fitness is mandatorily negative can very probably be deduced from the same premises that led Darwin to stress the importance of correlated variability. The decrease in fitness may, however, be temporary because of the possibility of eventual co-adaptation of the gene pool which could produce a recovery in fitness in the manner displayed by the SS line in figure 4.16.

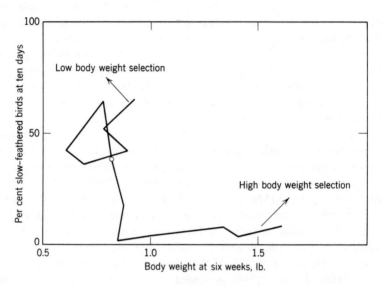

Fig. 4.18.   Correlated response to selection for body weight

The data are from the experiment of Godfrey and Goodman which were utilized in part for figure 4.4.   The circle is the starting point of selection for high six-week body weight in one line and for low in the other.   The gains in the plus direction of the selected trait are accompanied by a more rapid rate of feathering.   This correlated response was to be expected on the basis of many earlier studies (see references in Jull, 1952).

When selection is for traits such as those represented in curve E in figure 3.13, fitness will increase provided the population is not in equilibrium.   In any case, a positive correlation between characters of this kind and fitness may have a genotypic basis, even if correlated response in fitness does not materialize because of non-additivity.   A possible illustration is provided by the association of high egg number and viability observed in a production-bred flock of chickens by Dempster, Lerner, and Lowry (1952).

Another type of obligate response may occur in unselected traits when their variability is controlled pleiotropically by the alleles toward which selection pressure is directed.   Unless the originally pleiotropic effects of such alleles become separated either by selection of modifiers at other loci or by replacement by alleles which are without influence on the correlated trait,[2] the obligate nature of such response is permanent.

The facultative type of correlated response may affect certain characters in one selection program and completely different traits in another. The specific characters that may show a change are not *a priori* identifiable. Neither is the direction the change may take. Combinations of alleles with a net plus effect on character Y may be fortuitously linked with plus-acting alleles for character X in one population and with minus alleles in another. In such a case, selection to increase the mean of X in the two populations will be accompanied by correlated responses in Y of opposite direction. An illustration may be found in Prevosti's (1955) experiment with *Drosophila subobscura*, in which the signs of certain correlated responses were independent in geographically different populations. It is possible that the attribution to chance of the nature of association between the selected character and its correlate is due to our lack of understanding of the causal physiological relationship between them (e.g. see the confused picture in the correlated responses studied by Clayton, Knight, Morris, and Robertson, 1957). At any rate, in the absence of information on this point, responses of an unpredictable or variable type may be properly considered to be facultative.

There are several different genetic mechanisms underlying correlated response. The first and most obvious is pleiotropy. It is very likely that many metric traits are conditioned in part by the same fundamental processes, either on the level of primary gene action or early in ontogeny. Correlation due to pleiotropy may occur when the phenotypic expressions of the correlated traits are dependent on alleles with general effects on metabolic efficiency, or on the same hormones. Correlations between full and part performance (e.g. rate of growth and adult body size, winter lay of pullets and their annual output of eggs) are likely to be due to pleiotropy, at least to a degree.

Linkage is another important cause of correlation between traits. It may be present in the initial population or it may be generated by selection. Two types of origin of linked combinations may be recognized. First, if polygenic blocks are integrated under selection, they may contain locked within them alleles affecting traits other than those under selection. This is the basis of correlated response which was emphasized by Mather.

---

[2] Perhaps in the manner similar to that in the evolution of dominance according to Haldane's (1930) scheme, which has been more recently reinforced by Renwick's (1956) data. Selection may favor alleles which do not affect, concurrently with the trait under selection, other important characters. Such a process could be likely when the correlated character is a major fitness component.

The second source of origin of correlation between traits may be responsible for either pleiotropy or linkage. Its rationale is rather simple.
Different alleles or blocks may have net affects of various kinds on traits
X and Y. Thus, some may increase both X and Y, others increase X and
decrease Y, and so forth. The full list of possible combinations and their
fate under simultaneous selection for plus expressions of both X and Y is
as follows.

	Effect on X	Effect on Y	Fate under Selection
1.	+	+	
2.	+	0	Fixation
3.	0	+	
4.	−	−	
5.	−	0	Elimination
6.	0	−	
7.	+	−	Continued segregation
8.	−	+	

Although originally in this model X and Y were not correlated (assuming equal frequencies of all eight kinds of units), by the time only types 7
and 8 are left segregating in the gene pool a negative correlation between X
and Y has been established. Continued selection for X will then inevitably
lead to a correlated response in Y and vice versa. Such response can have
grave consequences in the selection for multiple objectives. The disastrous
effects that negative genetic correlations may bring about in artificial
selection programs have been discussed in detail by Dickerson (1955).
Their evolutionary significance has been commented upon by Haldane
(1956) in reference to paleontological studies such as those of Matthew
(1926) and Kermack (1954).

In addition to pleiotropy and linkage, correlated responses may be the
result of association of loci and blocks located on different chromosomes.
In particular, systems of correlations between selection coefficients of
independently transmitted genes based on gene interactions may produce
short-range correlated responses. Common origin of independent alleles
in a population of hybrid derivation may cause temporary correlations.
Any kind of non-random segregation can have a similar effect. For
instance, affinity or the attraction between non-homologous centromeres of
like origin (Michie, 1955) appears to be demonstrable in crosses between
subspecies or even between strains of mice. Whether it is of significance
in normally interbreeding populations of higher animals seems at present
problematic.

┌─────────────────────────BOX 14─────────────────────────┐

Genetic Correlation

The bases of correlation between two traits of an individual are pictured in figure 4.19. The phenotype for a given character (A) is shown as being determined by its genotype (G_A) and its environment (E_A), respectively connected to A by paths h_A and e_A. Character B similarly has genotypic and environmental components. A phenotypic correlation between A and B in a given individual may arise either because they are genetically correlated owing to common sources of genetic variation mentioned in the text, or simply because they developed in a common environment. Even when the magnitudes of the h and e paths are known, the phenotypic correlation is not very meaningful from the genetic point of view, since the two causes of covariance are confounded in it:

$$r_{AB} = e_A r_{E_A E_B} e_B + h_A r_{G_A G_B} h_B \qquad (1)$$

The genetic component of the phenotypic correlation may be isolated by determining the covariance of trait A in one individual with trait B in a relative, if the environment of the population is made random for all its members. The statistical techniques in this computation are analogous to the variance analysis in heritability determination. The papers of Hazel (1943), of Hazel, Baker, and Reinmiller (1943), of Reeve (1953), and of Jerome, Henderson, and King (1956) should be consulted for the details of the method. The latter article also has much useful information on heritability and on partitioning of genotypic variance.

Because of the high sampling variance of genetic correlations, few reliable values for characters of economic importance have been reported. In many instances, the correlations (as in Prevosti's, 1955, experiment commented upon in the text) may be reversed in sign in different populations. The genetic correlations which facilitate selection (i.e. those in which the desirable expressions show a positive association) include those between total egg production and its components (both temporal and biological), egg number and hatchability, body weight at different ages, and body weight and different linear dimensions. The important genetic correlations which hinder selection include those between egg number, on the one hand, and egg weight, egg quality, and meat quality characters on the other (see also section 25).

In addition to a number of abstracts appearing in *Poultry Science* in the years since 1952, the following sources of references may be consulted for estimates of genetic correlations in poultry: Abplanalp (1957); Godfrey and Goodman (1956); Jerome, Henderson, and King (1956); Johnson and Merritt (1955); Lerner, Asmundson, and Cruden (1947); Lerner and Cruden (1948); Peeler, Glazener, and Blow (1955); Wyatt (1954); Yamada (1955).

└───┘

All such mechanisms involve temporary or permanent *genetic correlations* between the characters in issue. Figure 4.19 and box 14 illustrate the distinction between phenotypic, environmental, and genetic correlations. The measurement of the latter not only between traits under

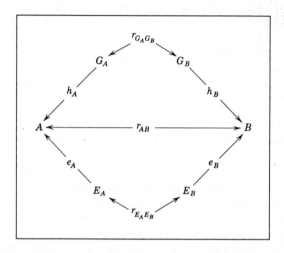

Figure 4.19.   The basis of phenotypic correlation between traits (see box 14)

selection but between others as well is a matter of considerable importance in selection practice. They are of significance in the construction of selection indexes (see box 18). They also permit the prediction of correlated responses, as demonstrated in box 15. However, prognoses of

---

BOX 15

Expected Correlated Response

No general formulation is available for the expected change in an unselected trait correlated with a character under selection. Difficulties may arise from such sources as partially genotypically determined maternal effects contributing to intertrait correlations and from other similar complications. For the simple situation in which only additive genetic variance and a constant linear genetic correlation between the traits are assumed, the expected correlated response is readily obtained. Designating the change in the selected trait (S) as $\Delta \bar{G}_S$, and that in the unselected one (U) as $\Delta \bar{G}_U$, the relationship between them may be written as

$$\Delta \bar{G}_U = \Delta \bar{G}_S \, \frac{h_U \sigma_U}{h_S \sigma_S} \, r_{G_S G_U} \qquad (1)$$

where $r_{G_S G_U}$ is the genetic correlation between S and U.

Abplanalp (1957) has computed several examples of expected correlated response in certain economic traits of poultry, which may be used to illustrate the subject.   He assumed mass selection directed, one at a time, to the following characters.

Trait		Phenotypic σ	Heritability
Winter egg production	(W)	13.7 eggs	0.26
Spring and summer egg production	(S)	23.0 eggs	0.14
Age at sexual maturity	(M)	3.7 weeks	0.12
March egg weight, per doz.	(E)	1.61 oz.	0.49

The system of genetic correlations in the flock studied by him was as follows.

Trait	S	M	E
W	0.55	−0.72	−0.38
S		−0.56	−0.47
M			0.33

If the selection differentials listed below (they are double those given by Abplanalp to allow for the fact that the traits are sex-limited) are assumed, the expected changes per generation of selection of female parents can be readily computed from formula (5) in box 12 for $\Delta \bar{G}_g$, and the expression for $\Delta \bar{G}_U$ given by formula (1).

Trait under Selection	Selection Differential	Direct Response	Correlated Response			
			W, eggs	S, eggs	M, weeks	E, oz. per doz.
W	20 eggs	2.56 eggs	–	0.36	−0.46	−1.15
S	20 eggs	1.38 eggs	1.72	–	−0.45	−1.72
M	2 weeks	0.12 weeks	−0.34	−0.07	–	0.18
E	2 oz. per doz.	0.49 oz. per doz.	−0.16	−0.05	0.03	–

Lerner, Asmundson, and Cruden (1947) give a similar example for selection on the basis of a selection index (see box 18).

this type are valid only to the degree that selection itself does not modify the magnitude of genetic correlations on which they are based.   Very little is known about this subject, largely because accurate estimates of correlations require data on a scale that is ordinarily not practical.[3] Similarly, with a few inconclusive exceptions, the effect of inbreeding on genetic correlations is known only in theory. Covariance between traits should be reapportioned under inbreeding in the same manner as variance, the between-lines component (on the assumption of additive gene action) increasing at the expense of the within-lines variation. In a completely homozygous line, the only source of correlation between traits should therefore be of environmental origin. In fact, however, hardly any empirical information is available on this aspect of the subject.

Genetic correlation will be alluded to once more in the discussion of aids to selection in the next chapter, which deals with selection techniques applicable to traits exhibiting additively genetic variation. Selection schemes when no or only a very limited amount of utilizable additively genetic variability is present will be examined in chapter 6.

[3] The study of Dempster, Lerner, and Lowry (1952) includes a possible example of change in a genetic correlation under selection. The statistical significance of this phenomenon, however, has not been established. In general, the changes in the values of correlations between traits may be related to the preservation of phenotypic balance between components of fitness. Morley (1955b) has suggested that this may be the reason why genetic and environmental correlations are often of opposite signs.

5

Selection Based on Additively Genetic Action

> . . . improvement is by no means generally
> due to crossing different breeds.

So far, discussion of expected selection responses from the quantitative point of view has been limited to mass selection. Considerably more complex forms of selection are possible in plant and animal breeding practice. The choice of the most efficient method in any given situation is then a major problem. Breeders have long been acquainted with selection procedures based on attempts to evaluate a genotype in ways other than from the individual's own phenotype.[1] But the possibility of arriving at a rational, even if not necessarily the best, decision in choosing between the various options available was opened only after the techniques for estimating selection accuracy (the regression of the genetic value on the criterion of selection) were developed.

When selection is ostensibly directed to a single trait, information about the breeding worth of a given individual may be sought from its own performance, as well as from the phenotypes of its ancestors, its offspring,

---

[1] Progeny testing was being recommended to animal breeders by authorities of the day nearly 2000 years ago (Lush, 1945). An early reference to sib tests is found in the ancient Hebrew law exempting from circumcision further children of a family in which two infants had died from bleeding produced by the ritual operation (cited by Coonen, 1956, from Garrison's history of medicine).

or its collateral relatives.   In addition, measurements of correlated traits
either of the individual itself or of its relatives can be turned to account
for this purpose.   When several characters are simultaneously objectives
of an improvement program, the number of sources of possibly useful
information becomes correspondingly larger.

Whenever there is an opportunity to employ more than one criterion of
selection, the breeder must ask himself two questions.   First, are the
selection gains expected under the more complex schemes sufficiently
greater than those obtainable from the simpler ones to warrant their
adoption?   Secondly, if the more elaborate selection scheme is also more
efficient, what are the respective weights to be given to each of the criteria,
so that selection progress is at a maximum?   Both questions can be
answered in theory when additively genetic variance is dealt with.   But it
is impossible to assert with great confidence that the conclusions reached
on theoretical grounds always accord with reality.   Some examples of
reasonable agreement with expectation and of actual observations on
selection advances attained under complex breeding plans may be found
in the literature.   The difficulty in evaluating them is often a logical one.
When expectation is met, the claim for validation of theory is readily
advanced (e.g. see Lerner and Hazel, 1947, and the amendment of their
conclusions by Kyle and Chapman, 1953); otherwise the discrepancy may
be attributed to non-additiveness of gene action or of genotype and
environment.   Since no accurate *a priori* estimates of non-additivity are,
as a rule, available for the traits studied, it is clear that the conclusions
reached in this manner can only be tentative.

One of the notable exceptions in which this difficulty does not arise may
be found in the elaborate investigations of Clayton, Morris, and Robertson
(1957) and of Clayton and Robertson (1957) on the selection for abdomi-
nal bristles in *Drosophila melanogaster*.   Having sufficient information on
the nature of the variance of this character before initiation of selection,
they were able to make predictions of expected gains from different
selection schemes and check them against the advances actually obtained.
They found that, in the early phases of the experiment, discrepancies
between their prognoses and their results were minor.   However, after
five generations of selection the responses in the various lines became
exceedingly erratic and moved the authors to conclude that "the classical
heritability approach appeared to break down completely."

Because of some special features of their material (small number of
chromosomes, lack of crossing over in males, presence of chromosomal
inversions and of lethals), it is not clear whether this diagnosis is intended
to suggest that the prediction equations possible at the present time have,
in general, no validity.   Such an extreme point of view would make the

better the enemy of the good.   A unified selection theory is preferable to a series of special theories for various species and for different stages of selection.   But, since no quantitative theory of this type free from epicyclic features is currently in sight, whatever possibility of making reasonably accurate short-term predictions there is should not be wastefully neglected.

We shall hence consider in this chapter the basis of selection practice when additively genetic variation is available in a population to be improved.   In the course of the discussion, departures from the conditions for which the theory outlined is valid will be mentioned when necessary. It may be worthwhile at this point to reiterate the premises under which prediction equations of the type developed in box 12, and extended in boxes 16 and 17, may be expected to be reasonably accurate.   Paraphrasing Clayton, Morris, and Robertson, they may be listed as follows for cases in which the realized selection differential can be computed: (a) diploid Mendelian inheritance, (b) presence of more than one allele at many loci, (c) small effects of allelic substitutions, (d) little epistasis, (e) independence of environmental variance from genetic values, (f) normal or quasi-normal distributions.

For successful long-term prediction of gains, further information beyond that discussed in the preceding chapter is needed, e.g. the distributions of allelic frequencies and of the magnitudes of effects produced on the selected character by individual allelic substitutions (Dempster, 1955b).

As was true of most of the quantitative theory presented in the earlier chapters, the biometric relationships underlying the choice of appropriate selection procedures derive from Wright's (1921) classical work on systems of mating.   Their application to the problems of artificial selection in animals was developed largely by Lush and his students.   Lush's (1947) comprehensive study of the use of family averages in selection, Hazel's (1943) development of selection index theory, and the analysis of selection plans for multiple objectives by Hazel and Lush (1942) are freely drawn upon in the following discussion.

The first point to be noted is the relationship between the selection gain possible and the degree of heritability.   When heritability is high, the expected advance from mass selection approaches the rate of genetic gain which could be obtained were the true genotypes of every individual in the population known.   The best that any complex combination of selection criteria can accomplish is this rate of progress.   Hence, the higher the heritability, the less worthwhile it is to investigate alternatives to mass selection.   It may be seen from figure 5.1 that auxiliary information in an improvement program for a character with an h^2 of 0.1 could at most permit a $3\frac{1}{3}$-fold increase in the gain per generation over that expected for mass selection. When h^2 is 0.8, this ratio is only 1.1. Although in both cases the cost of the extra work involved must be weighed against the value of the additional gains produced, it is obvious that at high heritabilities operationally sound opportunites for improving on mass selection are limited.

Figure 5.1 deals with the maximum possible genetic gains from selection. They represent, of course, only a potentiality. There are differences

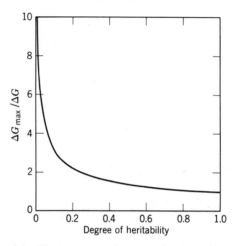

Figure 5.1.   Maximum rate of gain as a function of heritability

The expected gain from mass selection is

$$\Delta \overline{G} = ih^2 = \bar{\imath} \sigma_P h \sigma_G / \sigma_P = \bar{\imath} \sigma_G h$$

When the actual genotype of every individual in the population is known, effective heritability is equal to unity, and the gain expected is $\bar{\imath} \sigma_G$. It then follows that the ratio of the maximum possible gain ($\Delta \overline{G}_{max}$), when all sources of information about individual genotypes are taken into account, to the gain expected under mass selection ($\Delta \overline{G}$) equals $1/h$. This is the function plotted here.

between the various schemes open to the breeder in the degree to which they approach the limits set by the heritability of the character under selection. The efficiency of some of them will be considered in this chapter. The simplest one, apart from mass selection itself, is selection by family averages.

22. The Basis of Family Selection

A family may be defined as a group of individuals bearing a certain genetic relationship (r^G in box 4) to each other by virtue of common descent. In poultry breeding the two kinds of families of importance are full-sibs and half-sibs.   In a non-inbred population a *full-sib* or *dam family* is characterized by an r^G of 0.5.   Half-sibs (a *sire family*) in non-inbred flocks are assumed to have an r^G of 0.25.   In reality, this value is correct for sire families only when every family contains one offspring from each dam.   Otherwise sire families consist of a mixture of full-sibs and half-sibs and have average r^G values between 0.25 and 0.5, depending on the number of dams mated to each sire and the number of offspring produced by each dam (see caption to figure 5.6).   The deviation from 0.25 is, as a rule, not very serious and can be neglected for many purposes.   In inbred populations the genetic relationship within each kind of family is increased.   The effective or net r^G does not rise as fast when all inbred lines originate from the same population as when they are initially unrelated.   Thus, in a population of unrelated inbred lines, r^G between full-sibs is $(1 + 2F + F')/[2(1 + F)]$ where F is the inbreeding coefficient of the animals under consideration and F' that of their parents (see table in box 4).   When inbred lines are related, the gross r^G must be corrected for the fact that non-members of the family share a common descent with it.   The net relationship is

$$\frac{r_W^G - r_B^G}{1 - r_B^G}$$

where r_B^G is the average r^G between individuals belonging to different families and that for members within a family (Lush, 1945).

It is possible to base a selection program entirely on family averages, or more specifically on full-sib, half-sib, or progeny tests.   In non-inbred populations the genetic relationship of a sire or a dam to its offspring is 0.5, or the same as the intrafull-sib r^G.   Selection of dams, all of whose offspring were sired by one male, on the basis of a progeny test is equivalent to full-sib family selection in which the individual in issue does not itself contribute to the family average, as for example occurs in the selection of males for improvement of egg production or for other characters expressed only in females.   Selection of sires on the basis of a progeny test is different from full-sib family selection, because the intrasire-family r^G is usually closer to 0.25 than to 0.5.   In inbred populations there is a similar complication, the r^G between sibs being different from the r^G between parent and offspring.   In any case, since not every individual in a population can be progeny-tested, another selection criterion must be applied first to decide which animals will be subjected to the test.   Therefore, progeny testing is only rarely used without combining it with sib tests or mass selection.

The principle of family selection rests on the possibility of estimating the genetic value of a randomly picked member of a family from the phenotypic average of all its members. The greater the number of individuals contributing to the family mean, the closer does the average phenotype ($\bar{P}$) approach the mean genetic merit of the family, or its additive genotype ($\bar{G}$). This follows from the assumption that the non-additive genetic components as well as the E components of P are random in nature and, therefore, on the average tend to approach zero as the number of individuals per family is increased. In the discussion to follow, it shall be assumed that all individuals evaluated or selected contribute to the family average. Adjustments to the situations where this is not true (e.g. in selection of males for an egg production) are easily made (see, for instance, the formulas of Osborne, 1957b).

The heritability of family averages (h_f^2) takes intermediate values between the heritability of individual differences (h^2) and unity. When all

---

BOX 16

Family Selection

The derivation of gains expected from family selection, when the individuals selected contribute to the family average, can be made on the basis of part A of figure 5.2. Letting the subscript f stand for family,

$$\Delta \bar{G}_f = i_f h_f^2 = i \sigma_{\bar{P}} h_f^2 \tag{1}$$

where $\sigma_{\bar{P}}$ refers to the standard deviation of family averages. With n members in a family,

$$\sigma_{\bar{P}} = \sqrt{\frac{n\sigma_P^2 + \dfrac{2n(n-1)}{2}r^P \sigma_P^2}{n^2}} = \sqrt{\frac{1 + (n-1)r^P}{n}}\,\sigma_P \tag{2}$$

The genetic standard deviation of family averages is similarly,

$$\sigma_{\bar{G}} = \sqrt{\frac{1 + (n-1)r^G}{n}}\,\sigma_G \tag{3}$$

The value of h_f^2 is then

$$h_f^2 = \frac{1 + (n-1)r^G}{1 + (n-1)r^P}h^2 \tag{4}$$

and the expected gain is

$$\Delta \bar{G}_f = i\sigma_{\bar{P}} h_f^2 = i\frac{1 + (n-1)r^G}{\sqrt{n[1 + (n-1)r^P]}}\sigma_P h^2 \tag{5}$$

The ratio of gain from family to that from mass selection is therefore

$$\frac{\Delta \bar{G}_f}{\Delta \bar{G}} = \frac{1 + (n-1)r^G}{\sqrt{n[1 + (n-1)r^P]}} \tag{6}$$

The same result can be obtained by using the method of path coefficients. The following path relationships, derivable from part A of figure 5.2, will be used in box 17:

$$g = \frac{1}{\sqrt{n[1 + (n - 1)r^G]}} \tag{7}$$

and

$$p = \frac{1}{\sqrt{n[1 + (n - 1)r^P]}} \tag{8}$$

It may also be noted that

$$r_{\hat{G}\hat{P}} = ng[h + (n - 1)r^Gh]p = \frac{\sqrt{1 + (n - 1)r^G}}{\sqrt{1 + (n - 1)r^P}}h \tag{9}$$

and hence

$$h_f^2 = r_{\hat{G}\hat{P}}\frac{\sigma_{\hat{G}}}{\sigma_{\hat{P}}} = \frac{1 + (n - 1)r^G}{1 + (n - 1)r^P}h^2 \tag{4}$$

When n is indefinitely large, h_f^2 approaches the ratio r^Gh^2/r^P.

Here, r^P is used as a general symbol for the phenotypic correlation between members of a family. In box 4 and the figures related to it, the symbols t_{fs} and t_{hs} are, of course, equivalent to r^P for the respective cases of full-sib and half-sib families.

environmental variance is random, h_f^2 equals h^2 if there is only one individual per family and equals 1 when the number per family is infinite. On the basis of the biometrical considerations set forth in box 16 (and illustrated in figure 5.2), it is possible to compute the expected h_f^2 in terms of h^2, n, r^G, and the intraclass phenotypic correlation between the members of a family (r^P). Figure 5.3 shows how the ratio h_f^2/h^2 depends on heritability and number in a family of full-sibs, when no C effects are present.

Concurrently with an increase in family heritability the variation between family averages is reduced. The selection differential (i) corresponding to a given selection intensity is therefore lower under family selection than under mass selection. This follows from the facts that i in absolute units is a function of the σ of the population under selection, and that the σ of a population of family averages is smaller than that of a population of individuals (formula 2 in box 16). The ratio of $\sigma_{\bar{P}}/\sigma_P$ for full-sib families of different sizes approaches unity only at high heritabilities (figure 5.4).

Thus the advances expected from family selection as compared to those from mass selection are subject to pulls in opposite directions: accuracy of selection is increased, whereas the selection differential is reduced. The product of the two which specifies the gain to be obtained may be

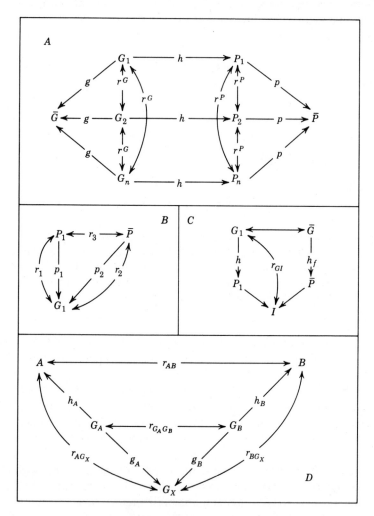

Figure 5.2. Biometric basis of family selection

Part A represents genetic (r^G) and phenotypic (r^P) relationships between n members of a family. The genetic values of each individual are represented by G with a subscript; the family average is symbolized by $\bar{G}$. Similarly, the individual phenotypic values and average are represented respectively by P_1 to P_n and by $\bar{P}$. The path between genotype and phenotype (square root of heritability) is indicated by h. The values of the paths g and p are given in box 16. Parts B and C are used in the development of the formulas in box 17. Knowledge of path coefficient techniques is necessary to follow the derivations presented. The symbols used, in addition to the ones described above, are I (selection index), p with subscripts (path coefficients), and r (correlation coefficients). Part D is used in box 18.

above or below that for selection on the basis of individuals, depending on the values of n, r^G, and r^P.   Figures 5.5 and 5.6 are based on computations using formula 6 in box 16; they compare the efficiency of full-sib and half-sib selection for different family sizes and values of h^2.

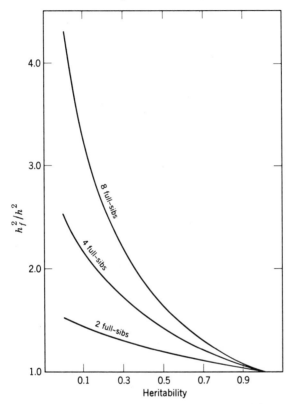

Figure 5.3.   Ratio of family to individual heritability

The curves are based on formula 4 in box 16 and on the assumptions (a) that the relationship between full-sibs (r^G) is 0.5 and (b) that $r^P = r^G h^2$.

The abcissa in all examples is the individual additively genetic heritability, and the ordinate is the ratio of expected gain per generation under family selection to that from individual selection.   Figure 5.5 deals with non-inbred full-sibs, the environment of which is completely random.[2]

[2] Lush (1947) devotes a section of his study to the examination of family selection under inbreeding.   In general, inbreeding may be expected to enhance the effectiveness of family selection, largely by increasing r^G.   This fact does not necessarily make the combination of family selection and genetic assortment an operationally efficient practice, because the economic and biological costs of inbreeding may be greater than the advantage it confers.

For each level of heritability there is a family size at which individual and family selection are expected to produce equal gains. Reciprocally, corresponding to any given family size there is a level of heritability above which mass selection is more effective than selection on the basis of family averages. For instance, by substituting 8 for n, 0.5 for r^G, and $0.5h^2$ for r^P into formula 6 (box 16), and by equating the expression to unity, h^2 is found to be about 0.44. This is the point at which the upper curve in figure 5.5 crosses the horizontal line at $\Delta\bar{G}_f/\Delta\bar{G} = 1.0$.

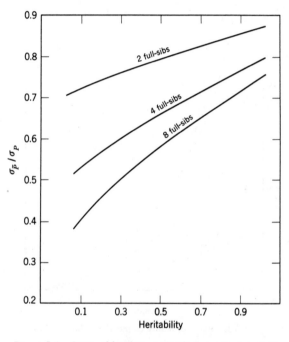

Figure 5.4.   Ratio of family to individual standard deviation

The curves are based on formula 2 in box 16 under the assumptions made for figure 5.3.

Similarly, it may be seen from figure 5.6 (note the assumption referred to in the caption) that for half-sib families the heritability below which selection based on families of 100 half-sibs is more efficient than mass selection is approximately equal to 0.24. Computations of this kind are not by themselves sufficient to decide whether family selection is to be preferred to mass selection, since the costs of gathering the information needed for one or the other breeding scheme must also be taken into account. But there are many situations in which the use of family

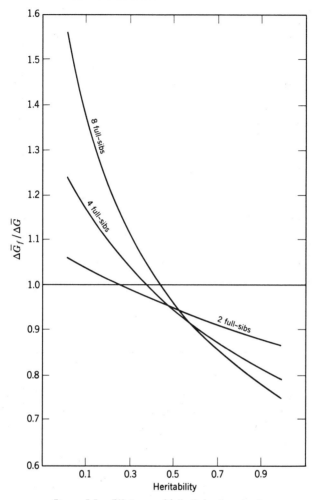

Figure 5.5. Efficiency of full-sib family selection

The curves are based on formula 6 of box 16 under the assumptions noted in the caption to figure 5.3. Family selection is more efficient than mass selection for heritabilities and family sizes above the horizontal line at the ordinate value of 1.0.

selection is dictated not by economics but by biology. For instance, in the improvement of sex-limited traits, mass selection of one of the parents cannot be used. Selection for carcass characters perforce falls into the same category if the animals have to be killed before breeding age. At the same time it should be remembered, especially with reference to chickens, that mass selection can be practiced without costly pedigreeing operations whereas family selection cannot. It may then be cheaper to

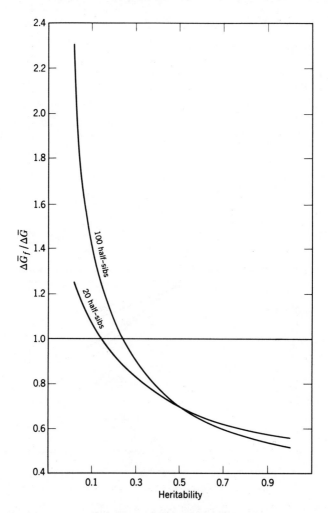

Figure 5.6. Efficiency of half-sib selection

The curves are based on formula 6 of box 16 and on the assumptions (*a*) that the relationship within each family (r^G) is 0.25 and (*b*) that $r^P = r^G h^2$. In practice, the first assumption is usually not valid, since half-sib families as a rule contain mixtures of full-sibs and half-sibs. The extent of underestimation of r^G here may be computed by comparing the value of 0.25 with the expected value of

$$r^G = \frac{n(d + 1) - 2}{4\,(dn - 1)}$$

where *d* is the number of dams mated to each sire and *n* the number of offspring per dam (see Osborne, 1957*a*).

neglect selection for a sex-limited character than to use family selection which may be otherwise not needed if pedigreeing thereby becomes necessary.

When the environment of animals forming full-sib or half-sib families is randomized, it is not always feasible to evaluate the family average without first measuring each individual. *En masse* measurement of the group average can be obtained for such traits as body weight. For others, e.g. egg production, the requirement of random environment precludes this possibility, because for mass measurement members of each family must be kept in quarters separate from other families. The usual choices for such characters are then between combined family and mass selection on the one hand and mass selection alone on the other, or between mass selection and family selection under non-random environment. Figures 5.7 and 5.8 show the latter comparison, but before examining them in detail a general consideration of C effects may be helpful.

23. Non-random Environmental Effects

The general expression for relative efficiency of group selection given in box 16 makes it clear that, for family selection to be preferable to mass selection, the genetic relationship between the members of the family (r^G) must be higher than the phenotypic correlation between them (r^P). Indeed, as pointed out by Lush (1947), it may be shown that only when r^P is less than $(r^G)^2$ can family selection be as efficient as the simpler forms of individual selection.

In the graphs hitherto considered, r^G was taken to be greater than r^P although not necessarily to the extent just noted ($r^G \geq \sqrt{r^P}$). In the presence of the so-called C effects (see section 10, figure 2.6, and box 4), r^P can become higher than r^G. These effects are present when the environments of members of a family are more alike than those of a group of individuals picked at random from a given population.

Many environmental factors which will make full-sibs resemble each other more than is dictated by their genetic relationship are possible. They are especially easy to visualize in such species as man in which siblings are subjected to a particular physical and cultural environment possessing continuity. But in addition to extrabiological variance components of this type which, at least under experimental conditions, may be controlled, there are unavoidable biological factors which induce C effects in full-sib families. They include (*a*) cytoplasmic inheritance, (*b*) maternally provided nutrition, (*c*) passive transmission of either pathogens or of antibodies from dam to offspring, (*d*) imitative behavior, and (*e*) under some conditions interaction between sibs either as a direct effect or indirectly through the dam.

The effects of these sources of sib resemblance are not easily recognized. Their evaluation is beset by difficulties unless appropriate experimental designs are employed to permit accurate partitioning of the phenotypic variance. Three examples of possible maternal influence of this type encountered in poultry-breeding practice may be cited. One is egg-borne transmission of the economically important neoplastic diseases (Burmester and Waters, 1955), which may interfere severely with selection for genetic resistance to them. Another is the maternal influence on the transmission of shell thickness (McClary and Lerner, 1950). Unfortunately the investigation of this aspect of egg quality inheritance was not carried far enough to substantiate or to disprove the evidence regarding the presence of C effects. The third instance of maternal influence in chickens is that of early growth rate. Apparently the size of the egg from which the chick hatches affects early body weight (see, among others, Skoglund and Tomhave, 1949). This can be a factor of considerable economic significance. It resembles the common phenomenon in mammals in which both intrauterine and early postnatal nutrition of the young are of paramount importance in determining preweaning body size (e.g. see Venge, 1950, and Chai, 1956), and the effect in chickens may persist to maturity (Hazel and Lamoreux, 1947).

Factors of this sort bear upon the relative efficiency of family selection, as is clear from the curves shown in figure 5.7. The magnitude of the non-random effects is designated in this figure, as in figure 2.6, as c^2 and is expressed in terms of h^2. When, for instance, c^2 is equal to h^2, mass selection under the conditions specified is more efficient than family selection at a heritability value as low as 0.15, which is about one-third of the comparable figure for the case of $c^2 = 0$. When c^2 is double the value of h^2, family selection would be warranted only at exceedingly low heritabilities.

Non-random C effects in sire families are as a rule a matter of management rather than of biologically determined inevitability. Selection on the basis of sire family averages is often practiced with cattle simply because the number of offspring in a dam family is very low. In poultry breeding, half-sib family selection has sometimes been recommended as a scheme in which great savings can be made in record keeping. The cost of trapnesting individual pullets could be presumably eliminated by housing all half-sisters together and recording total egg production for the house. This reasoning can be justified without further qualification only when such treatment does not result in significant C effects. The difficulty in practice is that the breeder can never be sure when such effects

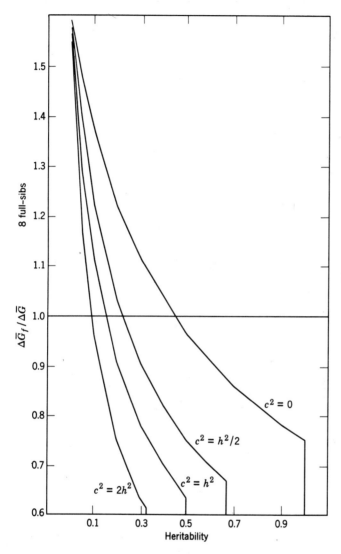

Figure 5.7. Efficiency of full-sib selection in the presence of non-random environmental effects

This plot is based on formula 6 of box 16. It differs from figure 5.5 in that r^P is taken to equal $r^G h^2 + c^2$, i.e. it assumes C effects, which make full-sibs resemble each other more closely than expected under random environment. The magnitude of c^2 is expressed here relative to that of h^2. The value of r^G is taken as 0.5. The curves (as in figures 5.8 and 5.10) extend to the maximum possible values of h^2, which are specified by the condition that $h^2 + c^2$ cannot exceed 1.0.

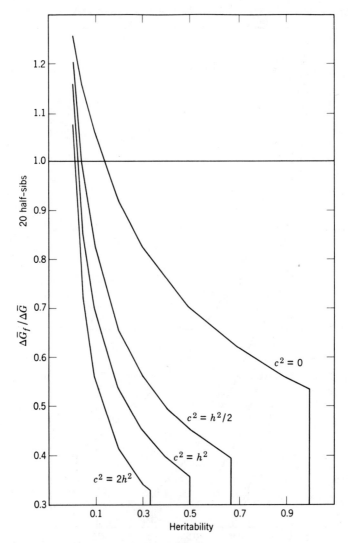

Figure 5.8.   Efficiency of half-sib selection in the presence of non-random
environmental effects

This series of curves is equivalent to the one in figure 5.7, r^P being assumed to be
equal to $r^G h^2 + c^2$ and r^G to 0.25.

may arise, as they can, for example, when disease outbreaks are limited to
single pens.

Figure 5.8 shows that, with families of 20 half-sibs, family selection
rapidly loses its effectiveness as c^2 is increased.   The curves cross the

horizontal line at very low levels of h^2, indicating the relative inefficiency of sire family selection in the presence of non-random environmental influences. Replication of samples from half-sib families under independent environments, such as would be provided by separate housing facilities for each of several groups of half-sibs by one sire, can overcome this difficulty to a certain degree.

24. Combined Selection

Combined selection is based on information on both individual phenotypes and family averages. The gains expected from this method of selection must, of course, always be higher than those obtained from either mass selection or family selection alone. But its net efficiency, when measured against the cost of applying it relative to the expected gains, may be lower than selection on the basis of one or the other of its components. This is a matter to be decided on economic grounds rather than on genetic grounds.

The quantitative principles of combined selection are expounded in box 17. Genetic theory must be called upon to provide the answers to two

---
BOX 17

Combined Selection

The points to be considered in discussing combined family and individual selection are: (*a*) the respective weighting to be given to each of the two criteria of selection and (*b*) the selection response expected. The diagram in part *B* of figure 5.2 can be used to derive by the method of path coefficients a general expression for the first of these.

The problem is to obtain the best estimate of the individual genotype (G_1) from a combination of the value of the individual phenotype (P_1), and the family average ($\bar{P}$), which includes the individual itself. The principles remain the same when more than one kind of family, e.g. full-sibs and half-sibs, are used. For the sake of simplicity, only one of such family averages will be considered here. The estimating equation is

$$\hat{G}_1 = b_1 P_1 + b_2 \bar{P} = P_1 + W\bar{P} = I \qquad (1)$$

Here, the family weighting coefficient W is equal to b_2/b_1 and I is the selection index.

The relationships between the regression coefficients and the paths in the diagram are given by

$$b_1 = p_1 \frac{\sigma_{G_1}}{\sigma_{P_1}} \quad \text{and} \quad b_2 = p_2 \frac{\sigma_{G_1}}{\sigma_{\bar{P}}} \qquad (2)$$

From the path diagram,

$$r_1 = p_1 + r_3 p_2 \quad \text{and} \quad r_2 = p_2 + r_3 p_1 \qquad (3)$$

so that

$$\frac{p_2}{p_1} = \frac{r_2 - r_1 r_3}{r_1 - r_2 r_3} \tag{4}$$

The values of the correlation coefficients in equation (4) may be obtained either directly from the diagram or from the relationships given in box 16:

$$r_1 = r_{P_1 G_1} = h \tag{5}$$

$$r_2 = r_{G_1 \bar{P}} = hp[1 + (n - 1)r^G] = \frac{1 + (n - 1)r^G}{\sqrt{n[1 + (n - 1)r^P]}} h \tag{6}$$

and

$$r_3 = r_{P_1 \bar{P}} = \sqrt{\frac{1 + (n - 1)r^P}{n}} \tag{7}$$

By substitution,

$$W = \frac{p_2}{p_1} \frac{\sigma_{P_1}}{\sigma_{\bar{P}}} = \frac{n}{1 + (n - 1)r^P} \cdot \frac{r^G - r^P}{1 - r^G} \tag{8}$$

The second problem, the expected gain from combined selection ($\Delta \bar{G}_c$), may be solved by examining the relationships in part C of figure 5.2. It is assumed that selection is made on the basis of the index in expression (1), $I = P_1 + W\bar{P}$.

We may write

$$\frac{\Delta \bar{G}_c}{\Delta \bar{G}} = \frac{ih_c \sigma_G}{ih \sigma_G} = \frac{h_c}{h} = \frac{r_{GI}}{h} \tag{9}$$

Here r_{GI} is the multiple correlation coefficient between G as the dependent variable and P_1 and $\bar{P}$ as the independent variables. But

$$r_{GI}^2 = \frac{r_{G_1 P_1}^2 + r_{G_1 \bar{P}}^2 - 2r_{G_1 P_1} r_{G_1 \bar{P}} r_{P_1 \bar{P}}}{1 - r_{P_1 \bar{P}}^2} \tag{10}$$

By substitution of expressions (5), (6), and (7) into (10),

$$r_{GI}^2 = \left[1 + \frac{(r^G - r^P)^2}{(1 - r^P)} \cdot \frac{(n - 1)}{[1 + (n - 1)r^P]} \right] h^2 \tag{11}$$

and

$$\frac{\Delta \bar{G}_c}{\Delta \bar{G}} = \sqrt{1 + \frac{(r^G - r^P)^2}{(1 - r^P)} \cdot \frac{(n - 1)}{[1 + (n - 1)r^P]}} \tag{12}$$

The theory underlying combined individual and family selection can be applied whenever more than one source of information is available for the evaluation of overall genetic merit. The method of index construction (box 18) is an example. However, complications in the computation of expected gains may arise when the choice of parents is arrived at not from a single culling but by a sequential series of eliminations of individuals undesirable for different reasons. The difficulties are largely due to the effects of the gradual decrease in the population size on its variation. Kyle and Chapman (1953) may be consulted for an example of computation of gains expected from the application of several criteria of selection.

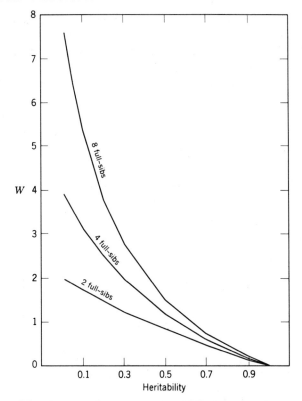

Figure 5.9.   Weighting factors in combined full-sib family and mass selection

The curves show the values of W as given by formula 8 of box 17 on the assumption that there are no C effects.

questions: (a) what are the optimum amounts of attention to be paid to individual performance relative to the family average and (b) what gains are to be expected from selection of this type.

In considering first the combination of only one kind of family average with individual performance, we may assign the coefficient W to the family mean in the estimating equation

$$I = P_1 + W\bar{P}$$

This expression is a selection index in which the information about the individual's phenotype (P_1) is added to the family average ($\bar{P}$ can stand for full-sib, half-sib, or any other type of family), which is weighted by the coefficient W.   The numerical value of W is chosen so as to maximize the regression of the true genotype of the individual in question (G_1) on the index.

The procedure of solving for W is explained in box 17.   Figures 5.9 and

5.10 provide examples of values of this coefficient under certain specified conditions. Both figures deal with full-sib families, the first one for varying values of n on the assumption that no C effects are present, and the second one for $n = 4$, for different values of c^2.

Figure 5.9 shows that the importance of the family average increases considerably with n, when h^2 is very low, and only a little when it is high. This fact is, of course, not in the least surprising. It may also be noted that the value of h^2 at which P and $\bar{P}$ make equal contributions to I ($W = 1$) increases with n.

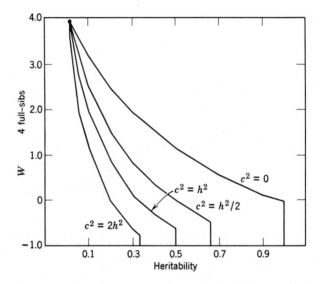

Figure 5.10. Weighting factors in combined full-sib family and mass selection in the presence of non-random environmental effects

The curves show the weights to be assigned to family averages when C effects are present. Note that, at certain h^2 values, superior individuals from inferior families should be preferred in selection, i.e., W is negative.

Figure 5.10 has a different point to make. It shows that, at certain values of c^2, W becomes negative. In other words, the existence of non-random environmental effects of the C type may make it sound practice to select individuals from phenotypically inferior families.

The paradox is only very superficial. Individual X, exhibiting a superior phenotype despite the fact that it, in common with the rest of its family, was exposed to an adverse environment, may well be a better choice for reproduction than Y, with a phenotype equally as good as that of X but representing a family provided with better environment.

Concrete examples of such a situation are often found in selection for disease resistance.   If exposure of different families to a disease is largely a matter of chance, then a surviving member of an exposed family might be preferred to a randomly chosen individual from a family which was not exposed.   Whether or not this is so must, of course, depend on the heritability of the character in question and on other parameters entering equation 8 in box 17.

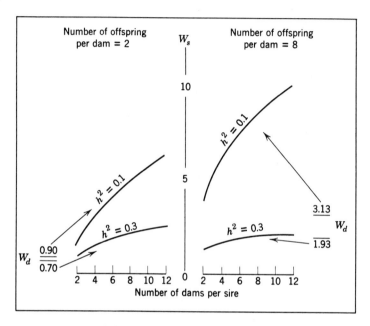

Figure 5.11.   Weighting factors in combined full-sib, half-sib, and mass selection

The values plotted are based on a selection index

$$I = P_1 + W_d\overline{P}_d + W_s\overline{P}_s$$

where W_d is the weight to be assigned to the average of full-sibs and W_s to that of half-sibs in the absence of C effects.   The values of W_d remain the same for a given heritability and number of full-sibs per family.   The scale for both W_d and W_s is given on the centrally located ordinate.   The illustrations are taken from a tabulation of values of W by Osborne (1957a).

Further complications arising from C effects are met in determining the optimum weights to be given to family averages in combined selection. In particular, traits in which these effects are themselves in part genetically determined may cause difficulties.   For instance, the early growth of mammals is to a great extent a function of the nutrition provided by the mother.   But this "environmental" effect is in turn a result of combined action of the maternal environment and of the maternal genotype, part of which is transmitted to the young. If a negative genetic correlation between the growth rate and quality of maternal nutrition (as found by Dickerson and Grimes, 1947, for pigs) is also present, the resulting interrelations between the different criteria and objectives of selection become veritably complex.

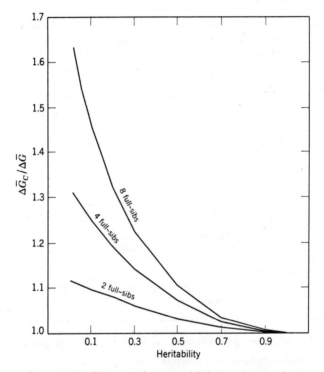

Figure 5.12. Efficiency of combined full-sib and mass selection

The curves are based on formula 12 of box 17 under the assumptions noted in the caption to figure 5.3.

Values which W can assume for combined selection on the basis of individual performance and both half-sib and full-sib family averages are shown in figure 5.11 for several types of breeding population. The number of offspring per dam in this figure is taken to be either 2 or 8. The number of dams per sire varies from 2 to 12, and only a limited array of h^2 values is considered. For other values, the papers of Osborne (1957a and b) may be consulted.

The remaining three figures in this section are devoted to illustrations of expected gains on the basis of combined selection and to a comparison

of full-sib and half-sib selection.   The theoretical basis of figure 5.12 is
fully given in box 17; that for figures 5.13 and 5.14 derives from Osborne's
studies.   All three plots should be taken only as illustrations of the general
situation based, for the sake of simplicity, on a number of assumptions
which may in practice be met only rarely.   In particular, the conclusions
derivable from figure 5.14 are open to doubt.   The figure is based on a

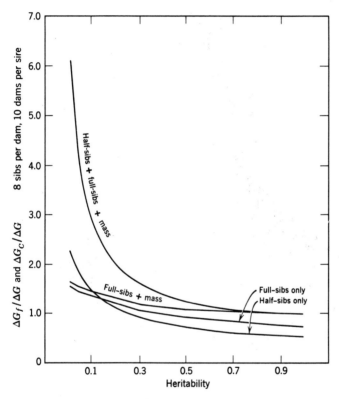

Figure 5.13.   Relative efficiency of combined full-sib, half-sib, and mass selection
(derived from Osborne 1957a)

postulate that no C effects exist and that gene action is completely additive.
A further point needs special emphasis in selection on the basis of half-sibs,
because with low heritability enhanced attention paid to half-sib averages
may result in a very rapid increase in the inbreeding coefficient.   It is
entirely possible that, in the absence of this factor, there are many traits
with enough additively genetic variance to make the general theory
developed here valid to a first degree of approximation.   Yet, as soon as
intense inbreeding is resorted to, the prediction equations may break

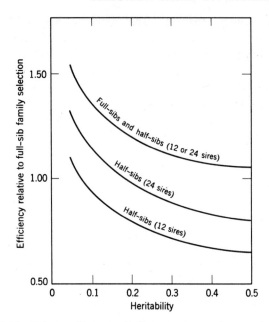

Figure 5.14.   Relative efficiency of half-sister selection for a sex-limited trait

The illustration (from Osborne, 1957*b*) assumes that every sire is mated to 12 dams, each of which produces 6 female offspring. Two male offspring are raised from each dam family. Selection among them is based on the performance of their full- or half-sisters. The curves show the efficiency of different selection methods relative to that obtained under full-sib selection.

down.   Considerable caution must therefore be recommended in choosing selection schemes that have a rapid increase in F as an inexplicit consequence.

25. Multiple Objectives

The difficulty of obtaining selection advances when the breeder addresses himself to more that a single character does not stem only from such complications as negative genetic correlations. Multiplicity of selection objectives, even in the absence of correlation between the traits under improvement, results in the lowering of selection intensity for each character selected.

In the simplest possible case it may be assumed that selection is directed to two uncorrelated characters A and B. If 10 per cent of the population is needed for reproduction, the selection intensity with respect to, let us say, A alone can correspond to a v value of 0.10, so that $\bar{\imath}_A = 1.75\sigma$ (box

11). But since A and B are not correlated, the average genetic value for B of the individuals selected for superiority with respect to A will equal the mean of the whole population. In other words, no pressure would be applied to B. Reciprocally, the best 10 per cent of the individuals, as judged by B, would have an i_A value of zero.

In order to include in the group selected as the parents of the next generation individuals excelling in both A and B, the selection differential for each must be lower than the 1.75σ possible for the reproductive rate specified. If equal weight is to be given to both characters, the effective v for each becomes $\sqrt{v}$ or, in our example, 0.316. This value represents an $\bar{i}$ of 1.12σ. In general, for n uncorrelated traits, the v possible for one character at a time increases to $\sqrt[n]{v}$ with a corresponding loss in $\bar{i}$. The selection differential for each of the traits may vary if their importance is not the same. Figure 5.15 illustrates how groups to be selected differ in composition, depending on the relative weight assigned to two traits under improvement.

The technique of selection for several objectives on which figure 5.15 is based is known as the method of *independent culling levels* (*ICL*). It, as well as *tandem* (*T*) selection, in which pressure is applied to one character at a time, and *index* (*I*) selection, based on a total score of combination of all desiderata, have been theoretically investigated by Hazel and Lush (1942). Their study indicates that on the assumption of no interference from the various complications discussed at the end of section 18, tandem selection is the least efficient and index selection the most efficient of the three methods. The advantage of total score selection over the other two rises with the number of characters entering the selection program, as is shown in figure 5.16.

The formulas developed by Hazel and Lush can become rather elaborate unless the simplifying assumptions noted in the caption to figure 5.16 are made. The rationale of their derivation is, however, simple. In particular, the curve of gains under index selection represented in the figure is simply the square root function of the number of characters. The gains expected from *ICL* selection are based on a somewhat more complex relationship between $\sqrt[n]{v}$ and the corresponding z (see box 11).

A graphic demonstration of the difference between *ICL* and *I* selection is provided by figure 5.17. It involves two characters which are negatively correlated. The index used for the chart was arrived at arbitrarily and represents a criterion of selection for an unspecified aggregate rather than for any rational combination of egg weight and number.

The method of constructing indexes is detailed in box 18. It calls for reliable information on the genetic parameters characterizing the population, including heritabilities and genetic and phenotypic correlations

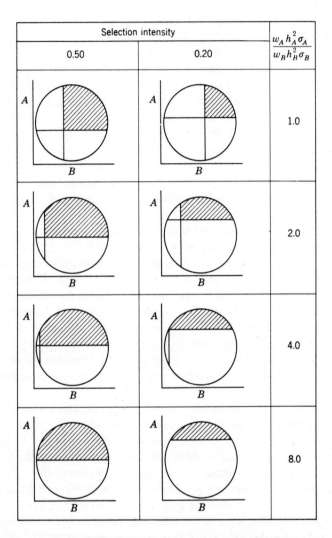

Figure 5.15.   Selection for two uncorrelated traits

The shaded area represents the group of individuals to be selected at different levels of v for maximum progress under the method of independent culling levels.   Different weights are given in selection to characters A and B, depending on their relative importance as measured by the ratio at the right.   The symbols used are the same as in box 18 (w = economic importance, h^2 = heritability).   The figure has been constructed from table 1 of Hazel and Lush (1942),

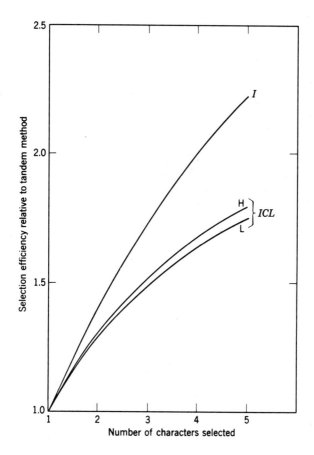

Figure 5.16.   Relative efficiency of different selection methods

The curves, based on the formulas of Hazel and Lush (1942), show the relative gains to be expected from index or total score (I), independent culling level (ICL), and tandem selection.   See text for definition of these terms.   The I curve applies to all selection intensities.   The two ICL curves represent high and low selection intensities:

	v for Males	v for Females
H (high)	0.005	0.05
L (low)	0.02	0.20

It is assumed that the heritabilities, phenotypic standard deviations, and economic weights of all traits are equal and that no correlation between the characters selected is present.

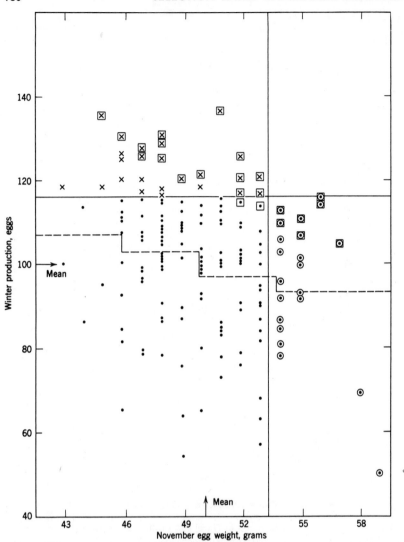

Figure 5.17.   Selection based on an index

The diagram shows a distribution of November egg weights and winter egg production figures (from beginning of lay to January 1) of 163 Leghorn pullets.   The horizontal line, above which the dots are replaced by crosses, truncates the 15 per cent of the birds highest in egg number.   The vertical truncation, to the right of which the dots are encircled, similarly separates the 15 per cent of birds with the highest egg weight. There is a negative correlation between the two characters, as is shown by the dashed lines which indicate mean egg production for different egg weight arrays.   Because of this correlation, no bird appears in both selected groups.   The squares enclosing dots and crosses indicate birds chosen on the basis of an arbitrary index ($I = 3EW + EN$).

BOX 18

Selection Indexes

Techniques for constructing selection indexes for multiple objectives have been described by Smith (1936) and by Hazel (1943). Many worked examples may be found in the subsequent literature (e.g. Wyatt, 1954). The rationale of deriving an index for many characters is essentially the same as that used in the construction of an index of combined family and individual selection (box 17), although certain additional constants are called for. For the sake of simplicity, selection for only two traits is considered here. Part D of figure 5.2 may help to explain the derivation.

Let the two characters to which selection is applied be designated as A and B, their respective genotypes as G_A and G_B, heritabilities as h_A^2 and h_B^2, and the correlations between them as r_{AB} (phenotypic) and $r_{G_A G_B}$ (genetic). An aggregate phenotype (X) may be defined which combines A and B proportionally to their relative economic values w_A and w_B,

$$X = w_A A + w_B B \qquad (1)$$

Corresponding to X there is also a genotypic aggregate, G_X, which is then subject to selection pressure and is defined by

$$G_X = w_A G_A + w_B G_B \qquad (2)$$

The variance of G_X is

$$\sigma_{G_X}^2 = w_A^2 \sigma_{G_A}^2 + w_B^2 \sigma_{G_B}^2 + 2 w_A w_B \sigma_{G_A} \sigma_{G_B} r_{G_A G_B} \qquad (3)$$

The contributions that each of the component genotypes make to G_X are, respectively,

$$g_A = w_A \frac{\sigma_{G_A}}{\sigma_{G_X}} \qquad \text{and} \qquad g_B = w_B \frac{\sigma_{G_B}}{\sigma_{G_X}} \qquad (4)$$

The correlations between the phenotype for each of the component traits (which are the criteria of selection) and the aggregate genotype may be derived from path relationships as

$$r_{AG_X} = h_A g_A + h_A r_{G_A G_B} g_B \qquad \text{and} \qquad r_{BG_X} = h_B g_B + h_B r_{G_A G_B} g_A \qquad (5)$$

If the relative weights to be given to A and B in the index for maximum gains are now designated as W_A and W_B respectively, two simultaneous equations may be written

$$r_{AG_X} = W_A \frac{\sigma_A}{\sigma_{G_X}} + r_{AB} W_B \frac{\sigma_B}{\sigma_{G_X}} \qquad (6)$$

and

$$r_{BG_X} = r_{AB} W_A \frac{\sigma_A}{\sigma_{G_X}} + W_B \frac{\sigma_B}{\sigma_{G_X}} \qquad (7)$$

By substituting the expressions numbered (5) into (6) and (7) and solving for W_A and W_B, the selection index

$$I_X = W_A A + W_B B \qquad (8)$$

can be constructed.

The efficiency of such an index as a tool for selection may be estimated from the regression of G_X on I_X,

$$b_{G_X I_X} = r_{G_X I_X} \frac{\sigma_G}{\sigma_I} \qquad (9)$$

where

$$r_{G_X I_X} = \sqrt{\frac{W_A \sigma_A r_{AG_X} + W_B \sigma_B r_{BG_X}}{\sigma_{G_X}}} \qquad (10)$$

The gain expected from selection on the basis of the index is, of course

$$\Delta \bar{G}_I = r_{G_X I_X} \sigma_{G_X} i \qquad (11)$$

The efficiency of index selection relative to that possible if the true genotypes of all individuals were known is given by the value of $r_{G_X I_X}$. The critical comments of Kempthorne (1957) on the subject of selection indexes should, however, be kept in mind.

between the different characters. Perhaps the most bothersome of the statistics needed are the economic weights to be assigned to each trait. No sound index for multiple objectives can be constructed without them. Unfortunately, a considerable element of arbitrariness has to be resorted to in the choice of economic weights, first because they are impossible to determine accurately and second because they are not constant.

For example, a breeder attempting to improve egg production of chickens must also select for egg size and for hatchability. The relative value of an increase of one standard deviation in egg number as against a similar gain in egg size will fluctuate with market conditions and with the actual level at which these traits happen to be. The relative weights to be given to egg weight improvement and to changes in hatchability are even more difficult to decide upon, because the values of the two characters are expressed on scales which are awkward to compare: the first is based on the monetary return to the breeder's customer, the second on the efficiency of the breeder's hatchery operation. Certainly both items can be reduced to dollars and cents, but the cost accounting needed to remove the subjective element in figuring the coefficients in the selection index may be rather complicated.

No problem of this sort arises when a single trait is to be improved and an index is used only in order to increase selection efficiency. The economic weights of the auxiliary characters in the index may be taken to be zero (as in the indexes constructed for changing the conformation of broilers by Lerner, Asmundson, and Cruden, 1947). The increase in efficiency of selection carried out on the basis of an index as against direct selection depends largely on the heritability of the character in question. For example, Krueger and his associates (1952) have constructed an index for selecting birds to improve egg production. The h^2 of their particular measure of this character was 0.28; that of the index which involved seven other traits (early and later body weight, sexual maturity, extent of short and long pauses in the course of the laying period, persistency of production, and viability) was 0.35. In indexes of this kind, as well as when improvement of several traits is at stake, any combination of individual performance and family averages may, of course, be used. In other words, a character can enter an index in the form of several separate but correlated criteria: individual value, half- or full-sib test, progeny test, and so forth.

The most difficult problem to handle in connection with multiple objectives is that of negative genetic correlations, whether induced by selection or originally present in the population. In poultry breeding the outstanding examples are breast width and fertility (especially in turkeys); short shank length (as an index of conformation) and body weight; and, above all, egg number and egg weight. The first of these correlations may be found to correspond to the situation represented by stages F and G in figure 4.6, and therefore might be remediable under continued selection pressure. The other two are more likely to be pleiotropically determined. Long shanks and high body weight on the one hand, and egg number and egg weight on the other, may involve general factors of metabolic efficiency, so that separation of genetic determinants of variation in each of the two instances is not a feasible goal. The egg weight–egg number correlation offers a further complication because of its non-linearity. The limitation on the amount of product a bird can manufacture seems to be operative only when the upper limits of egg production are reached. Thus, in a study of this problem, Blyth (1952a) found the negative relation between egg number and size of eggs only in birds producing more than 22 eggs a month.

There is no solution to *permanent* genetic correlations, at least within the framework of microevolution. Index selection minimizes the obstacles that they form in the breeder's path, but the assumption that this method can be effective when others fail completely is unwarranted. As noted by Dickerson (1955), the heritability of an aggregate consisting of n negatively correlated components, each having the same genetic and phenotypic variance, approaches zero as the average genetic correlation between them moves toward the value $-1/(n-1)$. In effect, this situation is equivalent to selection favoring a heterozygote. A very good analogy to it is provided by reproductive fitness, which is comprised of a variety of components and in a natural population in equilibrium cannot be improved by selection. It then seems a sensible procedure for breeders to redefine their goals rather than to waste selection pressure on unimprovable combinations of traits.   There are some selectors who still may be inclined to gamble on very long-term results, but since their sights are set on targets toward which the optimum approach is not known, there seems to be little reason to commend to them one form of selection rather than another.

26. Auxiliary Selection Methods

There are many methods other than index selection that are auxiliary to the basic technique of mass selection.   Some of these may be now briefly noted.   Of particular practical significance is the use of indirect criteria of selection which augment operational efficiency either by increasing gains or by lowering costs.

An example combining both features occurs in selection for increased egg production which was cited in section 18.   Dempster and Lerner (1947) computed the expected gains from combined full-sib family and individual selection for the first year's egg production, when (a) selection is based on the hen's full annual record and (b) when only the winter egg production of pullets is taken into account.   They (as well as Maddison, 1954) concluded that, because the interval between generations in the second system of selection is half what it is in the first, pullet selection is more efficient than hen selection.   Many further advantages are present in the scheme based on part records.   They include the possibility of exercising higher selection pressure because fewer pullets than hens are needed as dams to maintain constant flock size; lowered costs of commercial chick production for the same reason; the great saving in record keeping made possible by dispensing with trapnesting after selection of breeding birds has been made; and the economic as well as prophylactic benefits of earlier culling of unproductive and unhealthy birds (a practice that would interfere with obtaining accurate family averages for the full year).

To be weighed against these merits of the pullet selection scheme in small populations is the increased rate of inbreeding that may be connected with it.   Indeed, this factor, together with certain other limitations in the procedures used, prevented the experiment of Lerner and Dempster (1956), which was designed to test the validity of their theoretical inference, from being unequivocal in its results.   Strong indication was, however, obtained from it that the theory was basically sound.

Another type of short cut which has found a place in commercial practice is periodical instead of daily trapnesting.   The expected gains from using this method may be smaller than when complete trapnest records are kept (Nordskog, 1948), but the loss is insignificant compared to the savings effected. In fact, trapnesting for only two days a week seems to insure a reasonably accurate selection of dam families when they contain as many as eight sisters each.

Examples of this sort may be multiplied indefinitely, but in each situation an operational comparison of costs versus gains must be made. For instance, Martin, Glazener, and Blow (1953) found that in selection for increased 12-week body weight of broilers various combinations of earlier weights could be employed. Three-week weight as the selection criterion leads to 69 per cent efficiency as compared to 92 per cent obtained from the use of 6- or 9-week weights, gains based on the 12-week weight being taken as 100 per cent. The pertinent question is whether the respective losses of 31 and 8 per cent in efficiency are compensated for by any advantages. As a rule, exact information to make appropriate decisions is not available, and, in any case, the problem at this level, once the biological principles are understood, becomes one of economics.

Selection for traits on which repeated measurements are possible raises problems of a similar kind. Box 19 discusses certain aspects of the *repeatability* of traits under selection, which is a measure of the constancy of repeated observations on a given individual. The relative efficiency of selection based on single and multiple observations can be readily ascertained from this statistic.

An important aid to selection may be found in corrections for environmental sources of variation. It may be recalled that, since h^2 is a ratio

---

BOX 19

Repeatability

There are many traits for which repeated measurements on the same individual are possible. For example, the average first-year egg size characteristic of a bird may be estimated by weighing any number of eggs, from one to all, produced by her in the course of the laying year. The intraclass correlation between repeated measurements is known as *repeatability*. It measures the degree to which the phenotypic expression of the character is free from temporary influences of diverse origin.

The accuracy of selection is augmented by making repeated measurements on the same individuals, thereby also increasing the expected gain from selection. It may seem paradoxical at first sight that the benefit of repeated observation is the greater the lower the repeatability. But this is to be expected, since a very high correlation between successive measurements clearly indicates that the first contributes nearly all the useful information.

Designating the "heritability of multiple observations" by h_m^2, and repeatability by r_m, the same considerations that led to formula (4) of box 16 (with r^G taken as unity) yields the expression

$$h_m^2 = \frac{n}{1 + (n - 1)r_m} h^2 \tag{1}$$

Since

$$\Delta \bar{G} = ih^2 = i\sigma_P h^2 = i\sigma_P \frac{\sigma_G^2}{\sigma_P^2} = i\sigma_G h \tag{2}$$

and

$$\Delta \bar{G}_m = i\sigma_G h_m \tag{3}$$

the ratio of gain expected from selection based on multiple observations ($\Delta \bar{G}_m$) to that based on single ones is

$$\frac{\Delta \bar{G}_m}{\Delta \bar{G}} = \frac{h_m}{h} = \sqrt{\frac{n}{1 + (n - 1)r_m}} \tag{4}$$

Examples of using this formula in reaching decisions about the operationally optimum number of observations for various economic traits of chickens may be found in a series of studies by Nordskog and his students (Scheinberg, Ward, and Nordskog, 1953; Farnsworth and Nordskog, 1955; Hill and Nordskog, 1956). Considerable theoretical discussion is also included in these reports.

Of increasing significance in connection with the developments considered in chapter 6 is the formula (Lush, 1945) for comparing expected genetic values of animals from non-interbreeding populations when repeated measurements on them are available. If P_1 is the average of an individual's phenotypic values for a repeatable character and $\bar{P}$ that of the population of its origin, the best estimate of the individual's genotype is given by

$$\hat{G}_1 = \frac{(1 - r_m)\bar{P} + nr_m P_1}{1 - r_m + nr_m} \tag{5}$$

The use of this expression in comparing the performance of strains or groups of birds is illustrated by King (1954).

which includes environmental variance in the denominator, it is effectively increased whenever a component of non-genetic variation is eliminated. When such elimination is real and not only done on paper, the situation seems to be straightforward. But attempts to apply corrections by adjustment of raw data obtained under variable environment are not always successful.

In part this may be due to the fact that the environmental differences subjected to theoretical elimination are not systematic. For example, it may be generally true that a negative correlation between date of hatch and winter egg production exists. In any given year successively hatched groups of birds may, however, be subjected to other causes of environmental variation which can obscure or reverse the relationship. Correction for date of hatch by means of a standard regression may be of little use in such a situation. If part of the genetic variability is corrected away together with environmental variance, real harm may be done. Box 20 gives a rather simple illustration of overcorrection by introduction into the computations of a non-existent genotype-environment interaction.

Many workers have suggested criteria of performance designed to make corrections unnecessary. For instance, Skaller (1954a) examined a number of different ways of measuring egg production for this purpose, and Oliver et al. (1957) analyzed the gains to be expected from the use of various criteria of the annual egg record as bases of selection. Others have presented a variety of recipes for handling the effects of differences in hatching date on egg production and egg weight. That a considerable conflict of opinion exists about when and what corrections are helpful may be gathered from a sampling of literature on the subject, including the papers of Bohren, Rapp, and Arvidson (1952), Cochez and Pero (1954), King and Henderson (1954a and b), Skaller (1954b), Abplanalp (1956), and Düzgüneş and Yao (1956). It could be an instructive exercise to examine the grounds on which the recommendations for diverse procedures in the matter of corrections are based in these reports.

The attitudes of various investigators toward this matter depend not only on the use of different methods and materials but also on varying criteria for judging the significance of the results obtained. As has been repeatedly stressed, it is not enough to find out that a certain procedure increases selection efficiency by a certain amount. The cost of the procedure must also be taken into account. Clearly any corrections that reduce the expected gain need not be looked into further; those that augment it must be, whenever possible, evaluated with respect to their net effects. Otherwise judgment regarding the wisdom of using corrections must be offered as a guess.

There is one more form of correction that may be mentioned, although strictly speaking it refers to a matter outside the scope of the present chapter. In discussing prediction equations for gains from mass selection (section 18), the adverse effect of inbreeding due to the limited size of the breeding population was mentioned. Differences in F between individuals considered in the selection of parents of the next generation may be of such magnitude as to interfere with the evaluation of their additive genetic values. For example, Tebb's (1957) study (figure 3.11) indicates that within a given generation each per cent increase in inbreeding has an average effect of -1.0 egg on the annual record of pullets in the flock

┌─────────────────────────────BOX 20─────────────────────────────┐

Overcorrection

An arbitrary example without making generalizations may be used to illustrate overcorrection. Let there be three segregating loci, with all alleles designated by small letters given the value of zero, and the additive effects of respective allele substitutions being:

$$A - a = 4$$
$$B - b = 2$$
$$C - c = 1$$

Three families are assumed to segregate at two loci each, being homozygous for the third one:

    family I   segregating for Aa and Bb and homozygous for CC
    family II   segregating for Aa and Cc and homozygous for BB
    family III segregating for Bb and Cc and homozygous for AA

There are four houses in each of which one-quarter of every family is placed at random. The environments provided by the four houses are considered to differ so as to change the phenotype of every individual by a constant amount characteristic of each house. Thus

    house W adds   4 units
    house X adds   2 units
    house Y subtracts 2 units
    house Z subtracts 7 units

from each individual's genotypic value. Assuming that no other sources of environmental variation are present, an individual of the genotype $AaBBCc$ has a phenotypic value of 13 units if kept in house W, but one of only 7 units if kept in house Y.

The 16 individuals of each family were then assigned in a random fashion to the four houses. In one particular sample the house and family means were found to be as follows (on the basis of these stipulations).

House \ Family	I	II	III	Total
W	11.00	14.50	15.50	13.67
X	12.00	11.25	12.25	11.83
Y	6.50	6.50	9.50	7.50
Z	2.50	3.75	6.75	4.33
Total	8.00	9.00	11.00	9.33

└───┘

We may next assume that three levels of selection intensity (7/48 = 14.6%; 13/48 = 27.1%; 25/48 = 52.1%) are to be applied to the population on different bases: (a) true genotype; (b) phenotype; (c) phenotype adjusted to house mean, (d) phenotype adjusted both to house and family mean.

The accuracy of selection may be judged by the percentage of the superior genotypes (as originally defined) included in the groups selected by each of the methods. The following results (with some arbitrary adjustments to avoid ties in samplings) were obtained for this sample:

Selection Intensity	Selection by Genotype	Selection by Phenotype	Selection by Phenotype Adjusted to House Mean	Selection by Phenotype Adjusted to House and Family Means	Selection by chance (Theoretical)
7/48	100.0	71.4	85.7	57.1	14.6
13/48	100.0	61.5	84.6	69.2	27.1
25/48	100.0	72.0	92.0	72.0	52.1

Adjustment for the house means improves the accuracy of selection over that obtained by choosing the best phenotypes. Further correction, however, reduces the accuracy attained by this method at every level of selection intensity. The house effect is a non-random environmental condition, which the first adjustment removes. The house-family correction in this example is based on a non-existing interaction between genotypes and environment and thus, introducing a genetic correction, interferes with accurate estimation of the true genotypes. Carried a step further, correction for the average of all houses would assign an identical value to all individuals and thereby reduce selection accuracy to the level reached by selection at random.

Overcorrections have been frequently used in animal breeding, especially in dairy cattle. Lörtscher (1937) may be consulted for an analysis of the fallacies connected with byre corrections.

investigated. Hence, a correction for inbreeding may be considered worthwhile when selection is oriented toward methods appropriate in the utilization of additive genetic variation. This is a problem still to be investigated. Here it will only be pointed out that under the mating systems usually practiced in closed flocks, the correlation between F values of dams and daughters is not far from zero (figure 5.18). This fact suggests that high values of F should be given a *positive* rather than a *negative* weight if any correction is to be applied.

There are other selection aids available to breeders in search of methods for increased efficiency of selection procedures. Most of them depend on the principles already expounded. Such practices as polyallel matings, reliance on pedigrees, and so forth must be evaluated in the same way as the other auxiliary methods discussed in this section.[3] It should be kept in mind that the comparison between different selection procedures relates

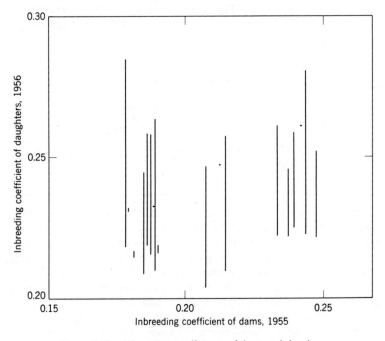

Figure 5.18.   Inbreeding coefficients of dams and daughters

An empirical illustration of the lack of correlation between the inbreeding coefficients of dams and daughters in the production-bred flock of Leghorns, described in section 31. Ranges of F values of 717 daughters are plotted against the F values of their 112 dams.

to the efficiency of immediate gains rather than to the total amount of selection advance possible. For the latter the disposable amount of additively genetic variation, the number of segregating units, and the magnitude of their effects are more relevant than the manner in which the breeding worth of selected animals is evaluated.

[3] An illustration of the dialectics which are on occasion involved in arriving at operationally sound decisions about the value of such methods is given by the sequence of papers by Lerner and Dempster (1951b), Hutt and Cole (1955), and Dempster and Lerner (1957).

27. Optimum Structure of Breeding Populations

Comparisons of efficiency of gains under different methods of selection, combined with a balance sheet of costs and returns, enable a breeder in theory to decide how many dams should be mated to each sire, how many offspring should be produced from each dam, and what the age distribution of the parents must be in order to attain maximum net gains in the objectives pursued by him. In practice, there are too many gaps in the knowledge necessary to obtain a complete *a priori* answer to this question in all but a few of the simplest situations. In spite of this fact there are certain features of the problem that deserve at least brief mention.

One is family size. Considering only full-sib families for the moment, a population of N individuals may be described as containing d families of n members each. The determination of the optimum relation between d and n is an eminently practical question which all breeders must ask themselves before initiating a program of selection. The answer depends on a number of factors amongst which reproductive capacity is of high significance, since it sets the uppermost value to n and thus the lowermost value to d.

Under mass selection, the maximum gain to be obtained in the absence of inbreeding decline might at first consideration be expected when n is high, equaling N in the limit, since such a reproductive rate would permit the biggest selection differential. This conclusion is of course not particularly realistic, because even when the trait under selection is not affected by inbreeding, reproductive fitness is, and selection of this order of intensity would call for continuous brother-by-sister mating. Furthermore, in relation to long-range objectives, such as the total amount of gain, rather than to the rate of immediate advance, the optimum v (i.e. d/N) can be shown to be much closer to 0.5 than to zero (Dempster, 1955b).

Be this as it may, the reproductive rate of most species does not permit n to be very high. In poultry it could be greater than in any other important domestic species, but in practice selection differentials must be lower than the maximum possible ones, in order to avoid inbreeding degeneration. The optimum values of n and d are, however, not known.[4]

[4] It is highly unlikely that either the reproductive rate or the number of males to be saved from each family would enter the determination of the optimum structure of poultry breeding flocks. Very few breeding enterprises are large enough to consider the employment in pedigree matings of all sires produced by a female, although in theory this may be an important factor (see Osborne, 1957b). In larger animals one-sire populations are more common. Inbreeding decline is arrested in them by continuous immigration, each male successively used originating from outside the herd.

All other things being equal, it may be assumed that, for the system of reproduction used in poultry, the balance between accuracy of family selection (which increases with n) and the variance of family averages (which decreases with n) leads to a maximum gain from selection on the

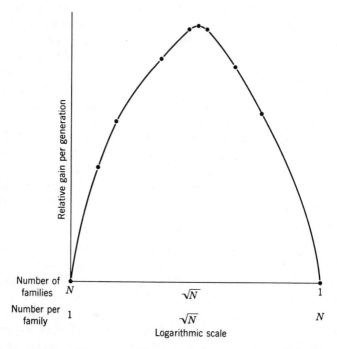

Figure 5.19.   Efficiency of family selection as a function of family size

This is a plot on a logarithmic scale of the first part of table 40 of Lerner (1950). It shows that the maximum gains are to be expected from selection based on averages of full-sib (dam) families when the number of individuals per family is equal to the number of families (N) in the population.   The optimum number of full-sibs per dam is then $\sqrt{N}$.   The simplifications underlying this relationship should be kept in mind, in particular the independence of h^2 and family size.   This condition may be violated when prolongation of the reproductive season introduces extra sources of environmental variation, although Abplanalp (1956) found it to hold for a number of economically important traits of chickens.

basis of dam-family averages, when $d = n = \sqrt{N}$ (see figure 5.19).   In reality, unfortunately, all other things are never equal.

   Reproduction of poultry is ordinarily carried out in a series of hatches rather than in a single one.   The question immediately arises whether prolonging the hatching season reduces family heritability of the character under selection by introducing additional sources of environmental variation. Should this be so, the optimum value of n might be different than otherwise computed. It should be parenthetically noted that Abplanalp (1956) failed to find this effect in a study of several useful traits of the chicken.

A broader approach to the problem of the optimum structure of breeding populations for straightforward family selection has been taken by Robertson (1957). He showed that a general solution is possible if the minimum permissible number of families to be selected for reproduction is specified, i.e. if an *a priori* limit of inbreeding tolerance is assumed. With N as the total population size, and f the number of families from which x individuals are to be allowed to have offspring, n (equal to N/f) is found to be a function of N/x, r^G within the family, and h^2. Robertson has prepared graphs from which the values of n and f may be derived for different values of h^2 in half-sib ($r^G = 0.5$) selection. He also gives formulas from which the same information for other values of r^G can be obtained, as well as the expressions to be used when C effects are present.

For combined family and mass selection the problems become correspondingly more complex. Despite the importance of the whole issue in poultry-breeding practice, little attempt has been made so far to solve it, probably because of the uncertainty regarding the precise nature of inbreeding effects. Once they are assumed to be non-significant, many aspects of this question can be readily analyzed. For example, the effect of size of breeding operation on efficiency of gains expected was investigated in a rather simple manner by Nordskog and Wyatt (1952).

The attenuation of the selection differential due to small population size was considered in box 11. Nordskog and Wyatt, using the principle discussed therein, computed the relative proportions of the maximum possible selection differentials realized under selection of different intensities in small populations. Their results are plotted in figure 5.20, from which it appears that, with 50 individual male matings, selection intensities approaching 98 per cent of those in populations of infinite size are possible. They suggest that 20 to 30 sires may provide a sufficiently wide base for selection. Unfortunately, the lack of information regarding other factors of significance (i.e., as noted before, inbreeding effects) limits the direct application of this analysis to breeding practice.

With respect to optimum-age structure, the computations carried out by Dickerson and Hazel (1944) and by Dempster and Lerner (1947), which have already been noted in section 18 and elsewhere, provide examples of the problems facing breeders and of the way they can be solved. Once more the warning must be made that not only additive gene action but absence of inbreeding degeneration in fitness must, as a rule, be assumed in determinations of this kind, at least for the present.

This condition clearly makes decisions, about which of the various possible practical breeding programs is the optimum one, provisional, since sooner or later non-additive effects will make themselves known.   Their importance is magnified by the fact that when selection is suspended and the population is propagated at random, the expectation on the basis of additively genetic variation of the trait selected is that its mean will remain unchanged.   If, however, the mean regresses, it must be concluded that non-additive variation, either directly in the determination of the trait itself or indirectly as when natural selection opposes artificial selection, has become of significance.

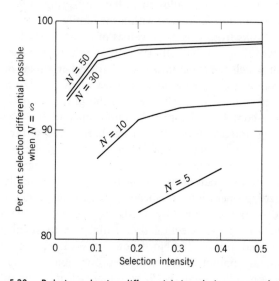

Figure 5.20.   Relative selection differentials in relation to population size

This graph shows the attenuation of the selection differential due to small population size.   It is taken from Nordskog and Wyatt (1952), who based their computations on the same considerations as those set forth in box 11; N refers to the number of sires.

This particular question has considerable practical importance, because if suspension of selection has no adverse effects, anyone could, by purchasing commercial stock, enter into competition with the breeder who produces it, without incurring the cost of a breeding program.   Since genetic improvement is a slow process, replenishing of the improved stock need be done only every few generations.   The economic significance of the problem is obviously high, a fact that makes the lack of studies on it unaccountable.   Only very recently has some investigation of this issue been undertaken, but so far it is impossible to specify precisely the homeostatic strength (Robertson's, 1956, parameter defining the rate of

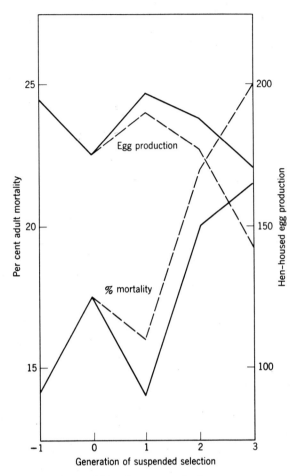

Figure 5.21. Suspension of selection

The solid line refers to a flock under continuous selection for reduced mortality, the dashed lines to an extraction from this flock in which selection has been suspended. The importance of these observations lies not in the trend shown by the two groups of birds but in the increasing difference between them in each generation. Note that the egg production is given in terms of hen-housed averages. This means that the observed difference may have been entirely due to mortality and that egg production of survivors was unaffected by suspension of selection. The data are from Moultrie, King, and Cottier (1953a) and Moultrie, Cottier, and King (1956).

reversion upon suspension of selection; see section 16) of the various characters. In addition to the study of suspended shank length selection (figures 4.12–4.17), other observations on this problem are being made at the University of California, suggesting that egg number does not drop very fast when selection is suspended, whereas deterioration of egg size and viability is detectable very soon. Moultrie, Cottier, and King (1956) have also supplied some evidence on this question. They concluded that mortality tends to increase when selection is suspended as compared to the level maintained under continued selection. Their data are reproduced in figure 5.21. It may be noted, however, that in absence of unselected controls, it is not possible to tell from the figures shown whether the suspended selection line actually deteriorated or merely failed to keep up continued genetic improvement which was obscured by interyear environmental fluctuations.

Perhaps the most important lesson to be learned from this illustration is that experimental tests of additivity by suspension of selection are not sensitive when conducted on the scale within the possibilities open to an average breeder. True, some notion about the amount of inbreeding degeneration or of heterosis expected in different traits may be obtained from theoretical considerations (Robertson, 1955a) or from empirical evidence (Blyth, 1952b). But, generally speaking, the decision whether a given complex of selection objectives should be handled in one of the ways mentioned in the present chapter or in one of those considered in the next must be based on trial and error.

Two of the most painful deficiencies in current selection theory are represented by the inability to foretell when and under what circumstances predictable responses give place to superficially capricious ones, and the inability to recognize immediately when a plateau has been reached in selection improvement. It is not easy to see at the moment how this shortcoming can be remedied, because each different combination of traits in every gene pool may be unique in its pattern of reaching a coadapted state under artificial selection programs. Hence, selection theory may have to address itself, as has been previously suggested, to predictions of population behavior given entirely in statistical terms. This may, in turn, mean that a breeder controlling one or only a few populations is at a great disadvantage. Breeding enterprises handling whole populations in the same manner as the breeder of yesterday handled individuals may then be the only ones able to survive. But this is a matter that only the future will reveal.

6

Selection When Variance Is Non-additive

Intercrossing plays a
very important part...

In recent years the commercial importance of poultry selection schemes which take into account non-additive variation has increased to a great extent. Three factors have contributed to this development. First, the rapid expansion of individual hatchery enterprises, which must seek markets for their product in an ever-widening area, raised the problem of genotype-environment interactions. The question whether stock selected for improved performance in one location and under a given management would perform equally well in other locations and under different managements became of great importance.

The second factor of significance has been the gradual approach of improved stocks to a plateau in performance. Exhaustion of genetic variability has not been demonstrated for any polygenic trait in flocks of reasonable size (although in experiments with mice reported by Falconer and King, 1953, allelic fixation appeared to account for cessation of selection response in body weight). Yet improvement has often been found attenuated to a degree that caused considerable concern to many breeders. It is likely that the remaining variation in populations exhibiting this phenomenon is non-additive.

The third factor which entered the situation was the utilization of heterosis in poultry production.   Even when further improvement seems readily attainable from the methods described in the preceding chapter, the widespread incidence of non-adaptive heterosis (or luxuriance in Dobzhansky's, 1952, terminology), as manifested by growth rate and other traits, makes crosses between breeds, varieties, strains, and lines commercially attractive.   As a consequence emphasis on crossing has greatly increased.   Figure 6.1 illustrates the startling postwar rise in the

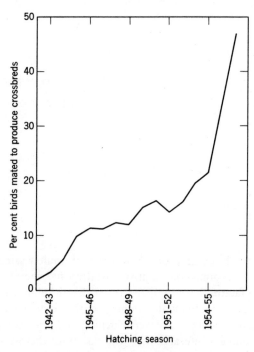

Figure 6.1.   Growth of poultry crossbreeding in the United States

The proportion of all birds mated that is devoted to the production of crossbred progeny rose from 2 to 47 per cent in sixteen years.   A news release from the United States Department of Agriculture is the source of this plot.

proportion of breeding birds devoted to the production of crossbred offspring in the United States.

The first of the factors mentioned refers to the non-additivity of genotypes and environments in the determination of the phenotype. Hence the opening section of the present chapter deals with genotype-environment interaction.   The remaining sections are devoted to a discussion of selection schemes appropriate for characters associated with the other two factors.   Traits with a significant proportion of epistatic and dominance deviations in their genetic variance fall into this category.

Selection schemes based on non-additive variance have only limited interest outside breeding practice, since no counterpart to the elaborate artificial selection and mating programs used by poultry breeders exists in nature. Furthermore, in spite of several brave attempts at formulating the quantitative theory of selection for heterosis, most of the information available is based on trial and error. The theoretical foundations of the current methods of breeding designed to utilize non-additive variation rest on much more flimsy grounds than those for selection directed toward additively genetic variance. In a book on selection practice, no doubt much space could be devoted to breeding for heterosis; in one on the genetic basis of selection, such procedure is hardly justified, especially when comprehensive summaries of the whole field (e.g. the volume edited by Gowen, 1952) are available.

The fact that it is probably not a sound policy to start an improvement policy directly with one of the schemes discussed in the present chapter should be noted. The high cost of selection based on the performance of crosses warrants its use only when cheaper methods of selection are ineffective. Furthermore, selection between populations at the very beginning of a program of genetic improvement is wasteful, because the additive variance within the groups discarded is not utilized. Hence, when selection is first initiated for various objectives, it is not unlikely that ordinary mass, family, or combined selection could be profitably employed with a relatively high degree of short-range accuracy in predicting results. At some point in the selection program the disposable additive genetic variance, as judged by selection response and not by intrageneration heritability analysis, may become reduced to such an extent as to make the transition to one of the selection methods dealt with in the present chapter worthwhile. Since currently it is not possible to identify the exact stage of selection progress when one approach should be substituted for the other, the decision to change must be arrived at in an arbitrary manner. For these reasons the treatment accorded here to selection when the important sources of variability are non-additive is more sketchy than that given to the various points considered heretofore.

28. Genotype-Environment Interaction

Statistical interactions between genotype and environment are produced by differential reactions of carriers of specific genetic constitutions to diverse external conditions. The simplest form of genotype-environment interaction in poultry-breeding practice is that between the date of hatch within a given year and performance at a single location. Although a number of investigators have found significant interactions of this sort for a variety of characters, it may be questioned whether they are of great practical significance. For instance, whereas Osborne (1952, 1954) and Skaller and Sheldon (1955) noted interactions between genotype and date of hatch in the determination of sexual maturity, Abplanalp's (1956) analysis shows that they may be disregarded without much damage in selection programs within closed populations (see the discussion of corrections for linear hatch effects in section 26). Of greater importance may be the interactions between genotype and (a) management, (b) location, and (c) complexes of conditions specific to particular years of hatch.

These types of interaction present two problems. First, is the expected improvement based on evaluation of genetic merit under one environment realized when the ameliorated stock is kept under another? Second, does the attenuation of effective heritability due to interaction interfere seriously with selection gains?

It is generally assumed that tests of performance on which selection is to be based should be carried out in the environment under which the improved stock is expected to be maintained. This point of view is, however, not necessarily correct. We may consider performance under two environments as two separate traits which are genetically correlated (see discussion by Falconer, 1952, and by Lowry, Lerner, and Taylor, 1956). Selection for one of these "characters" may produce, as a correlated response, changes in the other of a greater magnitude than had selection been directly for the second "character."

In figure 4.19 the characters A and B can stand for performance (expressed in standard deviations) in some trait under two environments. Direct selection for A will produce gains proportional to h_A^2 (since $\Delta \bar{G}_A = i h_A \sigma_{G_A}$). Selection for A on the basis of B will be (all else being equal) proportional to $h_B r_{G_A G_B}$. When this quantity is greater than h_A, indirect selection is more efficient than the direct kind. When there is interaction, $r_{G_A G_B}$ becomes reduced and indeed may be negative. Selection in one environment (B) may then be worse than useless, if improvement of performance in another (A) is sought.

There are practical breeders who insist that tests on which selection is to be based should be carried out, as a matter of principle, under the best environment. On strictly genetic grounds it is impossible to predict a priori whether such a policy would be effective. If it is, the success could no doubt be accounted for by the fact that the parameters determining correlated response, which in addition to the heritabilities, the genetic correlation, and the genotype-environment interaction also involve phenotypic variance, favored such outcome. Probable examples of this situation are to be found in characters, which require better than adequate environment for the expression of the full genetic potentialities of the "superior" individuals.

In point of fact, it seems more probable that tests under stress or under poor conditions, so long as they do not act as a sieve to pick out specific genotypes (that is to say, so long as genotype-environment interaction is not significant), are likely to be more effective than tests under favorable conditions. For instance, this was found to be true in selection experiments for body weight of mice on full and restricted diets (Falconer and Latyszewski, 1952). Similarly, Lerner and Bird (1948) presented limited evidence that selection for growth rate of chickens to be raised on normal diets is more effective when the criterion of selection is growth on a riboflavin-deficient regime than when adequate amounts of vitamins are provided.[1] The whole problem is an exceedingly complex one, in view of the fact that ordinarily there are not only two environments but a great variety. The important decision to be made by each breeder is which of the many possible environments should he provide for the stock under selection. Should he, for example, expose the animals being tested to all the diseases that the flocks of his customers are likely to encounter? Should he test his birds for performance in a variety of geographical locations? Should he vary the management and the diets supplied to the birds?

Answers to such questions must be arrived at operationally, but in practice little information on the economics of the problem is available. In contrast there are a number of studies on the biological issues at stake. One example deals with a major change in the managemental practice of poultry flocks which has come about in recent years. Many poultrymen, instead of keeping their birds in hen houses, now maintain them in individual laying cages. Should selection for one of these types of management not be effective in improving performance under the other, different strains for each might have to be developed. Fortunately for breeders, several economically important traits exhibit no genotype-environment interaction when these types of management are compared within a closed population (Lowry, Lerner, and Taylor, 1956). It should, however, be noted that *strain-management* interaction for survivors' egg production has been reported in a test involving floor pens and laying batteries (Gowe, 1956).

[1] In a more extensive experiment of the same type, Lamoreux and Hutt (1948) found their selection methods to be specific for resistance to riboflavin deficiency; on a normal diet the selected line did not grow faster than the controls.

Again, little or no interaction has been found between location and performance in a number of studies of strain differences in relation to egg production (e.g. Gutteridge and O'Neil, 1942; Gowe and Wakely, 1954; King, Cole, Hutt, and Cottier, 1952) and to broiler production (Merritt and Gowe, 1956). It must, nevertheless, be understood that diversity of location carries with it a variety of unspecified differences in some tangible and many intangible factors. Absence of significant interaction in a given experiment provides then no guarantee that in a different or more extended range of locations it could not occur.

This fact may be of particular importance not in relation to location but to differences between years of hatch, referred to under (c) at the beginning of the present section. The most comprehensive study of this point was carried out by Hill and Nordskog (1956). Their investigation was directed toward evaluating differences between various incrossbred (see box 22) combinations, but their results may throw some light on the failure of closed-flock selection to produce gains expected on the basis of intrageneration estimates of heritability.

In brief, Hill and Nordskog carried out two experiments. In the first, they compared the egg production and viability of 55 varieties of incrossbreds, each of which was maintained at 13 locations (in seven different states ranging from Nebraska to New Jersey). The second experiment compared the performances of 10 varieties of crosses at 4 locations in 3 successive years. Analysis of repeatability of variety performance revealed that equal efficiency of testing for egg production would be obtained from testing in 13 locations once, at 2 locations for 2 years or at a single location for 3 years.

Figure 6.2 illustrates this finding, together with corresponding information with respect to per cent mortality. The curves portray minimum significant differences at the 5 per cent level for different numbers of tests. For example, a variety tested a single time in 1 location must have a production higher by 60 eggs (or be 33 per cent lower in mortality) to be significantly superior to another variety. Retesting at the same location four times reduces these figures to 31 eggs and 12.5 per cent. Testing for 3 years at 3 locations calls for a minimum significant difference at this level of 25 eggs, and so forth. The practice recommended by Hill and Nordskog is to test varieties of crosses at 5 different locations and then retest the better ones for 1 or 2 more years.

The aspect of their study of greatest significance to closed-flock breeding is the comparison of repeatability of varietal performance in one or more locations, tested for one or more years. They found that, whereas repeatability of variety performance with respect to hen-day egg production for a single test in one location was 0.44, that based on different locations and different years was only 0.12.   Similarly for hen-housed mortality, the corresponding figures were 0.57 and 0.19.

Should the same proportions apply to intrapopulation selection, expected gains computed on the basis of intrageneration heritabilities would greatly overestimate gains obtained.   In effect, h^2 under such conditions would consist of two parts: h_G^2, the heritability of some general property of the animal which contributes to the phenotype independently of environmental changes between generations, and h_S^2, the heritability of response to the specific environment of the generation under test.   Only the former contributes to selection gains.   Indeed, h_S^2 may refer not only to a property that has no effect on the improvement in performance of the next generation, but to one that actually decreases it.

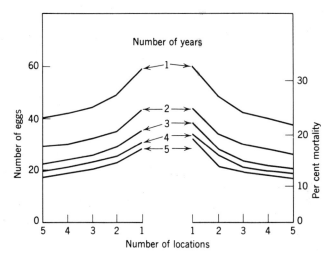

Figure 6.2.   Genotype-year-location interaction (see text)

This type of interaction is equivalent to a change in selection objectives every generation.   It is analogous to tandem selection, pressure being applied to a procession of different traits for a single generation each. There is no need to labor the theoretical aspects of this point since it seems apparent that severe attenuation of gains may be produced by inter- actions of this kind.   Thus, in selection for egg production, various diseases may interfere with selection advance.   It is obvious that when resistance to a particular disease is a major determinant of the egg record, selection in a generation when its incidence is high favors genotypes that have no selective advantage in the absence of the disease.   The greater the heritability of the specific resistance, the less effective is selection for the general ability to lay eggs independently of variation in the immediate environment. This is another way of saying that the sign and magnitude of the genetic correlation between components of performance may be of crucial significance in selection responses over a long period.

The only other point that needs to be noted here is the interaction of environment and the degree of heterozygosity of the genotype. The interactions discussed so far could be equally well taken to be either of the allele-environment or genotype-environment kind. Differential behavior of inbred and non-inbred individuals in different environments belongs to the latter type. A possible example of such interaction may be found in the egg production performance of hybrid and purebred birds. Lerner (1955) suggested that it is the better buffering of heterozygotes that permits them to continue laying in the face of diverse stresses and unsystematic pressures of their environment. Whether this hypothesis is correct or not, it points to the fact that gene-environment interaction, genetic correlation between traits, and non-additivity of gene action are abstractions. Statistically speaking, an organism or a population may be described in terms of one or another of these properties. But in a fundamental way they refer to a single entity, the genetic system. Division of the total into component features or description of it in these terms is only a matter of convenience to the observer and experimenter. Chetverikov (1926) in the classical paper, which inaugurated experimental population genetics, emphasized the fact that individuals are not mosaics of properties but wholes ("every individual is then literally '*in-dividuum*,' indivisible"). In the same way, the different aspects of a population which may be treated separately from each other for purposes of analysis are biologically inextricable from the whole organization of the interbreeding group or gene pool.

29. *Interpopulation and Cross-performance Selection*

The methods of selection appropriate when the postulated absence of overdominance (ordinary dominance presents little difficulty) and of epistatic deviations does not grossly misrepresent the real situation or, more generally, when a reasonable amount of additively genetic variance is available have been discussed in the preceding chapter. All of them are directed to the increase in frequency of desirable alleles at the expense of the undesirable ones. Under non-additive gene action, which sooner or later must become important for various aggregates of useful characters (such as fitness or dollars-and-cents value of a commercial product in which both quantity and quality are of importance), the goal of selection must be modified. There are no longer unqualifiedly good or bad alleles.

The process of coadaptation becomes of importance. Selection must address itself to complexes and not to individual alleles. The methods previously discussed are of limited usefulness when of themselves they do not secure the maintenance of desired genetic constellations without breakup between generations because of segregation. In the absence of inversions, of other restrictions on recombination, and of affinity and similar devices to preserve desirable genic associations in gamete formation, intrapopulation selection is not effective in the utilization of non-additive genetic variance.

This is particularly true when the optimum phenotype is produced by heterozygotes, since a self-reproducing population can then have its phenotypic average at the maximum only when homozygotes are lethal. Although such breeding systems can exist with respect to single loci, blocks, and chromosomes, the great reproductive waste involved does not permit their extension to many units of segregation.

Two solutions of the problem are possible in artificial selection: (A) to select between non-interbreeding populations and multiply the one closest to the optimum gene pool composition as judged by performance tests; and (B) to select within two populations for different alleles in such a way that crosses between them made anew in every generation are characterized by the desired genotype. As a rule, scheme B is used when maximum utilization of heterosis is being attempted.

Scheme A is interpopulation selection. Scheme B makes the greatest number of homozygous types absent in the cross (i.e. the crossbred population consists of heterozygotes) but requires at least two populations which, in addition to contributing parents for the cross, must also propagate themselves.

Many modifications and combinations of these two basic selection plans are possible. Because a wide variety of such methods has been used under different designations in commercial practice, some terminological confusion has arisen in the poultry industry. An attempt to standardize nomenclature with intention to prevent fraud has been made by a United States government business-regulating agency. Some of the definitions that have been thus endowed with a legal meaning are given in box 21.

Scheme B differs in several essentials both from A and from ordinary intrapopulation selection. In B, judgment regarding the genotypic value of selected parents is based entirely on the progeny test. Yet the offspring, whose performance constitutes the test, cannot themselves be employed as parents of the next generation. The interval between generations is thus greatly increased, although it is possible to reduce this lag to a minimum by mating sires simultaneously for progeny testing and for propagation. In such a variant of B, the offspring of sires not chosen to continue the line can be discarded as soon as the results of the progeny test are available.   This procedure, although reducing the average age of parents, obviously increases the breeder's operating costs.

More interesting from the theoretical standpoint is the fact that in *B* there is no predictable correspondence between the phenotype of the selected animals and their genotypic merit, at least for any of the usual objectives of selection.   In ordinary mass selection the presence or absence of the desired alleles is reflected by the phenotype of the individuals chosen as parents.   Family selection is essentially only an extension of this principle.   In other words, if the additive heritability of a character is zero, the auxiliary method of sib or progeny testing cannot help in selection.   On the contrary, scheme *B* is most effective precisely where overdominance is important and where the heterozygote thus differs from both homozygotes.   The aim of the breeder is then to change the frequency of alleles at overdominant loci in opposite directions in the two populations.   The point, however, is that these alleles do not necessarily have plus or minus values with respect to the trait of interest.   The

---

BOX 21

Legal Definitions of Inbred and Hybrid Stock

The proliferation of schemes of breeding intended to produce heterosis or at least to capitalize on the commercial popularity of crosses between inbred lines has led the United States Federal Trade Commission to include the following among the trade practice rules promulgated for the poultry industry:

RULE 20—MISREPRESENTATIONS AS TO BREEDING, ETC.

In the sale or offering for sale of poultry, chicks, or hatching eggs, it is an unfair trade practice to make any statement or representation relating to the breeding incident to the production of any such products, or to use any term or designation as descriptive thereof which denotes or implies a certain kind or extent of breeding employed in the production of such products, which has the capacity and tendency or effect of deceiving purchasers or prospective purchasers of such poultry, chicks, or eggs.

For the purpose of this rule and in its application, the following terms are acceptable when used in accordance with their respective definitions:

"CROSSBRED"—The first generation poultry, chicks, or eggs produced by crossing two different breeds or varieties, or first-generation combinations of breeds or varieties.

"INBRED LINE"—A group of inbred chicks resulting from breeding closely related poultry and in which the individuals in question have an average coefficient of inbreeding of 37.5% (equivalent to two generations of brother-sister matings).

"IN-CROSSBRED"—The first generation of poultry, chicks, or eggs produced by crossing two inbred lines, or the crossing of an inbred line with a first-generation combination of inbred lines.

(*Note*: To some purchasers and prospective purchasers of chicks and hatching eggs, the term "hybrid" implies application of genetic principles similar to those employed in the production of hybrid seed corn, and to others the application of a selective system of breeding dissimilar to that employed in the production of hybrid seed corn.

The term is generally regarded as denoting a superior quality and vigor resulting from systematic breeding and shall only be used to describe chicks and hatching eggs having such superior quality and vigor.

In the interest of avoiding deception of purchasers and prospective purchasers, industry members desiring to use the term "hybrid" as descriptive of such chicks and hatching eggs shall, in addition, confine the use thereof to established industry products obtained by crossing different inbred lines, or by crossing different breeds, varieties, strains, or lines, and shall qualify the word "hybrid" by stating in immediate conjunction therewith the type of cross used in the production of the industry product, such as "inbred line—cross hybrid" or "inbred hybrid," "crossbred hybrid," "strain-cross hybrid," "line-cross hybrid," etc.

Industry members will be expected to maintain adequate breeding records showing the establishment of the advertised product.)

heterozygote is superior to the homozygotes, the additively genetic merit of which is relevant only within the context of their own population. Hence, even when the homozygotes at given loci differ in their genetic values, so far as the desired trait is concerned, selection does not have as a goal the accumulation of all plus alleles in one line and all minus in the other. The genetic constitution of $+ + - + -$ for five loci in one of the populations used in the cross is optimal, when the other population has $- - + - +$ at the corresponding loci (assuming that overdominance is of importance), but not when the other population has $+ + + + +$ or another sequence as the most frequent type. When internal balance or intrachromosomal epistasis (including position effect) are also important, the situation becomes correspondingly more complex.

Figure 6.3 schematizes the difference between intrapopulation selection and selection between populations (method A). The term *strain* in the diagram is used to convey the notion that each of the isolates is a coadapted group capable of self-reproduction. In contrast, method B (figure 6.4) is based on the propagation of lines which themselves are likely not to be coadapted and may be poor in every respect except for their ability to produce the right kind of gametes to endow the cross they enter into with an optimum genotype for performance.

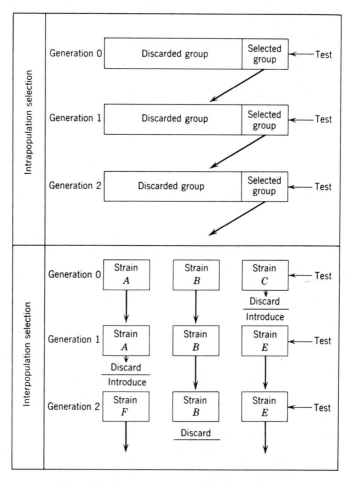

Figure 6.3.   Intra- versus interpopulation selection

Figure 6.4 will be referred to once more in the next section.   Here a simplified version of the principle involved in it may be considered. Figure 6.5 shows a method which is intermediate between *A* and *B* in that it does not include intrapopulation selection; discrimination between whole lines rather than between individuals within lines is at the basis of selection here.   In the example given, the parental populations are considered to be inbred.   The need for consanguineous mating arises

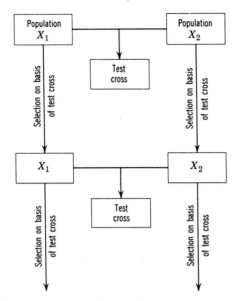

Figure 6.4.   Intrapopulation selection based on performance in a cross
This method is also known as recurrent reciprocal selection.

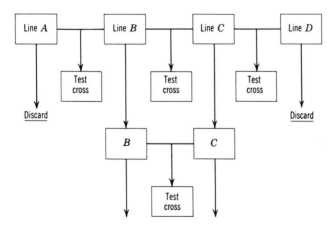

Figure 6.5.   Selection between inbred lines on the basis of incrossbred performance

because fixation of alternative alleles thus attained leads to maximum heterozygosity in crosses. Furthermore, in commercial practice, repeatability of performance is of great importance, and a high degree of it can be obtained only with parental lines whose genotypes remain stable and are not subject to change by natural-selection pressures.

Unfortunately intense inbreeding leads to serious losses in reproductive performance.   This means that the cost of producing stock by the method shown in figure 6.5 may be prohibitive.   Alternative schemes (which may have other defects) include crossing non-inbred populations of different breeds.   The rotational plan shown in figure 6.6 provides an example of such a technique.

Still another method is *topcrossing*, in which an inbred male is mated to females from non-inbred populations.   The population of origin of the dams may itself be under selection or not.   Another scheme calls for

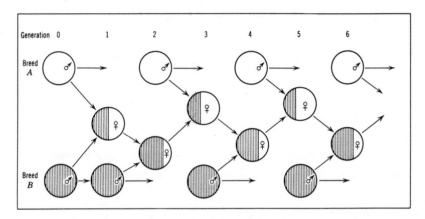

Figure 6.6.   Two-population rotation scheme

The diagram portrays a mating method which Skaller (1954*c*) on empirical grounds claimed is of value.   No selection is assumed here.   Reproduction of the paternal populations is needed to maintain a source of sires in alternate years.   The population of females is used for production and for propagation.   For generation 1 either breed can be used to supply dams.   Similar rotational schemes involving three or more breeds have been suggested for larger livestock, in particular swine (Winters, 1952).   See also figure 6.12.

three inbred lines, with males of one being mated to females produced by a cross of two others.   The reproductive capacity of such females is restored because they themselves exhibit hybrid vigor.   This method of three-way crosses can be extended to a four-way cross in which the males siring the commercial stock are also incrossbred (figure 6.7).

The numerous other mating plans conceivable need not concern us. Box 22 lists literature on the experimental results obtained with the different methods, although it is not possible as yet to evaluate all of them operationally.   A number of schemes already noted and some further ones are considered in the next section in connection with the problem of selecting for combining ability.

─────────────────────────────BOX 22─────────────────────────────

Literature on Mating Schemes in Poultry

In recent years an oppressively large number of reports has appeared in which results from many of the mating plans described here have been recorded. The wide variety of procedures combined with still greater diversity of material, usually of anonymous genetic origin, makes it impossible to deliver pragmatic judgment on the respective merits of the various schemes and the particular uses to which they are adapted. Perhaps even a greater accumulation of material of this kind is needed for safe generalizations of theoretical significance. In the meantime, of course, the poultry industry is finding practical solutions to the problem of efficient interpopulation selection by the method of trial and error.

The following listing of publications represents a sampling of the literature on poultry experiments relevant to the issue under discussion. Many other reports of a similar type may be found by examining the volumes of *Poultry Science* from approximately 1950 onward.

Mating System	References
Breed crosses	
Egg production	Glazener et al. (1952)
	King and Bruckner (1952)
Broiler production	Essary, Mountney, and Goff (1951)
	Smith and Wiley (1950)
Breed rotation	Skaller (1954c)
Strain crosses	
Egg production	Hutt and Cole (1952)
Viability	Moultrie, King, and Cottier (1953b)
Topcrossing	Coleman and Jaap (1954)
Incrossbreeding	
Single crosses	Maw (1949)
	Pease and Dudley (1954)
Single, three-way, four-way crosses	Glazener and Blow (1954)
Inbred line back-crossing	Blyth (1956)
Intra- and interbreed incrossbreeding	Dickerson et al. (1950)
Multiple comparisons	
Strain and breed crosses	Nordskog and Ghostley (1954)
Incrossbreeding and crossbreeding	Jaap, Grimes, and Coleman (1954)
	Knox (1954)
	Mueller (1952)

There is presumably an optimum rate of inbreeding that should be followed in the formation of inbred lines entering the various plans outlined.   As has already been noted in section 15, natural selection of heterozygotes will interfere with allelic fixation if the rate of inbreeding is slow (Hayman and Mather, 1953).   Hence, if the purpose of inbred line formation is to attain homozygosity, it seems that it can be best served by the closest mating possible.   Very rapid inbreeding, however, may also be expected to cause too many lines to become extinct or make interline selection favor either originally more heterozygous lines or those that

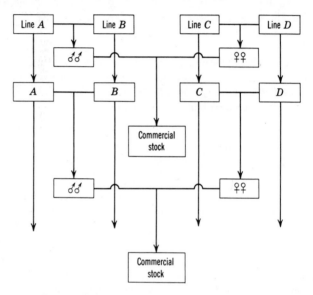

Figure 6.7.   Four-way cross between inbred lines

The production of commercial stock females from matings between incrossbreds is shown.   Arrows indicate continued propagation of the inbred lines.

possess some mechanism for preserving overdominant loci or blocks in a heterozygous state.   In general, the processes involved in survival or extinction of inbred lines are not at all understood.   The facile interpretations that can be advanced in terms of lethal and subvital alleles do not always fit the data.   The results of Dubinin (1948) and the general aspects of phenodeviant behavior may be cited in substantiation of the idea that more complex events than natural selection at single loci occur under enforced endogamy of normally outbred species.   Box 23 shows some examples of inbreeding crises.   The data therein cannot by themselves be used for interpretation of the nature of these events.   They are presented merely for illustrative purposes.

BOX 23

Inbreeding Crises

Inbred lines which survive must have a degree of tolerance to the mating system under which they are forced to exist. In the course of adapting themselves to consanguineous mating they may go through a series of crises, suffering a reduction in number and exhibiting a greater variety of visible defects. Having thus purged themselves of recessive lethals and subvitals, they become capable of existing at higher levels of homozygosity than those characteristic for the population of their origin, or they develop devices for maintaining requisite heterozygosity (Smith, Clarke, and Hollingsworth, 1955, have commented on this point).

The following table (based on the material of Shultz, 1953a) illustrates this process in several inbred lines of chickens propagated by one-sire matings. The number in each cell refers to the chicks produced by each line of each generation. Lines A, B, and C are likely to become extinct. At least for line B the outcome has definitely been fatal. Lines D and E have apparently overcome the crisis. The eventual fate of lines F, G, and H is still uncertain.

Generation of Inbreeding	0	1	2	3	4	5	6	7	8
Average Unweighted F	0.04	0.19	0.28	0.36	0.43	0.46	0.52	0.58	0.62
Line A	158	138	133	81	117	29	25	21	19
Line B	205	81	153	82	135	53	16	10	1
Line C	122	89	38	51	46	42	19	50	22
Line D	125	165	121	47	111	105	63	40	95
Line E	137	170	79	122	76	39	49	29	112
Line F	141	82	76	60	64	57	22	65	65
Line G	67	74	58	65	91	95	56	51	45
Line H	150	166	172	63	50	7	7	8	29

Another question that the breeder who is producing inbred lines may ask himself is whether artificial selection either between or within lines should be applied in the course of inbreeding. After a stable series of lines has been established, the breeder must, of course, choose the particular combinations he may wish to use in commercial production. But, before the lines are inbred enough to enter crosses, selection pressure may also be applied. During the period of inbreeding, artificial selection both between and within lines can be used, with respect either to commercial characters which are eventually exploited or to fitness. Selection for the latter would favor heterozygotes. This means that artificial selection would, similarly to natural selection, run contrary to the purposes for which inbreeding is being practiced. Selection applied to the useful characters themselves would not do so unless the traits are subject to inbreeding depression. In the latter case, selection could also have a damping effect on the rate at which the desired homozygosity is attained.

Selection between lines is worthwhile when it can be shown that there is a correlation between the expression of the desired trait in an inbred line and its expression in crosses in which the line is used as one of the parents. Although much work has been done on this problem in corn, there do not seem to be many data to go on in animals. Pilot experiments on this question carried out on Drosophila by Bell, Moore, and Warren (1955) did not provide unequivocal guidance. Thus, with respect to egg weight (a highly heritable trait assumed not to be subject to inbreeding depression), the best crosses were, as it might have been expected, those in which the parents were the best of the inbred lines. But since this character is largely additively determined, incrossbreeding need not be resorted to in its improvement. For egg number, Bell and his associates found that the best crosses were produced by high inbred lines mated to average ones. The genetic interpretation of this result remains obscure.

Not much light on the matter is shed by poultry-breeding experiments so far reported. One example of a reasonably high correlation (0.48) between the parental mean and the performance of strain crosses for resistance to respiratory infection (a character which is not highly heritable) is to be found in the study of Goodwin et al. (1956). For the behavior of incrossbreds, figures 6.8 and 6.9, based on the study of Shultz (1953a), may be examined. They show that selection within inbred lines was effective for egg weight but attained only very limited success for egg number. The crosses between inbred lines selected for high egg weight suggest that inbreeding prevented full expression of this trait. Upon release from this limitation, hitherto cryptic gains revealed themselves. That ordinary heterosis was not the cause of this phenomenon is demonstrated by the fact that the egg weight of crosses between other lines did not significantly exceed that of the inbred parents. Egg number, however, showed heterosis in all crosses shown, although (and this is the relevant point) the direction of selection seems to have had no bearing on the behavior of the F_1's.

There are many further aspects of the matter which are of practical significance in the selection of inbred lines that might be discussed. Some are trivial from the standpoint of theory (e.g. the best order in which combinations involving three or more lines are to be crossed, a question related to the differences between reciprocal crosses due to sex linkage or

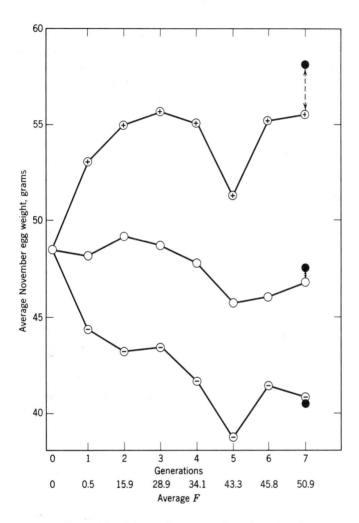

Figure 6.8.   Selection for egg weight under inbreeding

The circles containing plus signs represent averages of two lines selected for high November egg weight, those containing minus signs averages of two lines selected in the opposite direction.   The circles containing dots show the egg weight of four control lines, of which two were selected for high egg number and two for low (see figure 6.9). No direct selection in these four lines was practiced for egg weight.   The solid circles show the average egg weight of crosses within each of the three types of lines.   The data are derived from the material of Shultz (1953a).

to maternal effects).   For others, there is too little genetic information available to permit a meaningful discussion (for instance, the relationship between inbreeding, buffering, and egg production considered in the vaguest of terms by Lerner, 1955).   Still others are matters of technology rather than of genetics (numbers of individuals to be maintained per line, and so forth).   Most current answers to these questions are based on guesswork.   Indeed, in spite of the fact that programs involving inbred lines have become of such great significance in the poultry industry, it may well be asked with Donald (1955), who dealt with the same question in

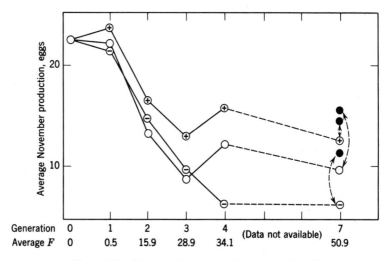

| Generation | 0 | 1 | 2 | 3 | 4 | (Data not available) | 7 |
| Average *F* | 0 | 0.5 | 15.9 | 28.9 | 34.1 | | 50.9 |

Figure 6.9.   Selection for egg number under inbreeding

See caption to figure 6.8 for explanation.   Here the controls are formed by the two plus and the two minus egg weight lines.   The dashed double-headed arrows connect the cross with the appropriate parental lines.

pigs, whether or not their operational soundness has actually been demonstrated.   It seems difficult to escape subjective judgments and impressions in this matter.   Thus, in a debate between proponents of different types of poultry mating schemes (Fox *et al.*, 1955), the very able summary by Quisenberry is based largely on *a priori* considerations instead of on data from controlled experiments, which unfortunately do not exist.

The basic issue is whether intrapopulation selection is to be preferred to incrossbreeding, even though there may be other methods available to exploit non-additive gene action.   In theory (see Wright, 1939, and Comstock, 1955), significant epistatic interaction dictates selection between inbred families.   On the other hand, overdominance makes intrapopulation selection based on results of interpopulation crossing the most effective method.   The difficulty in practice is that the various components of the aggregate objective have different genetic bases and hence call for different breeding procedures.   Index selection makes a compromise possible, but uncontrolled coadaptive processes within populations could make an index computed today obsolete tomorrow.

30. General and Specific Combining Ability

The present section considers some further details of selection for improvement in the performance of crosses.   The interest of investigators and breeders in mating plans based on selection for *combining ability* has been stimulated by theoretical considerations advanced by Hull (1945), Crow (1948), Brieger (1950), and a number of other workers.   The group of investigators in North Carolina (Comstock, Robinson, and Harvey, 1949) extended the theory and initiated a series of basic experiments on the nature of genetic variation in corn (see Robinson and Comstock, 1955).   The problems involved in this approach for swine breeding were considered by Dickerson (1952), and Bell, Moore, and Warren (1955) and Rasmuson (1956) carried out selection experiments with Drosophila, intended to test the validity of deductions from theory.   Very little else has been contributed by experiments to the evaluation of this technique for poultry breeding.   Nevertheless, selection for combining ability has, as noted, entered commercial practice.

Even were experimental data available, the validity of conclusions drawn from them would be temporary.   Different selection schemes are effective to a varying degree in transforming particular kinds of genotypic variability into selection gains.   But if the most efficient scheme with respect to the major source of variance is used, sooner or later all the advances possible under it will have been made, or, if not, further gains will become obtainable only under increasingly greater pressures.   The more effective the scheme, the sooner this will happen.   In the meantime, the sources of variability left untapped by the particular kind of selection practiced will have assumed increasing importance in determining the residual variance. At some point in the history of the selected population, the breeder is then warranted in changing his selection methods.

Operationally sound decisions must then depend not so much on general principles but more often on specific information about the genetic biography of a population.   This fact may explain why Rasmuson (1956) failed to obtain improvement in egg production in Drosophila either by ordinary intrapopulation selection or by selection on the basis of performance of a cross, whereas Bell, Moore, and Warren (1955) found both techniques effective, although to a different degree. It is also this fact that makes long-range operational decisions precarious. Bell and his collaborators noted that "in the long run" two particular methods of selection, A and B, were superior to a third one, C. However, a system productive of greatest gains for one initial population may not be as successful for another, especially if the two populations have had different kinds of artificial selection already applied to them. Therefore it cannot be inferred from the results of Bell *et al.* whether a breeder in order to achieve immediate "short run" gains should start with method C and then switch to one of the others; whether he would be wiser to start directly with A or B; or whether he should follow a plan that would use all three methods in some specific order.

Because of these uncertainties, little more than a series of descriptions of some of the possible schemes need be given here, although the reader may be urged to examine the theoretical foundations of the different mating plans discussed in the articles cited, in particular those by Comstock *et al.* (1949) and by Dickerson (1952).

The fundamental forms of selection on the basis of performance in crosses are schematized in four figures. Figure 6.4 represents *recurrent reciprocal selection*. The parents chosen to reproduce successive generations of population X_1 are selected not because of their own phenotypes, nor with regard to the phenotypes of their intrapopulation relatives, but on the basis of performance of their offspring by mates from population X_2. Reciprocally, selection within the latter population is based on the performance of offspring which X_2 individuals have by X_1 mates. Selection in both populations is then for combining ability with individuals of a foreign gene pool, rather than for superior genetic combinations within their own gene pool.

This method can hardly be called selection for coadaptation in Dobzhansky's sense, because it does not lead to an adaptively integrated gene pool. Indeed, the effects of this method of selection on the gene pools of populations X_1 and X_2 may be expected to be disintegrative, since it tends to disregard intrapopulation fitness. For instance, it is possible that a certain allele A_1 produces in population X_1 a subvital effect not only as a homozygote but also when it is in combination with A_2 and A_3. Ordinary intrapopulation selection would tend to eliminate A_1. But now suppose that population X_2 contains allele A_4 (absent from the X_1 pool), which in combination with A_1 but not with A_2 or A_3 produces luxuriance. Selection for combining ability will, under these circumstances, encourage the rise in the frequency of A_1, perhaps to the point of danger to the continuation of X_1 as a self-reproducing entity. This process can thus produce a pool which has contents that combine well with the alleles of another pool but which is not coadapted in the sense of maximizing the fitness of a self-reproducing population.

The selection scheme portrayed in figure 6.4 would be effective in increasing both the *general* combining ability of the two populations and the combining ability which may be called *specific*, that is, particular to the cross between X_1 and X_2, and not to any other cross which either of the two populations could enter with a third. Whether selection is largely directed to one or another form of combining ability depends on how the test crossing is carried out. For instance, when selection is not on the intrapopulation basis as in figure 6.4, but between populations or lines as in figure 6.5, test crosses can be made not only between pairs of lines as indicated but between each one and all the others. In such a method, general combining ability would be favored in the choice of the lines to be continued. Robertson (1952), in considering variation produced by recessive genes, demonstrated that variance between crosses of inbred lines is largely due to general combining ability when F is low. The component of the variation between crosses attributable to special combining ability is equal to $F^2q^2(1 - q)^2$. Thus for any initial level of q, the value of which in the absence of selection remains unchanged in inbred lines, the proportion of combining ability in the variance of the crosses, which is special, rises with the square of the inbreeding.

Two variants of recurrent (non-reciprocal) selection are shown in figures 6.10 and 6.11. The first deals with selection within a population X on the basis of a test cross with population A, itself not subject to selection. For maximum effectiveness, this method seems to depend on the constancy of population A from generation to generation. In other words, A should preferably be an inbred line. This form of selection is known as recurrent selection with a constant tester. It emphasizes specific and not general combining ability.

A commercially used modification in which the tester is not constant is schematized in figure 6.11. Population X is here selected on the basis of a test cross, whereas Y, the tester, is being improved by intrapopulation selection. For example, in broiler production, heterosis for growth rate is an important factor. At the same time it is necessary for the hatcheryman to maintain high reproductive capacity of the females producing the commercial chicks, since otherwise their cost would become exorbitant. One possible mode of operation is to select within breed X for combining ability with Y as judged by rate of growth, at the same time selecting for egg production on an intrapopulation basis within Y. The circumstances in which this plan is operationally more effective than that of figure 6.7 depend on a number of economic and biological unknowns.

Many combinations of recurrent selection with interpopulation selection designed to increase either specific or general combining ability can be devised.   Their relative success depends on the nature of non-additive variance in the characters under selection, and other factors, such as, for instance, the predictability of combining ability from *a priori* information. Obviously when the optimum combination of lines can be arrived at without elaborate testing (note the practical difficulties of testing crosses implicit in figure 6.2), economic applicability of crossing populations is greatly increased.   However, once again little useful information derived from experimental data on poultry is as yet available on this point, especially

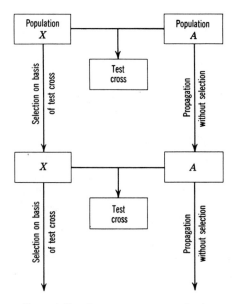

Figure 6.10.   One-way recurrent selection

Selection of one parental line on the basis of performance in a cross with an unselected line (*A*) is represented here.

for the more practical commercial methods.   Some notion of the average results expected from single crosses may be obtained from a knowledge of the population of their origin by making a series of assumptions of doubtful validity, but predictability of this sort is not very useful to a breeder.

For four-way crosses, it should be possible to make the necessary predictions from results of single crosses.   For additive gene action, accurate forecasts can presumably be made—from the mean performance of the six possible single crosses between the four lines producing the final commercial product, from the average of crosses of each of the lines with many others, or yet from the average topcross performance. As it happens, one of the few studies made in this connection on poultry (Wyatt, 1953) indicates that additive genes are not of importance in such breeding plans, and, in particular, that predictability of combining ability of inbred lines on basis of topcross results is very low.

The prediction method recommended by Jenkins (1934) for corn is based on non-additivity. It consists of computing the average performance of single crosses between the four grandparental lines, excluding those that

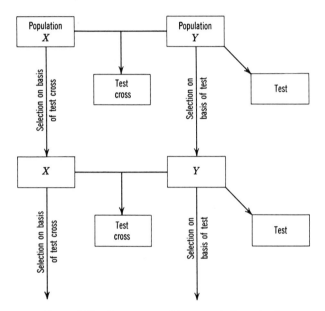

Figure 6.11. Recurrent and intrapopulation selection

A scheme in which one parental line (X) is recurrently selected for performance in a cross with another line (Y), which itself is selected on the basis of intrapopulation performance.

produce the parents. In other words the best estimate of performance of the four-way cross $(A \times B) \times (C \times D)$ is provided by the average of the four crosses, $A \times C$, $A \times D$, $B \times C$, and $B \times D$. Similarly, the average of $A \times B$, $A \times C$, $B \times D$, and $C \times D$ provides the best estimate of the four-way cross $(A \times D) \times (B \times C)$.

For rotational crossbreeding, prediction equations have been derived by Carmon *et al.* (1956) on the basis of simplifying assumptions, including absence of selection among gametes, zygotes or potential parents, no multiple alleles, constant allelic frequencies in all populations, and, what is especially serious, no epistasis. Figure 6.12 shows an example of

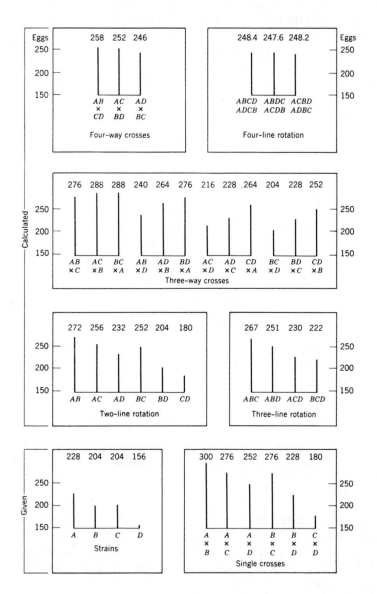

Figure 6.12.   Prediction of combining ability

An illustration of prediction of results of four-way crosses by the method of Jenkins (1934), and of the results of rotational crossbreeding by the formulas of Carmon *et al.* (1956).   The annual average egg production of four lines, *A*, *B*, *C*, and *D*, and of the single crosses between them are assumed to be known.

predictions made on the basis of Jenkins' method, and the formulas of Carmon and his collaborators.

Index selection can be used in all schemes mentioned. The basic principles underlying construction of indexes are the same ones as those in box 18. An example referring to improvement of line-cross performance in swine is given by Warren and Dickerson (1952). Their step-by-step outline of procedure can be readily adapted for preparing similar selection indexes for chickens or other animals.

These remarks on selection for combining ability are not intended for probing the subject in depth, but rather have the purpose of highlighting the uncertainties and guesswork on which present commercial practice is based. In any case, it may well be said that the general issue of breeding for heterosis falls more into the area of mating systems than that of selection. The relative brevity of the sections devoted to the subject here is accounted for in part by this fact.

7

Improvement of Specific Traits

> . . . great is the power of man in accumulating by his Selection successive slight variations.

It is problematic how much of the future improvement in the economic traits of domestic animals, and particularly in those of poultry, will be based on the selection methods of the type described in chapter 5. Their immediate utility for characters already subjected to a program of genetic amelioration is limited by the fact that if the selection techniques used have been successful, they will have exhausted much of the genetic variation which responds to them.

To a lesser degree the future of the procedures described in chapter 6 is also uncertain. Selection between populations, selection for performance in crosses, and other possible methods that do not depend for their success on simple additive genetic variance have come into exploitation only recently. Hence there are no doubt untapped resources of non-additive variation. But most of the techniques designed to utilize them are costly, either because they are intrinsically laborious or because they are operationally inefficient since they depend on trial and error. With the necessarily decreasing successive increments of progress from their use, it is questionable how successfully these methods of stock improvement can compete with non-genetic techniques for increasing agricultural production, which are being discovered in profusion day by day.

For example, pullorum disease, resistance to which can be increased by selection, has been virtually eliminated by prophylaxis; the rate of growth of broilers and the efficiency of their food utilization are being steadily augmented by dietary supplementation at a fraction of the cost of breeding programs; egg quality can be improved by controlling the age composition of the laying flock; the dread complex of neoplastic diseases, the study of resistance to which has long been the meal ticket of many poultry geneticists, is on the threshold of being rendered harmless by immunization. Thus, one by one, characters of economic significance yield to other than genetic approaches. Perhaps at the moment only a few highly heritable traits for which as yet no methods of control over the environmental fraction of variance has been devised are completely within the province of the geneticist. They include as selection objectives such characters as plumage color, egg size, and shape, and perhaps some others, the economic significance of which is of recent origin. With the rapid advances in biochemistry, endocrinology, and the applied aspects of nutrition and physiology, these may also soon become amenable to change by manipulation of environment.

This in no way diminishes the significance of selection theory in the improvement of animals and plants. Understanding of natural-selection processes, application of selection principles to new conditions, the possibility opened for checking the operational efficiency of improvement procedures, all could be invoked as *raisons d'être* of applied genetics. Furthermore, sooner or later the balance between genetic and environmental improvement will be redressed so that, after advantage has been taken of all the latter can do for the time being, the former will provide further possibilities of advance. There is, however, a more important two-fold justification for the foregoing discussion of the genetic basis of artificial selection. First, from the broad point of view, comprising interest in both artificial and natural selection, the new emphasis on *coadaptation*, as a fundamental aspect of selective processes involving Mendelian populations, can be appreciated only after acquaintance with the bases of evolutionary changes which have been discussed. Secondly, research in genetics in application to useful characters must now move into a new field. Its exciting future lies in attempts at meso- and macro-evolutionary modifications of populations, rather than in the realm of microevolution. Approach to these phases can be considered at the moment only in speculative terms and not at any great length. But before changes of this order of magnitude can be tackled, at least a brief summarization of what selection has done and can do at the lower levels is in order. Such indeed is the purpose of the first six chapters of this book.

In the current chapter a somewhat more specific survey of characters
dealt with by man in improving the economically useful (in contrast to
e.g. shank length, which is experimentally useful) traits of chickens is
undertaken.   Practically all of it refers, for reasons previously mentioned,
to intrapopulation selection.   Complete literature coverage is not intended.   As noted in box 24 (which lists the important early contributors

---

BOX 24

The Pioneers of Poultry Genetics

In concise surveys of present-day knowledge of a field of study, grave
injustices are often committed with respect to the first workers in the subject.   Because most of the germs of their thought are as a rule no longer
useful when presented in the original form, citation of the early contributors to theory is often neglected.   Because many of the early experiments
have been repeated in an improved manner, references to them are reasonably supplanted by those to more recent ones of better design.   Thus the
historical record is often rendered incomplete or unwittingly misrepresen-
ted, and the debts that every investigator owes to his predecessors remain
unacknowledged.   Obviously a line must be drawn somewhere, for otherwise every text would have to start with a discussion of Greek philosophers.
For the purpose of this and later boxes, it will be assumed that the history
of genetics starts after the rediscovery of Mendelism.

In chapter 8, references to works which played an important role in the
modern development of selection theory, but which are otherwise not
cited in this book, are given (boxes 29 and 30).   It may be appropriate
in the present chapter, devoted specifically to selection for various traits in
poultry, to mention a number of the pioneers who have made significant
contributions to poultry genetics but whose work is not specifically
emphasized in the discussion of selection presented here.   All the men
listed were born in the nineteenth century, and a majority of them are
still happily with us.

Full bibliographic references would occupy far more space than is
warranted by the purpose of the list.   The books of Hutt (1949) and Jull
(1952), however, contain extensive literature lists and are readily available
for consultation.

W. Bateson was the earliest of animal geneticists, who, with the collabo-
ration of *R. C. Punnett*, initiated the study of the formal genetics of the
fowl.

J. Dryden started one of the first successful selection experiments for
increasing egg production and advocated crossbreeding in the days when
the concept of the purebred dominated the poultry industry.

J. E. Rice and his successors at Cornell carried out one of the first and
longest selection experiments on economic characters of poultry.

C. B. Davenport was a pioneer of Mendelism, having established the mode of transmission of many morphological characters of chickens.

R. Pearl applied statistical methods of analysis to an early experiment on egg production in which he used family selection.

H. D. Goodale investigated egg production in terms of component physiological traits and initiated two separate long-range selection programs, one of which was continued for many years by *F. A. Hays*.

J. G. Halpin, in association with *L. J. Cole*, carried out early experiments on close inbreeding, which were followed by those of *L. C. Dunn* and of *Goodale* and later by those of a group at Iowa State College, including *C. W. Knox, W. V. Lambert, N. F. Waters*, and others.

M. A. Jull reported a wide variety of genetic experiments on economic traits of chickens and was responsible for the organization of the poultry research at the Experiment Station of the United States Department of Agriculture.

E. Roberts and *L. E. Card* carried out one of the early selection experiments on disease resistance (*Salmonella pullorum*).

D. C. Warren made important contributions to the formal genetics of chickens and was one of the early students of the effects of crossbreeding.

V. S. Asmundson investigated many aspects of selection for egg production, as well as the physiological basis of egg formation.

W. Landauer is the outstanding investigator of physiological genetics of the fowl and has carried out a number of selection studies of modifiers of major gene differentials.

A. W. Greenwood has conducted long-term experiments on selection under mild inbreeding.

F. B. Hutt has contributed notably to the formal genetics of the fowl.

L. W. Taylor initiated long-range selection studies on egg production and carried out a variety of experiments on selection for disease resistance, egg quality, and other traits of chickens.

to the field), the texts of Hutt (1949) and of Jull (1952) are easily available for extensive bibliographies of the subject. What follows then is a sampling of the attempts and the achievements of selection applied to economic characters of chickens, presented, as had been the preceding material, in the form of illustrations.

31. Egg Number

The character of greatest economic significance which has been the subject of selection experiments in poultry is egg number. Trials to determine the extent to which it is responsive to various types of selection date to pre-Mendelian days. Several long-term experiments have been described in detail in the literature. The most extensively documented ones are those carried out at the Agricultural Experiment Stations in Maine (Pearl, 1915), Cornell (Hall, 1935),[1] Massachusetts (Hays and Sanborn, 1939), and California (see box 25). Others, some of which are referred to in box 24, may be equally or more successful but are more difficult to interpret either because of a lack of published details or because of various complicating features of experimental procedures, such as small population size, in breeding, immigration, and unrecorded environmental changes.

The basic findings from the various experiments seem to indicate that in unimproved populations, egg production has a good share of

---

BOX 25

The University of California Production-Bred Flock

The University of California (Berkeley) flock of White Leghorns provides the source of material used in this book for illustrating progress of selection for egg number.   Selection was initiated in 1933 and continued to date.   The early history of the flock, the details of breeding methods, and many of the results have been recorded in a number of publications. In particular those by Taylor and Lerner (1938), Lerner and Hazel (1947), Lerner (1950), Lerner and Dempster (1951a), and Dempster, Lerner, and Lowry (1952) may be noted.   Box 26 gives some of the more recent data. The following figures may be consulted for other information relevant to the evaluation of changes observed under selection.

Figure 3.8	Inbreeding coefficients
4.9	Incidence of crooked toes
4.10	Average shank length
7.1	Hen-housed production
7.2	Number of elapsed generations
7.3	Survivors' production and mortality
7.4	Heritability of egg production
7.5	Fitness
7.6	Hatchability
7.11	Persistency
7.15	Bloodspot incidence

The accompanying table gives a sampling of data supplementary to those in these figures.   Various statistics for the population hatched in every fifth year are shown.

---

[1] This was one of the few poultry experiments in which selection was attempted in both directions (Lamoreux, Hutt, and Hall, 1943).   Petrov's (1935) critique of Hall's earlier conclusions regarding the efficiency of selection should be noted.

Year of Hatch	Number of Sires	Number of Dams	Number of Generations Since 1932	Chicks Hatched per Dam *	Pullets Banded per Dam *	Number of Pullets in Flock	Inbreeding Coefficient†		Hen-Housed Production, Eggs		
							Average	Range	to Dec. 1	to Jan. 1	to Oct. 1
1933	10	79	0.60	7.30	3.33	535	0.06	0–0.26	13.6	24.1	125.6
1938	12	99	3.32	10.30	4.79	604	0.08	0–0.18	32.9	47.3	154.0
1943	14	115	6.07	9.70	4.44	650	0.12	0.04–0.33	33.4	51.5	190.8
1948	12	106	8.75	11.70	5.57	549	0.14	0.10–0.20	58.6	75.2	224.7
1953	14	143	12.24	12.79	6.14	558	0.21	0.15–0.29	66.5	85.0	219.3

* Standardized to a hatching season of constant length.
† Computed to the base of the population hatched in 1925.

additively genetic variance and thus responds to intrapopulation selection more or less as expected on the basis of considerations set forth in chapters 4 and 5. Under continued selection, however, the character may have become refractory, although the reasons for the change are not always clear. As will be soon seen, interyear environmental fluctuations may severely interfere with the evaluation of progress in a character which is measured in terms of performance throughout a whole calendar year. Hence informative comparisons between expectation and realization must perforce depend on experiments of very long duration. Since in most experiments lasting, say, 25 or more years either the objectives of selection or procedures are usually changed, the evaluation of selection responses is rather difficult.

Perhaps some details of an actual experiment may help to clarify this and other points. Accordingly, in addition to the material in boxes 25 and 26, and the figures already presented, a further series of diagrams may be placed in evidence to illustrate some relevant aspects of experiments on selection for egg production.

First, it is necessary to specify the trait under selection and the procedures used. In brief, a flock of Single-Comb White Leghorns was constituted at the University of California in Berkeley in 1932 from a number of strains. Additions to it were made in the following years by the introduction of seven sires from four external sources. The progeny of all but three of these males which originated from one flock were gradually eliminated. Since 1941 the population has been entirely closed.

The original trait which was the main objective of improvement was

---BOX 26---

Recent Data from the University of California Flock

The flock described in box 25 was free from infectious diseases, except lymphomatosis and coccidiosis, for sixteen years after the beginning of the selection program. In 1949, a severe respiratory disease diagnosed at that time as atypical coryza (Lerner, Taylor, and Beach, 1950) made its appearance with the disastrous effects on egg production shown in figure 7.1. Since then nearly every year the population has been afflicted by one or another form of respiratory disturbance. The effects on the selection program of the novel conditions are difficult to evaluate. Figure 7.2 showing the average egg production to December 1, a period which, as a rule, preceded the disease outbreak (1949 being a notable exception), seems to indicate continued progress. On the other hand the annual record (figure 7.1) has not improved since 1951. Be this as it may, the accompanying table gives information on the flock since 1950, supplementary to that given directly or referred to in box 25.

Year of Hatch	Average Age of Parents, Years	Number of Sires	Number of Dams	Number of Pullets Placed in Laying House*	Fitness of Dams†	November Egg Weight, grams	April Egg Weight, grams	Survivors' Production to July 1, eggs	Percent Dead to July 1	Disease Outbreaks
1950	1.50	12	141	289	4.98	48.6	57.1	184.3	19.4	Newcastle
1951	1.40	12	138	324	4.75	51.2	58.1	201.0	14.8	Bronchitis
1952	1.32	13	130	424	5.42	50.4	56.5	205.3	27.1	Probably encephalomyelitis
1953	1.34	14	143	558	5.91	49.7	55.6	201.2	20.3	Encephalomyelitis
1954	1.20	12	144	728	4.95	50.3	56.4	207.0	26.6	—
1955	1.00	13	120	527	5.79	50.4	56.4	211.5	32.8	Encephalomyelitis
1956	1.00	12	112	717	5.69	50.9	57.5	206.9	17.9	Encephalomyelitis

* The flock from which breeding birds were selected was larger than indicated for the years 1950–1953. Part of the population was tested in individual cages (see Lowry, Lerner, and Taylor, 1956), but the data for these birds are not included in the tabulation or in the various graphs referring to the flock.

† Number of daughters alive on January 1, corrected to a hatching season of constant length.

annual hen-housed egg production, i.e. the average number of eggs produced by the unculled flock from the beginning of lay to the end of September of the next calendar year (approximately eighteen months of age). The character is an aggregate in the sense that both egg number and viability enter it, although not necessarily weighted in a manner that would lead to a maximum rate of gain in either or in the combination of the two. Some regard to other economic traits was also paid in the early years of selection, although no systematic pressures were applied to them. These traits included hatchability, egg size, egg color, freedom from blood spots and from various chick defects later identified as being of the phenodeviant type (e.g. crooked toes).

Until 1949 the criterion of selection of the females was the annual record. This meant that, by and large, the dams chosen were two years old when first mated. Progeny tests as well as sister tests of males were, however, based on part records, that is to say, production to January 1 of the first year of life. Most of the sires were one year old, the average age of all parents in the first stage of the improvement program being nearly two years.

After 1949 increasing use was made of younger birds. In order to simplify procedures the progeny test was gradually abandoned, although presumably some selection efficiency was thereby lost. By 1955 the inter-generation level became exactly one year. Selection was then directed primarily to the part record, being based on performance to January 1, except for two occasions upon which, for reasons extraneous to the goals of the project, the date was advanced by 15 and 30 days respectively. Selection pressure for other traits was also relaxed little by little. Maintenance of spring egg weight at 56–57 grams by selection for the correlated November egg weight was the only major objective pursued in addition to egg number. Other relevant details may be found in the publications listed in box 25. In particular it may be noted that the intensity of selection (v) was approximately 0.15–0.20 for females and 0.05–0.10 for sires selected on a dam-family basis.

Figure 7.1 shows the changes in the hen-housed average over the period of years. The four curves portray egg production ending at different points in the laying year. The top one (October 1) refers to the measurement which formed the main selection criterion in the early phases of the program. The July 1 curve is practically identical in shape with the October 1 curve. It is shown here because every year the surviving laying birds were moved early in July to other than the original laying houses in order to make room for the population of next year. It appears that whatever the effect of the change was, it did not differ greatly from year to year. The two lower curves are for part records, the December 1 and the

January 1 production values running parallel to each other, and, generally speaking, parallel to the first two curves. If the genetic standard deviations of the full and the part records are respectively taken as 19.3 and 7.5 eggs (Dempster and Lerner, 1947), the gains obtained may be estimated at $5-7\sigma_G$.

In 1949, a striking reversion to the initial preselection level of egg production took place. It was due to the appearance of a severe respiratory disease unknown in the flock up to that time. As indicated in

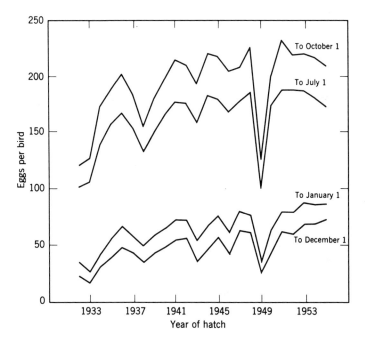

Figure 7.1. Selection for increased egg number

Changes in the hen-housed average egg production in the population described in boxes 25 and 26 and in the text.

box 26, since then hardly a year passed without further outbreaks, in particular of avian encephalomyelitis. However, in nearly all instances the epizootics occurred after December 1. The egg production up to that date may then, with the exceptions of 1949 and 1950 (when Newcastle disease made its appearance in October), be taken as representative of selection progress in the absence of this complication.

Figure 7.2 shows the lowest curve of the previous figure on an enlarged and somewhat modified scale. The abcissa shows the cumulative intergeneration interval (the reciprocal of the average age of the parents summed beginning with the offspring produced in 1933).   For the sake of convenience the year of hatch of several of the generations is also indicated. The dashed lines show unweighted five-year averages, which indicates steady progress in egg production over the period of the experiment.   As a matter of fact, it is impossible to determine for the full annual record whether or not gains have been produced at a constant rate or whether

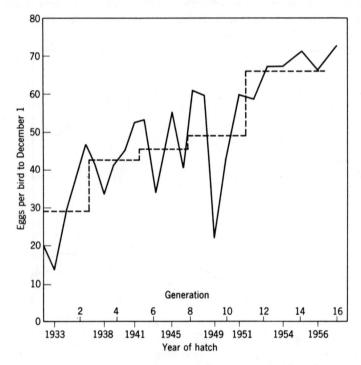

Figure 7.2.   Changes in the part production record under selection

The lower curve from figure 7.1 redrawn to a different scale with data for one more generation added.   The abcissa shows years of hatch as well as the cumulative number of generations (summation of reciprocals of the average age of parents) from 1932. The dashed line represents unweighted averages for five successive years.

they are still being obtained at all (see Dempster *et al.*, 1952).   Yet for the short period to December 1, it appears highly likely that the advance still continues.

Figure 7.3 shows the changes in two of the components of the hen-housed production in the last ten years for which data are available.   Its main function is to illustrate the erratic nature of the interyear variation which makes the accurate determination of the observed rates of change so difficult.   Neither of the two components (viability and the egg

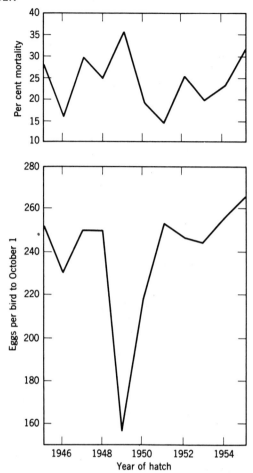

Figure 7.3. Survivors' production and mortality under selection

The lower part of the figure shows the average egg production from beginning of lay (4–5 months of age) to October 1 of the following year (about 18 months of age) of birds that survived this period.   The upper part of the diagram shows the percentage of the birds placed in the laying house at about 3½ months of age that died before October 1 of the succeeding year.

production of birds surviving till the end of the year) may be said to have improved significantly over the period portrayed. The year-to-year changes in these two characters and in the hen-housed average for the year (figure 7.1) are not intimately dependent on each other.

Figure 7.4 shows the estimates of heritability of the hen-housed production and the survivors' production for each of the first fifteen years of the selection program. There is no indication that additive genetic variance for either trait is being exhausted or that the rise in the inbreeding coefficient, which increased in this population by approximately 10 per cent in the period shown (figure 3.8), has affected the h^2 values. It seems, on the other hand, entirely possible that the lack of exact correspondence between selection gains expected (on basis of the formulas discussed in chapter 5) and those realized even in the early stages of the selection program is in part due to the increased inbreeding. It may be recalled that Tebb (1957), in analyzing the intrageneration regression of egg production on F in this particular flock, found a loss of one egg in the

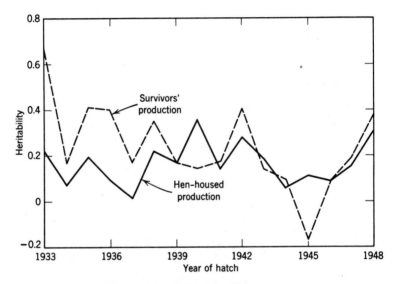

Figure 7.4.   Heritability of egg number

The estimates of h^2 of hen-housed and survivors' annual egg record in each of sixteen years (from Dempster, Lerner and Lowry, 1952).

annual record for each per cent increase in the inbreeding coefficient. Since the gain per generation expected under the conditions of the experiment is not more than five to ten eggs per year, whereas ΔF has been near 0.01, it is possible that 10–20 per cent of the expected gain is dissipated by the antagonism between inbreeding and high production levels. This, in general, seems to be a problem meriting attention. The attrition of selection pressure by inbreeding is a feature of closed population selection that should be remediable by increasing flock size, but, as has been noted in section 27, there is little information to be guided by.

Figures 7.5 and 7.6, relating to changes in fitness and one of its components, suggest that the inbreeding degeneration in reproductive capacity is not a serious problem under the conditions of this experiment. As indicated in figure 7.6, better hatchability was obtained in the latter stages of the project owing to improved incubation. However, it may also be seen that even before 1954 no deterioration in hatching capacity occurred, while fitness as a whole increased throughout the twenty years represented in figure 7.5.

In the light of all the facts, it seems probable that the rate of progress in the selection for annual production had diminished in this experiment.

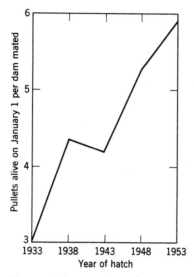

Figure 7.5.   Changes in fitness under selection for egg production

The index of fitness here is the average number of female offspring surviving to approximately eight months of age, per dam mated.   These values served as the control for the fitness indexes of the various lines in the shank length experiment in figure 4.16.

It is, however, not easy to explain this in terms of the various possible reasons discussed in section 18. Opposition of natural selection to the direction of artificial selection is clearly not the case here, as has been shown by Lerner and Dempster (1951a) and by Dempster, Lerner, and Lowry (1952). Multiplicity of objectives may have been a factor, but it would be strange if it applied to the annual record and not to the part record, especially since the two are strongly correlated (Lerner and Cruden, 1948). Inbreeding effects, if playing a role, were apparently not entirely linear, for the rate of inbreeding did not differ in the early and middle phases of the experiment (figure 3.8). Conversion of additive to non-additive variance has not been shown (e.g. as judged by the h^2 values in figure 7.4). Mutation pressure in the direction of lowered egg number may, of course, be a factor, but since its importance is impossible to evaluate, there is nothing that can be said about it. Absence of selection pressure can be definitely ruled out. Deterioration of environment and genotype-environment interaction are however possibilities, especially in connection with the respiratory diseases. It must, nevertheless, be emphasized once more that, although this selection experiment has

Figure 7.6. Hatchability of the production-bred flock

The percentage of fertile eggs set which hatched is shown here. Improvements in incubation practice were introduced at the points marked by arrows concurrently with increased use of younger dams.

been carried out for a quarter of a century, the number of generations has been only sixteen to the end of 1957. Judgment about the nearness of the selected population to an ultimate or even a temporary plateau in performance must be reserved.

32. Other Fitness Components

The average reproductive fitness of a population in equilibrium cannot be expected to respond to selection. Yet under domestic conditions, many components of fitness, and, indeed, the absolute reproductive capacity of animals under man's control, may be improved by selection. There are of course many reasons for this possibility. They are connected with the changes of environment of domesticated animals from that of their feral ancestors, a process leading to a biological redefinition of fitness and to shifts of emphasis from one component to another. For example, it seems reasonably certain that in nature the number of eggs laid by a bird is a major fitness component which has its optimum not at the maximum but at an intermediate value. A bird must pause in her lay in order to incubate the eggs. If she laid too many eggs before becoming broody, the hen would not be able to incubate all of them, and the number of young surviving may be smaller than that produced by a less ambitious dam.

With artificial incubation, the optimum number of eggs, so far as fitness is concerned, is shifted toward the maximum.[2] The same is true of other components of fitness such as fertility and hatchability. Their relationships to each other and to total fitness are also modified. Manipulation of the initiation and length of the hatching period, supplementation of diets of both parents and young, prophylactic measures, artificial insemination, and other husbandry practices change the amount, the kind, and the additive proportion of variability which is available for selection to operate upon. In a very general way, domestic populations of poultry may then be said to be in genetic disequilibrium.

The fact that poultry have been domesticated from time immemorial does not modify the situation greatly. Artificial incubation on a grand scale is not much more than 100 poultry generations old. Environmental changes of considerable magnitude, such as blood tests for removal of carriers of certain infectious diseases, the extension of the hatching season to the whole year, the rise of battery and individual cage management, supplementation of rations with trace elements and with antibiotics and so forth are constantly being introduced and thus provide opportunity for genetic differentials hitherto of secondary importance, to assume major status.

At the same time, many of the direct fitness components have, as a result of selection (natural as well as artificial) and of improved environment, reached levels that are so high as to be too difficult or too costly to improve further. For instance, it is not known what the practically possible maximum hatchability is. There may be an irreducible minimum loss of embryos due to uncontrollable non-genetically determined accidents in egg formation or development. But even without making any allowance for this possibility, when hatchability exceeds 90 per cent (figure 7.6),

[2] Indeed, Harland (1927) suggested that the response to selection for egg production under domestic conditions has been largely due to elimination of rest periods between clutches, some of which were, of course, taken up by maternal duties.

comparatively little room for additional improvement is left.   Irrespective
of the scale used (percentages, probits, angles), the heritability of hatchability is bound to be low and the rate of selection progress limited (see
the estimates of gains expected from different selection schemes computed
by Crittenden, Bohren, and Anderson, 1957a and b).

The presence of recessive lethals in many populations of poultry is
another point of interest in discussing the genetic control of hatchability.
Landauer (1951) listed seventeen lethals and sublethals of chickens which
have so far come to light.   There is little doubt that this number represents

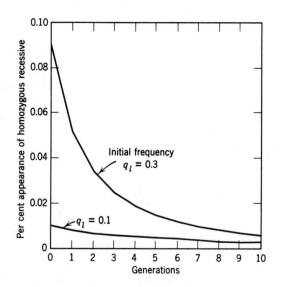

Figure 7.7.   Elimination of recessive lethals by natural selection

Theoretical progress in eliminating a recessive lethal by natural selection.   For the
case in which the heterozygote is favored over the normal homozygote, see figure 3.2.

only a very small fraction of those actually present in commercial flocks.
Many of them are carried in populations of large size so that their
manifestation is rare enough to pass unnoticed.   In establishments
producing incrossbred chicks, it is rather likely that many lethals have been
eliminated in the process of creating inbred lines.   The question, however,
may be raised regarding the policy with respect to lethal genes to be
followed in maintaining closed populations.

Considering first alleles which produce lethality when homozygous but
have no significant effect in a heterozygous state, it seems clear that the
wisest procedure for a breeder is simply to ignore them.   As may be seen
in figure 7.7, natural selection against strongly deleterious alleles will soon

bring the incidence of homozygous recessives down to harmless proportions. The effort of progeny testing and the sacrifice in selection pressure
for other characters which is needed to eliminate completely the offending
allele represent a poor investment when viewed operationally. It is
possible that in small flocks chance, especially when combined with
family selection, may result in a temporarily uncomfortable increase in
the frequency of the lethal allele, but this is a rare situation and it can
usually be handled without much difficulty.

Should the lethal allele also have deleterious effects in a heterozygous condition, this reasoning applies *a fortiori*. When, however, the heterozygote
has some advantages over the homozygous normal type, the situation is
changed. Figure 3.2 showed the equilibrium frequencies of lethals
favored in the heterozygous state. Such selection of undesirable alleles
may lead to biologically and economically grave consequences as, for
example, has occurred with the dwarf alleles in cattle (Gregory and
Carroll, 1956). The matter may be made worse when other mechanisms
favoring retention and spread of lethals or subvitals (e.g. Dunn's, 1957,
abnormal segregation ratio in mice) enter the picture. There can be no
general answer to the procedure the breeder should follow under these
circumstances. In order to arrive at a specific solution of the problem,
the advantage of a high proportion of the heterozygotes in his population
has to be weighed against the increased costs of reproduction chargeable to
the rise in the incidence of the lethal. It should be obvious that no scheme
of crossing two reproductively isolated populations to produce only the
superior heterozygote is possible when one of the alleles entering it has
lethal effects in a homozygous state.

The components of fitness operating in the post-hatching period have
been studied with much industry by poultry geneticists. In box 27
various viability-determining factors known to have a genetic component

---

BOX 27

Inheritance of Disease Resistance

The purpose of this box is to provide a list of the various pathological
conditions, resistance to which has been found to have a genetic component. In some of the reports cited only breed differences were noted.
In others, genetic variation in the behavior of strains of a single breed,
or of inbred lines, or of families within a strain was observed. Presumably, presence of genetic variability would permit a successful selection
program to be undertaken. The fact is, however, that Gowen's (1937)
dictum, that "no investigator who has adequately sought inherited host
differences in disease response has failed to find them," is as true today as

it was twenty years ago.   Hence a list of specific poultry diseases, susceptibility to which might be reduced by selection, reflects only the possibilities that geneticists have had for studying them and the industry with
which their investigations have been pursued.

The following then are the pathological conditions of chickens that have
been examined from the genetic point of view.   Hutt (1949) and Jull (1952)
may be consulted for bibliographic references to the early work; the
citations given here include a sampling of only the more recent literature.

1. Abnormalities brought about by monogenic differentials with major
effects on form or function.

2. Pathological conditions produced by nutritional deficiencies (see
box 28).

3. Non-specific mortality with a genetic component (Hyre, 1951;
Moultrie, King, and Cottier, 1953a; see also two of the curves in figure
7.8).

4. Mortality caused by specific environmental effects, e.g. extreme heat
(Kheireldin and Shaffner, 1954).

5. Infection with parasitic worms (Reid, 1955).

6. Cecal coccidiosis (Champion, 1954; Rosenberg, Alicata, and Palafox,
1954).

7. Infestation with external parasites.

8. Avian diphtheria.

9. Pullorum disease.

10. Fowl typhoid (Bell, 1949; Smith, 1956).

11. The complex of neoplastic diseases including lymphomatosis, leu-
cosis, and fowl paralysis (see Campbell, 1954, for a description of the
various entities included in this group; King, Cole, Hutt, and Cottier,
1952; Hutt and Cole, 1954; Waters, 1954; Coles, 1955; Nighthall, 1956).

12. Sarcomata.

13. Atypical infectious coryza.

14. Blue-comb disease (Moultrie, Cottier, and King, 1955).

15. Newcastle disease (Godfrey, 1952; Francis and Kish, 1955).

16. Avian encephalomyelitis (Taylor, Lowry, and Raggi, 1955).

17. Mortality from staphylococcus infection (Scossiroli and Coen,
1958).

Only a few heritability determinations for disease resistance in closed
populations have been attempted.   The values reported range from close
to zero for number 13 in the list above to about 0.3 for number 17.

are listed.   The catalogue tends to show more the opportunities which
have arisen for investigation than the actual genetic variability to be found
in poultry populations.

In chapter 3 it was noted that any mutant making an appearance in a population seems to find a segregating system of modifiers already present in the gene pool.   Similarly, genetic variability for resistance to any disease to which a flock is exposed, even apparently for the first time, can as a rule be demonstrated to exist.   Sometimes the resistance may be rather specific and fail to protect the birds possessing it from other diseases. For example, Lambert (1935) found that although resistance to *Salmonella gallinarum* conferred some protection against *S. pullorum*, birds selected for resistance to *S. pullorum* infection were susceptible to *S. gallinarum*.   In other cases general vigor factors (for example, in the resistance to avian encephalomyelitis studied by Taylor, Lowry, and Raggi, 1955) appear to be of greater significance.   Pleiotropy may be involved where there is correlation between resistance to a particular unfavorable environmental influence and other properties of the animal.   It is also possible that non-specific disease resistance is the property of the genotype as a whole rather than of the individual alleles, as has been suggested with particular reference to the ability of birds to maintain production under stress.

Very little is known about the relationship of different types of pathological conditions to fitness in the sense of figures 3.12 and 3.13.   Indeed, most of the information on the genetic basis of disease resistance of poultry is derived from gross observations.   Selection experiments to increase resistance or susceptibility to a number of pathological conditions are abundantly represented in the literature, but little can be said about them beyond the fact that, provided enough effort is expended, success to some degree can be attained.

In figure 7.8 the results of selection in three lines of Leghorns for increased incidence of three kinds of pathological conditions are illustrated.   The first of these is lymphomatosis, a complex of neoplastic diseases, at least some of which are virus-produced.   Differentiation by selection between lines high and low in incidence of the pathological syndromes entering this complex has been demonstrated on a number of occasions (see references under number 11 in box 27).

The group of diseases represented by the lymphomatosis complex has until recently defied either therapeutic or preventive measures, except for the partial effectiveness of isolation of young from old stock discovered by Hutt and Cole (1948).   Selective breeding thus appeared to be the only effective way of reducing losses from this source.   In addition positive genetic correlations of variable magnitude between mortality from this and other causes have been reported (Lush, Lamoreux, and Hazel, 1948; Robertson and Lerner, 1949).   Programs of selection for resistance to lymphomatosis could also be effectively combined with those directed toward increased egg number, as was the case in the production-bred flock described in the preceding section, and in the experiment portrayed

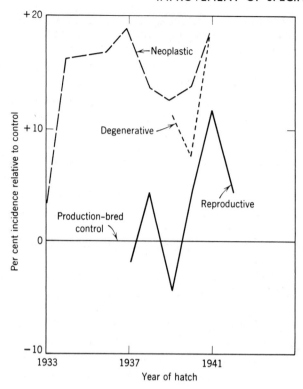

Figure 7.8.   Selection for disease susceptibility

The curves show the progress of selection in three separate lines for increased incidence of three types of pathological conditions: neoplastic diseases (largely lymphomatosis), degenerative breakdown of the kidneys and to a lesser degree of the liver, and non-specific disturbances of the reproductive system.   Only the information on the first of these lines has been previously published (Taylor, Lerner, DeOme, and Beach, 1943).   The other two were maintained by Taylor and Lerner between 1937 and 1942.   Members of the Department of Veterinary Science of the University of California performed the autopsies in these experiments.   The production-bred line of Leghorns was used as the control.   The experimental lines were derived from this population, either directly or by way of previously made extractions.

in figures 7.9 and 7.10.   All these facts made the incorporation of resistance to neoplasms among the criteria of selection in the improvement of poultry for egg production highly advisable.

Gradually, as the levels of incidence dropped, selection became less effective, for one thing, because of reduced opportunities for exposure. Furthermore, the demonstration that some components of the disease complex were transmitted through the egg (Burmester and Waters, 1955) tended to shift the problem from the area of breeding to that of hygiene.

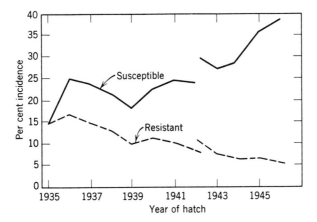

Figure 7.9.   Selection for resistance and susceptibility to lymphomatosis

The curves are taken from the report of Hutt and Cole (1948) on their long-term experiment on selection for resistance and susceptibility to lymphomatosis. The percentage incidences are based on three-year shifting averages ("except for terminal points"). In 1942 part of each population was exposed more severely than the rest of the flock to the disease. From 1943 onward opportunity for increased exposure was provided for all birds in the experiment. The break shown in 1942 reflects this circumstance.

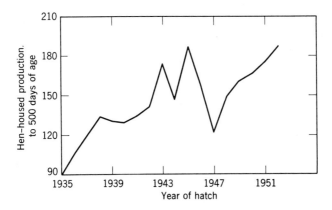

Figure 7.10.   Changes in egg production of the lymphomatosis-resistant line

The curve shows the increase in hen-housed egg production of the resistant line of Hutt and Cole (1948, 1953), data for which appear in figure 7.9. The changes in egg number observed in this line should not be viewed as a simple correlated response, since this character was one of the criteria of selection employed.

Advances in the understanding of the nature of the causative agent, which promise to lead to effective prevention (Burmester, Walter, and Fontes, 1957), are also being made. Thus it appears that this phase of selection can soon be discontinued in commercial practice.

The other two curves shown in figure 7.8 fall into a different category. They deal with non-specific and presumably non-infectious disturbances, for the control of which neither non-genetic techniques nor selection seems to be practical. Attainment of only a minor degree of success in the differentiation between susceptible and resistant lines may be noted in the figure. The experiments, however, were conducted on a very small scale. It is likely that more extensive tests could produce clear-cut demonstrations of the possibilities of breeding control. Yet in the absence of known causative agents and considering the various complications, in part relating to the threshold nature of the character and in part to the highly probable non-additive component, it is difficult to become enthusiastic over selection for resistance to these particular causes of death as a practical solution to the problem of high-laying flock mortality.

In general, levels of exceedingly high mortality can be readily reduced by selection (e.g. Hyre, 1951; Moultrie, King, and Cottier, 1953a). But, as already implied, the returns from a selection program diminish as the irreducible loss from accidental and uncontrollable sources of death is approached. At some point the breeder may find it more worthwhile to concentrate on other selection criteria in preference to viability. Where this point may be cannot be currently told, because it is certain that the minimum inevitable losses vary with the environment. Nor is it easy to suggest what measurement should be substituted for the relatively inefficient all-or-none character of survival to some age.[3] One possibility is suggested by data on the flock described in section 31, which indicate that one of the major sources of improvement in the hen-housed production average was the number of eggs laid by birds which died before the end of the laying year. It may be worthwhile to investigate the heritability of this trait and its genetic correlations with other useful properties. At the same time, it should be kept in mind that the current trend in commercial poultry production toward earlier culling tends to reduce the producer's and breeder's emphasis on increased viability.

Other traits which contribute less directly to fitness than egg production, fertility, hatchability, and viability have also been investigated. Genetic differences in many nutritional requirements, which would most certainly affect fitness under marginal conditions, have been demonstrated (box 28).

[3] The use of the average age at death was shown by Lush, Lamoreux, and Hazel (1948) to be no improvement.

BOX 28

Genetic Differences in Nutritional Requirements

It may be expected that the existing genetic variability in nutritional requirements of poultry would permit successful selection for differences in optimal levels of almost any ingredients of a normal diet. It may not always be clear whether the genetic variation utilized in selection is of a specific or of a more general type (e.g. for rate of growth or general efficiency of food utilization). Furthermore, it seems that from the practical standpoint inherited differences of this kind are of trivial significance despite assertions often made to the contrary. Their existence, however, cannot be entirely neglected. The brief list of nutritional elements with respect to which genetic variation has been described, parallel to that in box 27, includes only the few references to work on this topic which are of a later date than those found in Hutt (1949) and Jull (1952).

1. Thiamine (Howes and Hutt, 1956).
2. Riboflavin.
3. Animal protein factor (vitamin B_{12}).
4. Vitamin D (Lillie, Knox, and Bird, 1953).
5. Vitamin E (Howes and Hutt, 1952).
6. Manganese.

But here, even to a greater extent than with disease resistance, improvement by non-genetic means may be obtained at such a relatively low cost that from the economic standpoint it is pointless to consider these characters in a selection program. One possible exception lies in the efficiency of food utilization which, being a function of growth rate, is amenable to rapid improvement by selection. Otherwise, breeders are at the present time justified in occupying themselves with characters of this type only when unequivocal demonstrations of operational efficiency of selection schemes compared to changes in management are available.

Geneticists have often been known to deplore the alleged shortsightedness of poultry and livestock producers in relying on non-genetic means of improvement instead of on selection. For instance, it has been said that control of pullorum disease by the elimination of carriers of the *S. pullorum* organism following identification by blood testing is a dangerous procedure. Should the pathogen mutate to a form that would not be detectable in this manner, drastic consequences would supposedly ensue. Hence, the argument proceeded, selection for resistance should be practiced. The validity of this reasoning may be questioned. It could well be that mutation to a more virulent form, or to a form against which the alleles previously selected for would fail to protect, is just as likely as mutation to a type not identifiable by blood tests. In general, the economic cost of selecting against even a fraction of the multitude of ills to which poultry flesh is subject would be unsupportable. Similarly, writing off losses of a small fraction of birds, the nutritional requirements of which are not met by standard rations (which in any case could be modified if it were so desired), is a much more economical procedure than attempts to lower needs for specific nutrients by selective breeding.

There may well be genetic methods other than selection open to the breeder, in particular those based on controlled mating systems such as incrossbreeding. It is known that crosses between inbred lines can produce adequate hatchability. The picture for viability and specific disease resistance is somewhat obscure, the reports in the literature on this issue being confusing. Discretion hence demands suspension of judgment on the application of such methods for improving this character. Similarly, little can be said about the use of immigration to improve this and other fitness components. In Drosophila, Buzzati-Traverso (1955) produced experimental evidence that hybridization between strains, followed by natural selection, can eventually increase reproductive capacity above that of either of the parents. No doubt a theoretical possibility of this happening also exists in poultry populations. Yet the dangers of loss in other economic traits, which have reached a high degree of perfection in the parents, dictates caution in proceeding with strain hybridization schemes for the sole purpose of improving fitness.

33. Egg Production Traits

The total number of eggs laid and the fitness components—fertility, hatchability, and viability—do not by any means comprise all the characters of economic significance to the breeder and the egg producer. Other traits of interest fall into two groups: (a) characters which relate to the pattern of distribution in time of the eggs laid and (b) characters affecting the market quality of eggs.

Figure 2.11 shows under the heading "Egg production" the range of heritability values reported for a number of egg-record components which may be used to specify differences in the pattern of egg production. As noted in box 24, it was Goodale (1918) who initially interpreted the number of eggs produced by a bird in the first year of lay in terms of contributing physiological traits. These include age at attainment of sexual maturity, freedom from winter and summer pauses, some of which are due to broodiness, average clutch size and interval between clutches, and persistency or ability to continue laying late into the fall.

It is by no means certain that these characters are entirely independent of each other. They are undoubtedly under control of endocrine glands, but neither their physiological nor their genetic bases have been adequately investigated. Data on heritability, results of a few selection experiments, indications that non-additive gene action is involved in some of them (e.g. broodiness), and other isolated bits and pieces of information are available. But no comprehensive picture of interrelationships between each and every other one of them, or of their contributions to variance of egg number and of fitness, is available. Such information could undoubtedly help in the construction of efficient selection indexes and in other aspects of breeding practice.

The results of a selection experiment dealing with one of the individual components of the egg record, age at first egg (rate of sexual maturity), have already been shown in figure 4.8. Although prompt differentiation between a slow and a fast maturing line was obtained in that study, the progress portrayed is probably not as great as might be expected on the basis of available heritability estimates. As with many other experiments the small scale on which it was conducted may be responsible for this.

Small numbers as well as low heritability of persistency of lay are accountable for the results shown in figure 7.11. Interyear fluctuations in this character are of considerable amplitude. The fact that the fraction of the population in lay on October 1 swings from 40 per cent up to 80 and down to 50 is, of course, much more of a reflection of variation in some as yet unidentified environmental conditions than it is of the genetic composition of the production-bred flock. Clearly, if persistency is amenable to modification by selection, a more adequate measurement of it than that used in the experiment reported here is needed. Since current commercial practice is oriented toward replacement of laying birds before persistency can be manifested, the problem is largely an academic one.

For traits affecting egg quality, selection is of greater importance. Some egg characters, such as yolk color, are rather readily modified by nutritional means. Others, e.g. the average thickness of egg shell (which deteriorates with age), may best be improved by controlling the age composition of the flock. Dietary supplementation may eventually be found to be an efficient method of maintaining at a high level other egg quality traits. But the improvement of some of the characters determining the market value of eggs produced by a given flock still depends almost entirely on genetic techniques. Indeed, it may be seen that the highest heritability values shown in figure 2.11 are those for egg quality factors.

This fact explains the ease with which such traits as egg weight are modified by selection (figure 6.8). An additional illustration is provided by figure 7.12. It must, however, be recalled that the intermediate

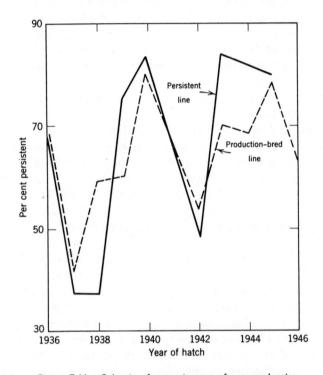

Figure 7.11. Selection for persistency of egg production

Unpublished results of a selection experiment by Taylor and Lerner are shown here. Persistency of production is defined as the percentage of the population in active lay on October 1 of their second year of life. Because of the low heritability of the trait (see figure 2.11) and the small scale on which the experiment was carried out (one or two sires per year), the selected line failed to become differentiated from the control (the University of California production-bred flock).

optimum (both biologically and economically) and particularly the non-linear negative correlation between egg weight and egg number (Blyth, 1952*a*) create some special problems in the application of egg weight selection in actual practice. In the flock discussed in section 31, no difficulty was experienced in maintaining egg size at a constant level by mild selection. At the same time it seems probable that the imposition of an egg weight requirement inhibited progress with respect to egg number.

Another selection experiment for an egg quality trait, shell thickness, is shown in figure 7.13. As in some previous examples, differentiation between lines, in this case characterized by thick and thin shells, could be rapidly established, although here selection progress appears to have been

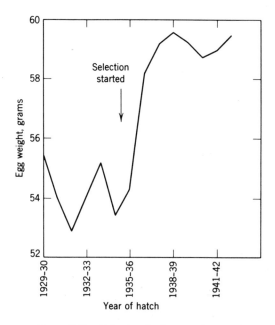

Figure 7.12.   Selection for increased egg weight

The curve gives the two-year shifting average of February (according to Hutt, 1949) egg weight in the selection experiment conducted by Snyder (1945). The high heritability of egg weight led to immediate responses followed by a plateau. In the absence of further information, the precise reasons for lack of gains after 1938–1939 cannot be established.

attained mostly in one direction. On the other hand, more or less symmetrical responses were obtained in the experiment in which selection was addressed to modifying egg shape (figure 7.14). The results of crosses between lines selected in opposite directions also indicate that the genetic variation in egg shape on the scale of measurement used in this experiment was largely additive.

Although a variety of other egg quality characters have been subjected to selection experiments (Jull, 1952, gives references to a number directed

toward changing the percentage of firm albumen in the egg, shell perme-
ability and porosity as measured by keeping quality, and shell finish), only
one more will be given here.   Figure 7.15 shows the progress of selection
for raising the incidence of blood spots in eggs.   No complications were

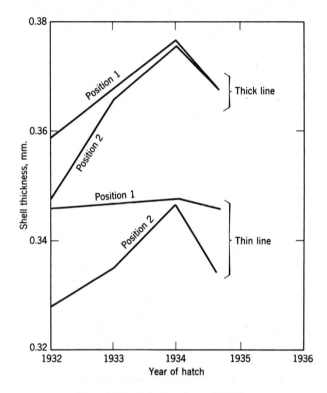

Figure 7.13.   Selection for shell thickness

The curves show the results obtained by Taylor and Lerner (1939) in a selection
experiment for modifying shell thickness.   The position of the egg in a clutch affects
shell thickness, the second egg being as a rule thinner than the first one.   Hence
averages for them are given separately.   The response obtained is asymmetrical.
Variation of this trait may be in part determined by C effects (McClary and Lerner,
1950).

experienced in increasing the annual incidence of this defect some 25-fold.
Its complete elimination from the production-bred flock shown in the
graph would have most certainly presented much greater difficulties.   However, commercially successful application of selection in that direction has
also been reported (Dickerson, 1955).
The present section, in contrast to the preceding one, has dealt with

characters for which selection is an important technique of improvement. A number of these traits are likely to drop out of selection programs as non-genetic methods of improvement are found. For the time being,

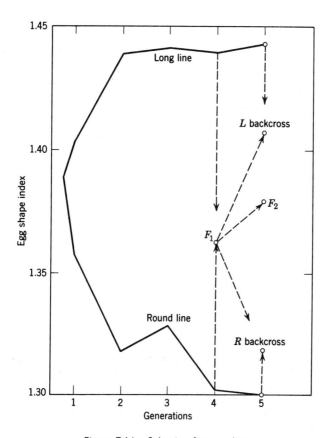

Figure 7.14. Selection for egg shape

The data for this diagram are taken from Marble's (1943) report, although the egg shape index shown here (ratio of egg length to egg width) is the reciprocal of the one used by Marble. The birds were characterized by the average shape of ten eggs laid at approximately twelve months of age. The relationship between the h^2 of this measurement and the maximum h^2 based on an infinite number of eggs (repeatability estimates) may be found in Shultz's (1953b) study.

barring startling discoveries in nutrition and physiology, it seems likely that at least egg weight will continue to be an important selection criterion. The main problem in selection for egg weight is to establish a way of reconciling the somewhat contradictory objectives of egg size and egg

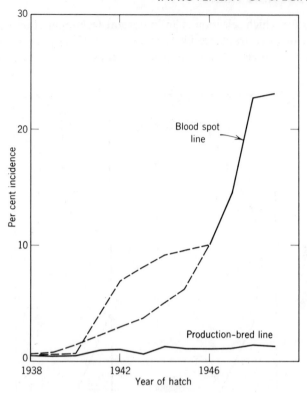

Figure 7.15.   Selection for increased incidence of blood spots

In the early stages of the selection experiment of Lerner, Taylor, and Lowry (1951), only two-year-old dams were used as parents of the blood spot line. Hence, in alternate years distinct populations were being measured. The two lines were combined in 1946 when one-year-old dams began to be employed. The control flock is once again the University of California production-bred line.

number. One possibility may lie in adjusting marketing procedures to the biological situation by lowering the commercial standard of excellence for egg weight.

34. Meat Production Traits

The operational opportunities for the application of selection are greatest in the improvement of meat poultry. Even though enormous progress in raising the level of such traits as rate of growth has recently been made through advances in nutritional knowledge, there is still much room for economically attainable genetic advances.

Two important reasons which are not entirely independent account for this fact: (*a*) artificial selection for meat production has only recently started, and (*b*) many characters of significance in meat production, fortunately for the breeder, are peripheral to fitness (see figure 3.13) and therefore can be altered at little or no loss of reproductive capacity. Hence at present a large share of successful selection work in the poultry industry relates to the field of meat production.

The traits which contribute to the quantity and quality of poultry meat are numerous. Relationships between them have not been fully explored, although data on their heritability and genetic correlations are gradually being accumulated. The most important characters are rate of growth (or body weight), conformation, early feathering, plumage color, and freedom from carcass-disfiguring defects, such as crooked keels or breast blisters. A number of selection experiments on them have been reported. Some will be referred to in the course of discussion, but, by and large, they do not demonstrate any new features of selection theory or practice.

As a solitary graphic illustration, figure 7.16 presents an example of highly successful selection in increasing early rate of growth. The average 12-week body weight of the initial generation (males and females combined) in the chart was 2.56 pounds; that of the high line in the last generation shown was 3.77 pounds. Thus an increase approaching 50 per cent of the mean body size of the original population was obtained in six generations. Even when cheap nutritional supplementation can lead to similar gains, opportunities for genetic improvement of such a large magnitude should certainly not be neglected. The unpublished observations of Godfrey and Goodman, who carried out this experiment, indicate that other characters of economic significance, such as hatchability and egg production, did not suffer in the course of increasing body weight of the high line. This was also true in a selection experiment for improved broiler qualities carried out by Clark and Cunningham (1953). On the other hand, the dynamic nature of the relation between a metric trait and fitness must always be kept in mind. A relevant lesson may be found in the history of turkey improvement. In the early attempts to change body size and conformation, no difficulties arose. Under intense and prolonged artificial selection for these traits, their relative importance in determining fitness became increasingly greater. In consequence, reproductive capacity of the large broad-breasted turkey declined alarmingly, and the efforts of breeders had to be directed toward restoration of fitness rather than toward improvement in meat qualities.

It may be noted here that although increases in body size have been obtained by exploiting polygenic variability, specific major size-inhibiting genetic differentials have also been identified in poultry (Maw, 1935;

Godfrey, 1953). They characterize bantams and are probably of no importance in commercial practice. Yet, when major single locus effects enter combinations with the ubiquitous polygenic variation in body size, difficulties in the interpretations of selection results could, of course, arise. Once more the texts of Hutt (1949) and Jull (1952) may be referred to for citations of literature and discussion of the large number of genetic

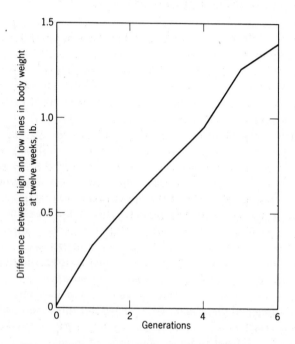

Figure 7.16. Selection for twelve-week body weight

The unpublished material of Godfrey and Goodman drawn upon for figure 4.4 is also utilized for this graph. Instead of six-week weight, twelve-week weights are shown here. The low line did not respond to selection; hence the curve plotted may be considered to have been corrected for interyear environmental differences. Progress for six generations appears to have been made at a steady rate.

experiments carried out on the body size of chickens since the early days of Mendelism. Of the more recent studies, that of Brunson, Godfrey, and Goodman (1956), relating to the analysis of types of gene action in body weight inheritance, is of particular interest. As expected on the basis of selection responses experimentally obtained, partitioning of variance of body weight indicated that the non-additive fraction of genotypic variance contributes little to the total variability.

Of the numerous selection experiments on other characters of importance in meat production, the study of Abplanalp and Asmundson (1956), although not as yet fully reported, has a bearing on the theory of selection indexes. In it, gains under direct selection (without using any ancillary information) for increased breast width were compared with those obtained in the same character selected on the basis of an index which included several other simple measurements (body weight, shank length, keel length). The index attached no economic value to changes in the other traits, addressing itself solely to conformation as measured by breast width (Lerner, Asmundson, and Cruden, 1947). The theoretically expected superiority of index versus direct selection (based on the considerations set forth in box 18) was 13 per cent. The actual response in breast width was 20 per cent higher in the index-selected line than in the population selected directly for it. As much as can be judged from a single test of this sort, the theory underlying selection index construction may be considered to have found confirmation for a short-range selection program.

The incidence of crooked keels has also been a subject of selection experiments. As a rule, it has been treated in an all-or-none manner. Its particular interest lies in the demonstration of genotype-management interaction. Both Warren (1937) and Hyre (1955) found variation in the degree of difference in the level of expression between high- and low-incidence lines, depending on whether the birds were provided with perches or not. Selection for increased incidence of the defect under an environment which promoted the higher frequencies of occurrence (i.e. with perches) appeared to be a rather simple matter.

Inferences about the possibility of successful selection for other characters affecting the value of meat birds can be made from heritability analyses (e.g. Hurry and Nordskog, 1953, with respect to rate of feathering) and other information. This, however, should not lead to a precipitate conclusion that selection for meat quantity and quality presents no difficulties of any kind. On the contrary, even in the short history of breeding improvement of meat poultry, incompatabilities between various selection objectives have come to light. In addition to negative genetic correlations, such as, for instance, found by Lerner, Asmundson, and Cruden (1947) between body weight and shortness of shank (a desideratum from the standpoint of conformation), other types of complications have also arisen. Thus it appears that the allele responsible for dominant white plumage, carriers of which have a decided economic advantage over colored birds, may have an inhibiting effect on growth (Jaap and Grimes, 1956; Jerome, Slinger, Huntsman, and Pepper, 1956). The implications of such interactions between major genetic differentials and polygenic variation may be serious, but they have not as yet been fully explored.

It does not seem probable that any novel aspect of fundamental selection theory is involved in these situations; the problems are more likely to be purely technical.

In spite of the ease with which the traits under discussion respond to selection in closed populations, crossbreeding is being used very extensively in commercial broiler production. The advantages of this mating system include not only the fact that growth rate is a heterotic trait but also the possibility of combining efficient reproduction with market qualities by means of breed and strain crosses. Many years ago, before the broiler industry came to be an economically important sector of the poultry business, Warren (1942), among others, was systematically exploring various crossbred combinations. Since then a large number of synthetic breeds or varieties designated by brand or trademark names have appeared on the scene to provide one of the parental lines in crosses. The developments in this area of the poultry industry are very rapid and are of great fascination to students of breeding techniques.

In general, meat production is a field in which a close integration of population and physiological genetics may be legitimately expected. The polygenic basis of growth rate has now been established in broad outline; the study of endocrinology of growth is also in a relatively advanced stage. The two aspects are beginning to be brought together, for example, in the study of Shaklee and Knox (1956) on the heritability of thyroid weight. A fruitful field of investigation appears to be opening in the direction of such a synthesis.

8

Prospects

It would be somewhat rash to assert that the limit has been attained in any one case.

The preceding discussion made it apparent that, although much has been learned about the genetic basis of selection since the methods of population genetics have come into being, there are still many gaps in our knowledge to be filled. The assumption that the selection theory developed from the current outlook on the inheritance of quantitative traits will remain valid indefinitely is probably overly-optimistic. Nevertheless, even within the framework of the present approach to the subject, much effort can be usefully expended in procuring further experimental evidence on the behavior of populations under selection.

It would be no easy task to outline in general terms the directions toward which further research on selection must turn. Many lacunae, especially in the field or practical breeding, are purely technical in nature and involve the comportment of specific traits in specific populations. Search for highly heritable characters strongly correlated genetically with traits under selection, study of techniques to increase the reliability of direct genotype evaluation, identification of signals which would indicate when a given breeding system may be profitably abandoned in favor of another, investigation of the effects of relaxing or suspending selection pressure on fitness and on the selected characters—all these and many similar research projects would be of basic significance to breeders. But the goals of such endeavors are primarily those of industrial research rather than of academic pursuits.

The business of breeding has undergone a radical change since the Second World War. At least so far as the improvement of poultry in the United States is concerned, the 1950's are characterized by the virtual elimination of small breeding establishments and by the concentration of the control of chick production in a small number of organizations blanketing the country. The newly arisen corporations have been forced by increasingly severe competition, and enabled by virtue of their size, to mechanize and rationalize breeding schemes, to expand open field trials of stock, and to inaugurate tests (perhaps less open) of the value of various selection and mating plans.

Owing to this development, technological research in breeding is gradually being removed from the province of the universities and experiment stations. These institutions were originally engaged in studies of such type as a public service for breeders incapable, because of lack of training and small scale of operation, to find their own answers to their problems. As matters stand at present with chickens, and perhaps before long with other domestic animals, research on practical aspects of breeding can be carried out more efficiently and on a vaster scale by the breeders themselves than by public agencies. The functions of the American land grant colleges and agricultural experiment stations hence need no longer include either practically oriented research on poultry breeding or advisory work. They can concentrate on the training of geneticists and on research of a broader and perhaps more far-reaching kind than that called for by immediately pragmatic aims.

There are, however, many problems deserving study which cannot be sorted into basic or applied categories. A number of them, surveying a few of the various avenues now open for further investigation of artificial selection, are considered in the following sections.

35. Research in Artificial Selection

An obvious undertaking in this field is to determine the practical value of intermittent or cyclic selection, i.e. of alternating periods of selection and no selection. On the assumption of additive gene action, there seems to be little promise either in periodic relaxation of selection pressure or in varying the objectives of selection in successive generations. Hazel and Lush (1942) have shown that tandem selection, tantamount to these procedures, is not particularly efficient. The fact that loss of fitness may occur when the direct objectives of selection are additively determined does not necessarily suggest that occasional suspension would be desirable. On the contrary, it may be argued that what is needed under such circumstances is an index which would take fitness into account. This reasoning would be valid were fitness itself additively determined which it is not. There also seems to be some indication from experiments, carried out for other purposes, to suggest that occasional relaxation of selection may be an efficacious practice, thus making intermittent selection worth investigating. The underlying objective of such a procedure is the attainment of a coadapted gene pool at a new level of the desired character, yet with preservation of genetic variability to permit revision of the selection goals upward.

The empirical evidence on the subject is admittedly meager, but it is not inconsistent with the possibility that intermittent selection may have practical value. For instance, in the experiment of Mather and Harrison (1949) with Drosophila, suspension of artificial-selection pressure at a certain point in the phylogeny of a line selected for bristle number not only saved it from extinction but permitted the line eventually to reach a higher level of the selected trait. Of course, increases in inbreeding were also prevented by this intervention, but no real reduction of F occurred, unless relaxation of artificial selection permitted natural-selection pressure in favor of heterozygotes to become stronger.

Further relevant information is given by Scossiroli's (1954) experiment on selection for bristle number in Drosophila. Others have tried unsuccessfully to produce new genetic variation by means of X-rays in order to enable the population to rise above an apparent plateau in a selected character. Different procedures were used in the various experiments conducted with different ends in view. Thus, Clayton and Robertson (1955), who summarized the earlier attempts of Serebrovskaya (1935) and Rokizky (1936) to utilize X-ray-induced variability in selection, addressed themselves to the question whether irradiation produces polygenic mutations or increases crossing over. To prevent the latter from occurring, they started their experiment with inbred material. In Scossiroli's experiment irradiation was applied to lines which failed to respond to further selection but which nevertheless were genetically variable. At any rate one of the differences in procedure between the comparatively unsuccessful attempts and that of Scossiroli, which succeeded, is that he applied artificial selection pressure only every other generation, allowing natural selection for fitness to interpose itself in the mass matings producing the alternate non-selected generations. It may not be particularly profitable to discuss at this stage whether it is this fact that accounts for the differences in results obtained. Suffice it to say that intermittent selection may present a possible alternative to selection of low intensity (see Dempster, 1955b) because of operational considerations. Since under cyclic selection measurements need be made and costs of pedigreeing be incurred only every second or third generation, it could be used so as to produce advances identical to those obtainable under continuous selection but at a reduced cost.

Although means for making theoretical comparisons for the efficiency of various schemes of selection for economically useful characters are available for many situations, empirical tests are by and large lacking or, when on record, are expected to apply only to the material on which they were performed. This deficiency is aggravated by the fact that, so far, no precise methods for assessing genetic progress under selection relative to unselected controls have been used in experiments with the larger animals.

The difficulty lies in the fact that the environment of the different generations is not identical. This means that whatever unselected controls are maintained, they are subject to variable natural-selection pressures and hence do not necessarily remain constant in their genetic composition throughout the experiment. For traits not ordinarily influenced much by differences in interyear environment, the effect may be minor, although even here in some instances difficulties may arise (e.g. the 1948 and 1954 peaks noted in the control line in figure 4.10). Furthermore, genetic drift may also enter the situation in control populations of small size.

The ideal but impractical solution to this problem would be to have a sufficient number of readily identifiable markers segregating in the control population, thus permitting a continuous check on changes in gene frequency to be made. In the absence of this possibility, randomly reproducing unselected control populations (e.g. the SS line in section 20) provide a partial answer to the problem. A rather complex design for maintaining controls, so as to obtain greater accuracy in the estimation of genetic changes in traits subject to environmentally induced fluctuations and to maternal influences, was proposed by Goodwin, Dickerson, and Lamoreux (1955). Whether it is a sufficiently practical one to become part of routine procedures in artificial selection experiments or improvement programs is hard to say. But it may be found from pilot experiments with their design that the difficulties of maintaining constant populations, the possible existence of which may be surmised on theoretical grounds, are of little significance in practice. Great simplifications in experimental and breeding programs could then be introduced, and the interpretation of results could be thereby much facilitated.

Another question to be answered is whether genetic correlations between various characters remain constant when correlated traits are exposed to effective selection pressure. In theory, changes in these correlations (for the worse, from a breeder's standpoint, as may be deduced from the considerations set forth in section 21) can be expected. But there is little factual evidence about them. Indeed, the very sign of many correlations in populations which are in the initial phases of selection is not known.

Not long ago it was important to find out whether birds excelling in both meat and egg production could be bred. Since chicken meat production has become a specialized industry, dual-purpose birds no longer present an attraction to either egg or broiler producers. Efficiency of management demands completely different schedules of operations and kinds of equipment for broilers and for layers. Only the breeders and the hatcherymen marketing broiler chicks are now interested in having a stock with high laying capacity, the offspring of which could be raised for meat. The requirement of high egg production, of course, is related to the reproductive potential of the parental generation, i.e. to the cost per chick of breeding and hatching operations.

One possibility lies in the development of maternal lines characterized by high egg production and low maintenance costs. They could be crossed with paternal lines which would confer good meat production properties on the commercial chick. This solution would clearly not be as satisfactory as one that would permit the combination of both kinds of useful traits in the same line. A difficulty is raised here by the fact that the rate of growth of broilers is genetically positively correlated with adult body size (Peeler, Glazener, and Blow, 1955). The cost of producing chicks with a genotype for rapid growth is therefore increased by the high maintenance requirements of the parents. Reversal of the sign of the correlation, were it possible to accomplish, would then be a first step in the desired direction.

A broader problem involving genetic correlation involves the search for physiological or biochemical indexes of genotypic capacity for meat or for egg production. Success in this quest not only may mean more direct, more accurate, and cheaper methods of identifying desirable genotypes, but, by leading toward a fuller understanding of the pathways between gene and character, should prepare the ground for attacks on more revolutionary goals (section 37).

Considerable preliminary work along these lines has been done, some of which is encouraging. For example, the studies of Kushner (1941) on the relationship between, on the one hand, the biochemical constituents of blood of the larger animals and their productivity and heterosis, on the other, suggest many possibilities. The indications of genetic correlations between blood-glutathione levels and egg production of chickens reported by Stutts, Briles, and Kunkel (1956) also appear to be promising. Similarly, the high heritability of thyroid weight already noted (Shaklee and Knox, 1956) and the apparent relationship between growth rate and response to thiouracil feeding (Shaklee and Shaffner, 1952) point the way to a direct approach to genetic improvement of production characters by way of the endocrine glands. The investigation of the physiological basis of the ovulatory cycle (Fraps, 1954; Bastian and Zarrow, 1955; see also the review of Albada, 1956) has not yet been attacked from the genetic standpoint, but the prospect of a profitable combination of endocrinology and biochemistry with physiological and statistical genetics is clear. As Blyth (1952c) has emphasized, no major advances in the genetics of egg production can be expected until a more thorough understanding of the underlying physiology of egg production and of the relation between ovarian activity and other organ systems is obtained. The need for more information on the fundamental physiology of other useful traits is just as urgent.

Immunogenetics offers another exciting experimental approach to selection studies. The possibility of identifying by blood groups the genotypes which are likely to produce heterosis upon crossing is only one of a number offered by this field of study. Even broader in its ramifications is the likelihood that the solution to the problem of the mechanics of maintenance of heterozygosity in inbred lines and closed populations of small size will come from immunogenetic studies. More light on this subject is required if the desire to enforce heterozygosity in closed populations is to be implemented, as well as for the purposes of eliminating it in inbred lines to be used for crossing.

Selection is known to operate with respect to blood group alleles (section 16). Yet it seems impossible for selection to account for many heterozygous loci in a population with as high a fitness as that displayed by the University of California production-bred flock (section 31). It therefore appears highly probable that some other mechanisms will eventually be found to be responsible for this phenomenon. The more obvious answers to this problem, such as preferential fertilization of eggs by genetically unlike sperm, seem to be at variance with the observations on record (Bonnier and Trulsson, 1939; Parker, McKenzie, and Kempster, 1942; Allen and Champion, 1955). Neither does preferential mating, as appears from the unpublished results of experiments by Taylor and Lerner, account for it. On the other hand, mutation still remains an unexplored area, which studies on blood group alleles may illuminate.

A list of examples of unsolved problems of significance to selection theory and practice could be made indefinitely long. It is perhaps sufficient for the purposes followed here to have indicated a few of the more general questions for the attack on which adequate experimental methods are now available. One other issue which seems of particular importance may be considered. It relates to the ways and means of extending the limits of selection.

36. Selection Limits

The difficulties of judging whether a ceiling is being reached in selection experiments with such traits as egg production have already been noted. Since it is very likely that the approach to a plateau is asymptotic, rate of attainment of gains may become uneconomically slow long before advance ceases. There seem to be two general ways in which the speeding up of lagging progress or the renewal of advance after total cessation of gains may be promoted: (a) by utilizing the genotypic variability which is present but which is not expressed under the particular conditions of the selection program in question, and (b) by the production of new variation either through immigration or by mutagenic agents. The change from methods appropriate for closed population selection to selection between populations or to mating inbred lines falls into the second of these categories. But there are probably other ways of breaking through apparent barriers to selection progress.

In the utilization of existing variation, the basic problem is to change the environment of the population in such a way as to bring to phenotypic expression differences at loci which segregated up to that time for reasons unrelated to the objectives of selection (as noted in section 32 with regard to fitness). This would be analogous to the changes in dominance or penetrance of newly arisen mutants by selection of modifiers already present in the population.

In breeding for economic characters, unusual environments or stress may allow the identification of desirable alleles or of favorable genotypes. For this purpose, shocks may be applied in the form of periodic starvation, of deficient or unbalanced diets, of changes in the length, temperature, humidity, or other aspects of the incubation regime, or by the use of a number of other procedures, many of which have already been investigated in other connections. They include intermittent light stimuli for laying birds (Wilson and Abplanalp, 1956), exposure to low temperature of embryos (Olsen, 1951) or of chicks (Siegel and Mueller, 1955), and a variety of other methods bounded largely by the investigator's ingenuity.

Introduction of competition between members of a population by restricting food may produce a form of stress. In some plants at least, competitive ability may be partly independent of productive ability

(Sakai, 1955). Whether this is true of different useful traits in animals may be worth investigating. In chickens, the lack of interaction between genotype for egg production and cage or floor management (i.e. maintenance of laying birds in individual cages without competition as against keeping mixed groups in large laying houses; see section 28) suggests that competition for food and shelter would have to be very intense or start very early in life, if isolation of genotypes for yield from genotypes for competitive ability is attempted. In general, the investigation of the genetics of peck-right order, aggressiveness, and other aspects of animal behavior (see reviews by Guhl, 1953, and by Wood-Gush, 1955) may be valuable in this relation.

It is very likely that testing performance under stress will lead to modifications in the relative proportion of additive and non-additive variability contributed by the loci already segregating in a population (see discussion in section 9). This effect not only may of itself dictate alterations in the optimum breeding plan to be followed but also may actually change the levels of performance of populations in equilibrium.

Ceiling breakthrough by immigration is in principle a rather simple matter. By the introduction of new variability from another gene pool, new levels of expression of a trait under selection should be attainable. The natural selection experiment of Buzzati-Traverso (1955) noted in section 32 provides an example. The results of Falconer and King (1953), who crossed two lines of mice which were apparently at a plateau for body weight and by selection from the crosses were able to increase the body size beyond the ceilings of the two parental lines, provide another. The economic application of this principle is, of course, not as simple as the experiment suggests, largely because in breeding practice not a single desideratum but many diverse objectives are pursued. Maintenance of a desirable constellation of characters at a high level hence may be economically more rewarding than a rise above the plateau for one trait with a possible loss of excellence in others. Nevertheless, there is little doubt that circumstances under which it is economically justifiable to bring together two or more gene pools, and then to select for a coadapted contents at a new level of expression of the desired characters, are not uncommon.

A less certain procedure would seem to lie in an attempt to produce new genetic variability by mutagens. Encouragement, however, may be taken from many sources, although the possibility of commercial application of such techniques to the larger animals still remains to be demonstrated. Irradiation of plants to produce useful variation has been discussed by Gustafsson and Tedin (1954), Gregory (1956), and Mac Key (1956). The X-ray experiment of Scossiroli (1954), who succeeded in producing selection advances in Drosophila populations stabilized with respect to bristle number, has already been referred to. Whether he or Buzzati-Traverso (1954b), who was able to increase egg production and reproductive capacity of Drosophila by the same means, induced polygenic mutations or produced rare recombinations, translocations, inversions, or other gross effects may not be clear at the moment. But in any case, genetic variation of an utilizable type was brought into existence in populations otherwise not responding to artificial (in Scossiroli's experiment) or natural (in that of Buzzati-Traverso) selection.

Extensive studies on natural selection in connection with artificially induced genetic variability have also been carried out by Wallace (e.g. 1956). One of the early conclusions of this series of investigations on Drosophila was "that heterotic combinations are selected for and become established in populations at an extremely rapid rate . . . and radiation induced genetic variants are seemingly incorporated in these combinations" (Wallace and King, 1951). Encouraging as this finding may be, it still remains to be seen whether X-rays or chemical mutagens have application in poultry-breeding practice for the specific purpose of creating polygenic variation designed to overcome the forces keeping the population on a plateau. Other uses of X-rays may be envisaged, even though they are still on the experimental level. For example, should it be possible to make translocations produced by X-rays homozygous, a breeder could market crosses between lines containing the standard and the rearranged chromosomal complements without the danger of his stock being pirated for reproduction by others. On an even more speculative level, X-rays or other means of artificially changing the heredity of populations may provide tools for experimenters who may wish to carry work on selection beyond the microevolutionary level.

37. Macroevolutionary Horizons

Macroevolutionary processes in nature may be considered to arise from a cumulative action of small selection pressures over a long period of time (e.g. see Haldane, 1958). But experimental macroevolution or the border area between meso- and macroevolution should perhaps be approached in a more radical manner, because otherwise the cumulative lifetimes of several generations of investigators may not be long enough for the induction of irreversible changes of specific or quasi-specific rank. In the absence of recipes for success and of guideposts to possible procedures, it may be argued that undertakings of this sort are not rewarding. Yet the immense theoretical importance and the potential practical consequences of any positive achievements along this line warrant expenditure of some effort on trials to obtain macroevolutionary changes. Considerable imagination and a bold and daring attitude of thought may be required for this purpose. Instead of relatively mild selection directed toward a gradual alteration of allelic frequencies, catastrophically severe pressure must be applied if any hope of creating new forms deserving specific or species-hybrid status is to be fulfilled. As a first step in the making of new species, establishment of reproductive isolation between part of a currently existing gene pool and the remainder of it is needed. To produce viable species hybrids, breakdown of isolation between two or more present species is called for.

The creation of new types of organisms may be aided by the production of genetic variation ranging in magnitude from polygenic point mutations to polyploidization, and by committing various biological outrages on the population via environmental pressures directed to either the germplasm or the soma. Natural selection will, no doubt, continue its intervention to block the experimenter's efforts, but obstinacy or good luck may still work on his side. A "shattering of the heredity," not in the naive manner of Lysenko but in the sense of producing decanalization of development, destabilization of the genotype, and disruption of the gene pool, should be the primary objective. Alleles which are highly specific in their action and not jacks-of-all-trade (Mayr, 1954) should be afforded increased selective advantages. Environments which would permit particular genetic combinations characterized by poor fitness in their present milieu to regain reproductive capacity should be searched for. Selection for potentially crucial modifications of the breeding system, e.g. for conversion to a parthogenetic mode of reproduction,[1] for the production of several eggs a day instead of one, or for the twinning of embryos within an egg, might be undertaken. Attempts to induce genetic assimilation (Waddington, 1953a) of different traits currently enjoying the status of abnormalities might be followed up. The manufacture and propagation of various bizarre variants may be tried. In fine, not only imitation of processes which have occurred in nature but also attempts to add an unprecedented wrinkle or two to them should be undertaken.

New kinds of animals might also be created by hybridization between various feral and domestic varieties and species of gallinaceous birds. To obtain self-reproducing populations of novel types may be more difficult than to find a new hybrid of commercial value such as, at one time, was the mule. It is by no means impossible that manipulation of incubation regimes or of other aspects of early environment could make

[1] A glimpse of this possibility may be seen in the work of Olsen and Marsden (1956) on parthogenetic development of the turkey.

forms, currently assumed to be inviable or of very low viability, commercially useful, even though they remain sterile. After all, incrossbreeding has been found profitable!

The production of single specimens of a new kind would be merely the first step. Whether a new self-reproducing type or a new hybrid is obtained, integration of one or more gene pools would be needed before the goal of macroevolutionary change could be reached. For a novel kind of gene pool (new "species" would probably be an incorrect term here), the original reproductive capacity would be expected to be very low. But artificial selection may be used to aid natural selection in arriving at an optimum balance of all fitness components of the newly arisen interbreeding group. In the case of a new hybrid, selection for cross-performance on a somewhat grander scale than that considered in chapter 6 may be needed. The fundamental principle of producing coadaptedly integrated gene pools is, however, the same here as at the microevolutionary level. The contributions of King (1955), of Wallace and Vetukhiv (1955), and of Mayr (1955) to the discussion of gene pool integration may be profitably reread in reference to this problem.

At this stage of our knowledge it may be pardonable to be vague about the details of the means by which macroevolutionary changes may be expected to be brought about. It is clear that unorthodox approaches are needed. They may be difficult to justify in the eyes of those who have full faith in the validity of current interpretations. But since in science, as in war, the victors are seldom put on trial, it may be hoped that the prospects of success, so long as its probability is finite, will spur the uninhibited to make the effort.

38. Envoy

In the course of the previous discussion many generally accepted and some personal points of view have been expressed. Little harm can come from such a mixture, especially since various sources of information redressing any bias have been constantly cited. As a further safeguard less against giving offense to dissenters from the views voiced here than against leading the highly impressionable astray, it might be of value to list a number of important or interesting contributions on selection and related topics to which, for one or another reason, no reference has been made heretofore. These are annotated in boxes 29 and 30.

In genetics and evolution, as in other fields of study, periods of enthusiasm which follow major syntheses or discoveries may alternate with waves of pessimism which lead to grave doubts about the validity of

┌─────────────────────────── BOX 29 ───────────────────────────┐

Literature on Selection Experiments

A large number of selection experiments have been performed by many investigators intent on a variety of aims and working with many species. Only a small fraction of reports on them has been referred to in the text. A limited number of others may be cited here as a bibliographic aid. Only publications not specifically mentioned in the text are included in the following brief listing. They were chosen because of historical interest, because the experiments are extensively reported, or because they illustrate aspects of selection not otherwise considered in this book.

Castle (1919). An important landmark in genetics which concluded a controversy of several years' duration on the question whether or not selection creates new genetic variability. Coat pattern in rats was the character under selection.

Craft et al (1951). A symposium on selection in livestock, which includes a valuable section with a bibliography on experiments with laboratory animals.

Dickerson et al. (1954). A report of a cooperative project on developing selected inbred lines of swine at seven experiment stations.

Goldschmidt, Hannah and *Piternick* (1951). A study of the pheno-deviant *podoptera* in Drosophila, which includes data from selection experiments for modification of penetrance.

Goodale (1942). A study of selection for extension of white spotting on the heads of mice by a pioneer of poultry selection studies (see box 24). Goodale also carried out a long-term selection experiment on body weight in mice (see Falconer and King, 1953, for reference to this and the parallel work of MacArthur). An earlier paper by Goodale (1938) provides a valuable catalogue of other selection studies.

King (1955). One of a series of independent studies on selection for resistance to insecticides. Merrell and Underhill (1956) and Milani (1957) reviewed many of these investigations.

Pearl (1912). The first of the selection experiments for economic characters (egg production in chickens) interpreted in Mendelian terms is reported upon in this article.

Rasmuson (1955). One of the analyses based on a number of long-term experiments on selection for bristle number in Drosophila, comparable in scope to those of Mather and Harrison (1949) and of Scossiroli (1954).

Robertson and *Reeve* (1952). The first of a long series on selection for metric traits in Drosophila.

Sturtevant (1918). A report of experiments in Drosophila which contains a comprehensive statement of the basic problems in selection that the creators of the gene theory of inheritance were attempting to solve. Among others who have carried out the first cycle of extensive selection

└──┘

experiments in Drosophila were MacDowell, May, Payne, and Zeleny (all referred to by Rasmuson, 1955). Mather may be considered to have initiated the second cycle.

Woodworth, Leng, and *Jugenheimer* (1952). A description of what is, perhaps, the longest selection experiment in duration (fifty years) which has been reported upon in detail. The material used was corn; the objectives of selection were protein and oil contents.

---BOX 30---

Miscellaneous References

In addition to the reports of specific selection experiments given in box 29, a number of other publications of interest and importance to the subject should be noted. They include several recent volumes of collected papers on different aspects of evolution and population genetics. Individual articles in them have already been mentioned. Their titles and publishers may be found in the list of literature cited under the names of their editors: Gowen (1952), Reeve and Waddington (1952), Brown and Danielli (1953), Buzzati-Traverso (1954a), Heberer (1954), Huxley, Hardy, and Ford (1954), and Warren (1955).

Several other contributions of historical or general interest, most of which have not been otherwise cited, may be commented upon.

Buzzati-Traverso, Jucci, and *Timofeeff-Ressovsky* (1938). This article, written in Italian, contains an extensive bibliography of the significant papers dating to the early days of experimental population genetics.

Crow (1955). A stimulating discussion of recent developments in some theoretical aspects of population genetics.

East and *Jones* (1919). An historically important treatment of inbreeding depression and heterosis.

Ford (1955). A review of observations on morphism in nature with particular reference to factors effecting evolutionary changes.

Hagberg (1953). A comprehensive discussion and review of heterosis.

Hardy (1908). The classical note on gametic and zygotic population equilibrium which appeared in the same year as the report of Weinberg's discovery of the identical principle.

Henderson (1952). An important mathematical treatment of selection procedures with particular reference to the subject matter of chapter 6 of this book.

Jennings (1916). The earliest of the papers on population genetics based on Mendelian considerations which received wide attention among geneticists. It deals with consequences of different mating systems.

Johnson, Robinson, and *Comstock* (1955). An example of the investigations of the North Carolina group of workers on quantitative inheritance.

This particular article deals with genetic and phenotypic correlations in soya beans in relation to selection procedures.

Kempthorne (1957). An exceedingly useful book on statistical rationale and procedures for geneticists. Among other topics, the statistics of gene interaction, inbreeding, quantitative inheritance, and many aspects of selection are discussed. The book appeared after the manuscript of the present volume was in the hands of the publishers.

L'Heritier (1954). An exposition of the mathematical aspects of population genetics largely on a single locus level (in French).

Ludwig (1954). A broad statement of current quantitative selection theory (in German).

Malécot (1948). An approach to genetics via the mathematics of probability, presenting more generalized and powerful methods than those in earlier use (in French).

Morley (1952). This is one paper of a series relating to improvement in sheep and presenting an example of a comprehensive study of artificial selection of a particular species in all its phases.

Weinberg (1909). The first attempt to treat Mendelism quantitatively. It was, however, entirely overlooked by the geneticists of the day. A year earlier, Weinberg published a paper on what has become known as the Hardy-Weinberg equilibrium.

Although the following works have been cited in the text on one or more occasions, their exceptional significance in the development of our understanding of selection warrants a reference to them in this box: Dobzhansky (1951), Fisher (1918, 1930), Haldane (1932), Lush (1945), Wright (1921, 1931).

the basic concepts on which current knowledge rests. Thus, the exuberant confidence of the early Darwinians, who saw no limits to the possibilities of selection as an agency for transforming nature, was succeeded by a period of an eclipse of the Darwinian doctrine, which was considered not to have solved many problems after all. But when the fuller implications of Mendelian inheritance were understood, Darwinism in its broad interpretation once more produced an explosion of research activity (which may now be subsiding because of the even more startling developments in other phases of biology). Similarly, the introduction of quantitative methods into genetics, the successive invention of techniques for artificial production of mutations and for the study of genetically controlled biochemical pathways, and the discovery of microorganisms as subjects for genetic research all in turn gave promise of yielding the key for unlocking the ultimate door, only to disappoint and leave us facing still another door to be opened. It is, therefore, not to be expected that the keys which we can forge now will unlock anything but another door in a probably infinite series. But it is still a fountainhead of excitement to make even a small step forward in the pursuit of truth, which is the purpose of scientific endeavor.

The current developments in genetics which have a direct bearing on selection give reason for at least tempered optimism for the immediate future. Synthesis of several independent approaches on a much broader front than has been hitherto achieved seem likely. Thus, experimental population genetics based on a neo-Darwinian outlook, mathematical genetics characterized by more inclusive and more rigorously defined statistical models of inheritance, physiological and biochemical genetics directed not only to the pathways from the gene to the trait but also to those from the trait to fitness form some of the strands which are beginning to be woven together to make a whole.

What may unite them is the idea that has been stressed throughout this book. In brief, the principle that may be most fruitful in advancing selection theory and practice is that interrelationships between different populations, between each population and its environment, between members of a population, between the components of a gene pool, between properties of a single individual or parts of its genotype—all of these—are not static but are subject to change by *coadaptation* in the broadest sense of this term. The roots of this concept can, no doubt, be traced to the philosophers of classical antiquity. But the succession of students of evolution, from Darwin, Mendel, and Galton of the last century to Wright, Fisher, Haldane, Dobzhansky, and their followers of our day, have provided us with the means of attacking it experimentally. It is to the study of the specific mechanisms underlying the coadaptive process at each level of its operation and expression that we must turn to now for elucidation of the role of selection in nature, of its uses in augmenting man's control over his environment, and, more generally, for increasing both our powers of prediction and our understanding of evolutionary change.

Literature Cited

Abplanalp, H. 1956. *Poultry Sci.*, **35**: 1285–1304.
Abplanalp, H. 1957. *Poultry Sci.*, **36**: 226–228.
Abplanalp, H. and V. S. Asmundson. 1956. *Poultry Sci.*, **35**: 1129.
Albada, M. van. 1956. *Arch. Geflügelk.*, **20**: 321–370.
Allen, C. J. and L. R. Champion. 1955. *Poultry Sci.*, **34**: 1332–1342.
Allison, A. C. 1955. *Cold Spring Harbor Symposia Quant. Biol.*, **20**: 239–255.
Anderson, E. 1953. *Biol. Rev.*, **28**: 280–307.
Bader, R. S. 1956. *Quart. J. Florida Acad. Sci.* **19**: 14–34.
Bastian, J. W. and M. X. Zarrow. 1955. *Poultry Sci.*, **34**: 776–788.
Bell, A. E. 1949. *J. Infectious Diseases*, **85**: 154–169.
Bell, A. E., C. H. Moore and D. C. Warren. 1955. *Cold Spring Harbor Symposia Quant. Biol.*, **20**: 197–211.
Benzer, S. 1957. *Symposium on Chem. Basis Hered.* (Johns Hopkins Press): 70–93.
Berg, Raisa L. 1941. *Drosophila Inform. Serv.*, **15**: 20–23.
Bernstein, F. 1930. *Z. Induktive Abstammungs- und Vererbungslehre*, **56**: 233–273.
Blow, W. L. and E. W. Glazener. 1953. *Poultry Sci.*, **32**: 696–701.
Blyth, Janet S. S. 1952*a*. *Poultry Sci.*, **31**: 254–268.
Blyth, Janet S. S. 1952*b*. *Empire J. Exp. Agr.*, **20**: 133–141.
Blyth, Janet S. S. 1952*c*. *Proc. Roy. Soc. Edinburgh*, **B65**: 52–65.
Blyth, Janet S. S. 1956. *J. Agr. Sci.*, **47**: 107–111.
Bohren, B. B., G. D. Rapp and R. B. Arvidson. 1952. *Purdue Agr. Exp. Sta. Bull.* 574.
Bonnier, G. and S. Trulsson. 1939. *Hereditas*, **25**: 65–76.
Brieger, F. G. 1950. *Genetics*, **35**: 420–445.
Briles, W. E. 1956. *Poultry Sci.*, **35**: 1134–1135.
Briles, W. E., L. W. Johnson and M. J. Garber. 1953. *Poultry Sci.*, **32**: 890.
Briles, W. E. and W. F. Krueger. 1955. *Poultry Sci.*, **34**: 1182.
Brncic, D. 1954. *Genetics*, **39**: 77–88.
Brown, R. and J. F. Danielli, eds. 1953. *Evolution* (*Symposium Soc. Exp. Biol.*, **7**). Cambridge Univ. Press.
Brunson, C. C., G. F. Godfrey and B. L. Goodman. 1956. *Poultry Sci.*, **35**: 524–532
Buri, P. 1956. *Evolution*, **10**: 367–402.
Burmester, B. R., W. G. Walter and A. K. Fontes. 1957. *Poultry Sci.*, **36**: 79–87.
Burmester, B. R. and N. F. Waters. 1955. *Poultry Sci.*, **34**: 1415–1429.
Buzzati-Traverso, A. A., ed. 1954*a*. *Symposium on Genetics of Population Structure*. UIBS Publ., B15.
Buzzati-Traverso, A. A. 1954*b*. *Proc. 9th Intern. Cong. Genet.*, **1**: 450–462.
Buzzati-Traverso, A. A. 1955. *Heredity*, **9**: 153–186.

Buzzati-Traverso, A. A., C. Jucci and N. W. Timofeeff-Ressovsky. 1938. *Ricerca Sci.*, 9: 584–610.

Cain, A. J. and P. M. Sheppard. 1950. *Heredity*, 4: 275–294.

Campbell, J. G. 1954. *Rept. 10th World's Poultry Congr.*, 2: 193–197.

Carmon, J. L., H. A. Stewart, C. C. Cockerham and R. E. Comstock. 1956. *J. Animal Sci.*, 15: 930–936.

Caspari, E. 1952. *Evolution*, 6: 1–18.

Castle, W. E. 1919. *Am. Naturalist*, 53: 370–376.

Chai, C. K. 1956. *Genetics*, 41: 157–164.

Champion, L. R. 1954. *Poultry Sci.*, 33: 670–681.

Chetverikov, S. S. 1926. *Zhur. Eksp. Biol.*, A2: 1–54.

Clark, T. B. and C. J. Cunningham. 1953. *Poultry Sci.*, 32: 893.

Clarke, Jean M. and J. M. Smith. 1955. *J. Genet.*, 53: 172–180.

Clayton, G., G. R. Knight, J. A. Morris and A. Robertson. 1957. *J. Genet.*, 55: 171–180.

Clayton, G., J. A. Morris and A. Robertson. 1957. *J. Genet.*, 55: 131–151.

Clayton, G and A. Robertson. 1955. *Am. Naturalist*, 89: 151–158.

Clayton, G. and A. Robertson. 1957. *J. Genet.*, 55: 152–170.

Clough, Margaret and A. G. Cock. 1957. *Nature*, 179: 1030–1031.

Cochez, L. P. and R. Pero. 1954. *Rept. 10th World's Poultry Congr.*, 2: 16–19.

Cock, A. G. 1956. *Poultry Sci.*, 35: 504–515.

Cock, A. G. and Margaret Clough. 1956. *Nature*, 178: 136–137.

Cockerham, C. C. 1954. *Genetics*, 39: 859–882.

Cockerham, C. C. 1956. *Genetics*, 41: 138–141.

Cohen, C. 1956. *Science*, 123: 935–936.

Coleman, T. H. and R. G. Jaap. 1954. *Poultry Sci.*, 33: 958–965.

Coles, R. 1955. *Poultry Sci.*, 34: 312–322.

Comstock, R. E. 1955. *Cold Spring Harbor Symposia Quant. Biol.*, 20: 93–102.

Comstock, R. E., H. F. Robinson and P. H. Harvey. 1949. *Agron. J.*, 41: 360–367.

Comstock, R. E. and L. M. Winters. 1944. *J. Animal Sci.*, 3: 380–389.

Coonen, C. P. 1956. *Sci. Monthly*, 83: 57–65.

Craft, W. A., A. B. Chapman, C. F. Sierk, L. M. Winters, G. E. Dickerson, C. E. Terrill and J. L. Lush. 1951. *J. Animal Sci.*, 10: 3–21.

Crittenden, L. B., B. B. Bohren and V. L. Anderson. 1957a. *Poultry Sci.*, 36: 90–103.

Crittenden, L. B., B. B. Bohren and V. L. Anderson. 1957b. *Poultry Sci.*, 36: 104–110.

Crow, J. F. 1948. *Genetics*, 33: 477–487.

Crow, J. F. 1952. *Heterosis* (Iowa State College Press), 282–297.

Crow, J. F. 1955. *Cold Spring Harbor Symposium Quant. Biol.*, 20: 54–59.

Crow, J. F. and M. Kimura. 1956. *Proc. 3rd Berkeley Symposium Math. Statis. Prob.*, 4: 1–22.

Crow, J. F. and N. E. Morton. 1955. *Evolution*, 9: 202–214.

Cruden, Dorothy M. 1949. *J. Heredity*, 40: 248–251.

Darlington, C. D. 1939. *The Evolution of Genetic Systems*. Cambridge Univ. Press.

Darlington, C. D. 1956. *Proc. Roy. Soc. (London)*, B145: 350–364.

Darlington, C. D. and K. Mather. 1949. *The Elements of Genetics*. Allen and Unwin.

Darwin, C. 1872. *The Origin of Species*. 6th ed. Murray.

Darwin, C. 1875. *The Variation of Animals and Plants under Domestication*. 2nd ed. Murray.

Demerec, M. 1956. *Cold Spring Harbor Symposia Quant. Biol.*, 21: 113–121.

Dempster, E. R. 1955a. *Cold Spring Harbor Symposia Quant. Biol.*, 20: 25–31.

Dempster, E. R. 1955b. *Biometrics*, 11: 535–536.

Dempster, E. R. 1956. *Am. Naturalist*, 90: 385–386.

Dempster, E. R. and I. M. Lerner. 1947. *Genetics*, 32: 555–579.

Dempster, E. R. and I. M. Lerner. 1950. *Genetics*, 35: 212–236.

Dempster, E. R. and I. M. Lerner. 1957. *Poultry Sci.*, 36: 143–146.

Dempster, E. R., I. M. Lerner and Dorothy C. Lowry. 1952. *Genetics*, 37: 693–708.

Dempster, E. R. and L. A. Snyder. 1950. *Science*, 111: 283–285.

Dickerson, G. E. 1952. *Heterosis* (Iowa State College Press), 330–351.

Dickerson, G. C. 1955. *Cold Spring Harbor Symposia Quant. Biol.*, 20: 213–224.

Dickerson, G. E., C. T. Blunn, A. B. Chapman, R. M. Kottman, J. L. Krider, E. J. Warwick and J. A. Whatley, Jr. 1954. *Missouri Agr. Exp. Sta. Res. Bull.*, 551.

Dickerson, G. E. and J. C. Grimes. 1947. *J. Animal Sci.*, 6: 265–287.

Dickerson, G. E. and L. N. Hazel. 1944. *J. Agr. Research*, 69: 459–476.

Dickerson, G. E., Q. B. Kinder, W. F. Krueger and H. L. Kempster. 1950. *Poultry Sci.*, 29: 756.

Dobzhansky, Th. 1950. *Am. Naturalist*, 84: 401–408.

Dobzhansky, Th. 1951. *Genetics and the Origin of Species.* 3rd ed. Columbia Univ. Press.

Dobzhansky, Th. 1952. *Heterosis* (Iowa State College Press), 218–223.

Dobzhansky, Th. 1954. *Proc. 9th Intern. Congr. Genet.*, 1: 435–449.

Dobzhansky, Th. 1955. *Cold Spring Harbor Symposia Quant. Biol.*, 20: 1–15.

Dobzhansky, Th. 1956. *Am. Naturalist*, 90: 337–347.

Dobzhansky, Th. and H. Levene. 1951. *Am. Naturalist*, 85: 247–264.

Dobzhansky, Th. and Olga Pavlovsky. 1957. *Evolution*, 11: 311–319.

Dobzhansky, Th. and B. Wallace. 1953. *Proc. Nat. Acad. Sci.*, 39: 162–171.

Donald, H. P. 1955. *Proc. Roy. Soc. (London)*, B144: 192–203.

Dubinin, N. P. 1948. *Zhur. Obshcheï Biol.*, 9: 203–244.

Dunn, L. C. 1957. *Proc. Nat. Acad. Sci.*, 43: 158–163.

Düzgüneş, O. 1950. *Poultry Sci.*, 29: 227–235.

Düzgüneş, O. and T. S. Yao. 1956. *Poultry Sci.*, 35: 1309–1315.

East, E. M. 1936. *Genetics*, 21: 375–397.

East, E. M. and D. F. Jones. 1919. *Inbreeding and Outbreeding.* Lippincott.

Emerson, S. 1952. *Heterosis* (Iowa State College Press), 199–217.

Essary, E. O., G. J. Mountney and O. E. Goff. 1951. *Poultry Sci.*, 30: 552–557.

Falconer, D. S. 1952. *Am. Naturalist*, 86: 293–298.

Falconer, D. S. 1954a. *Symposium on Genetics of Population Structure.* UIBS Publ., B15: 16–41.

Falconer, D. S. 1954b. *J. Heredity*, 45: 42–44.

Falconer, D. S. 1955. *Cold Spring Harbor Symposia Quant. Biol.*, 20: 178–196.

Falconer, D. S. and J. W. B. King. 1953. *J. Genet.*, 51: 561–581.

Falconer, D. S. and M. Latyszewski. 1952. *J. Genetics*, 51: 67–80.

Falconer, D. S. and A. Robertson. 1956. *Z. Induktive Abstammungs- und Vererbungslehre*, 87: 385–391.

Farnsworth, G. M., Jr. and A. W. Nordskog. 1955. *Poultry Sci.*, 34: 16–26.

Fischer, H. 1956. *Arch. Geflügelk.*, 20: 118–127.

Fisher, R. A. 1918. *Trans. Roy. Soc. Edinburgh*, 52: 399–433.

Fisher, R. A. 1930. *The Genetical Theory of Natural Selection.* Oxford Univ. Press.

Fisher, R. A. 1949. *The Theory of Inbreeding.* Oliver and Boyd.

Fisher, R. A., F. R. Immer and O. Tedin. 1932. *Genetics*, 17: 107–124.

Fisher, R. A. and F. Yates. 1953. *Statistical Tables.* 3rd ed. Oliver and Boyd.
Ford, E. B. 1945. *Biol. Rev.*, **20**: 73–88.
Ford, E. B. 1955. *Cold Spring Harbor Symposia Quant. Biol.*, **20**: 230–238.
Fox, T. W., E. F. Godfrey, S. C. King and J. H. Quisenberry. 1955. *Poultry Sci.*, **34**: 1194–1195.
Francis, D. W. and A. F. Kish. 1955. *Poultry Sci.*, **34**: 331–336.
Fraps, R. M. 1954. *Proc. Nat. Acad. Sci.*, **40**: 348–356.
Gilmour, D. S. 1954. *Heredity*, **8**: 291.
Glazener, E. W. and W. L. Blow. 1954. *Poultry Sci.*, **33**: 1055.
Glazener, E. W., R. E. Comstock, W. L. Blow, R. S. Dearstyne and C. H. Bostian. 1952. *Poultry Sci.*, **31**: 1078–1083.
Godfrey, E. F. 1953. *Poultry Sci.*, **32**: 248–259.
Godfrey, G. F. 1952. *J. Heredity*, **43**: 22–24.
Godfrey, G. F. and B. L. Goodman. 1956. *Poultry Sci.*, **35**: 47–50.
Goldschmidt, R. 1940. *The Material Basis of Evolution.* Yale Univ. Press.
Goldschmidt, R., Aloha Hannah and Leonie K. Piternick. 1951. *Univ. Calif. Publs. Zoöl.*, **55**: 67–294.
Goodale, H. D. 1918. *Am. Naturalist*, **52**: 65–94, 209–232, 301–321.
Goodale, H. D. 1938. *Am. Naturalist*, **72**: 243–267.
Goodale, H. D. 1942. *Am. Naturalist*, **76**: 515–519.
Goodwin, K., G. E. Dickerson and W. F. Lamoreux. 1955. *Poultry Sci.*, **34**: 1197.
Goodwin, K., G. E. Dickerson, W. F. Lamoreux, K. Schaaf and W. D. Urban. 1956. *Poultry Sci.*, **35**: 915–924.
Gordon, C., Helen Spurway and P. A. R. Street. 1939. *J. Genet.*, **38**: 37–90.
Gowe, R. S. 1956. *Poultry Sci.*, **35**: 430–435.
Gowe, R. S. and W. J. Wakely. 1954. *Poultry Sci.*, **33**: 691–703.
Gowen, J. W. 1937. *J. Heredity*, **28**: 233–240.
Gowen, J. W., ed. 1952. *Heterosis.* Iowa State College Press.
Graybill, F. A., F. Martin and G. Godfrey. 1956. *Biometrics*, **12**: 99–109.
Graybill, F. A. and W. H. Robertson. 1957. *Poultry Sci.*, **36**: 261–265.
Gregory, P. W. and F. D. Carroll. 1956. *J. Heredity*, **47**: 107–111.
Gregory, W. C. 1956. *Brookhaven Symposium Biol.*, **9**: 177–190.
Griffing, B. 1956. *Heredity*, **10**: 31–50.
Grüneberg, H. 1952. *J. Genet.*, **51**: 95–114.
Guhl, A. M. 1953. *Kansas Agr. Exp. Sta. Tech. Bull.* 73.
Gustafsson, Å. and O. Tedin. 1954. *Acta Agr. Scand.*, **4**: 633–639.
Gutteridge, H. S. and J. B. O'Neil. 1942. *Sci. Agr.*, **22**: 482–491.
Gyles, N. R., G. E. Dickerson, Q. B. Kinder and H. L. Kempster. 1955. *Poultry Sci.*, **34**: 530–539.
Hagberg, A. 1953. *Hereditas*, **39**: 349–380.
Haldane, J. B. S. 1930. *Am. Naturalist*, **64**: 87–90.
Haldane, J. B. S. 1931. *Proc. Cambridge Phil. Soc.*, **27**: 131–136.
Haldane, J. B. S. 1932. *The Causes of Evolution.* Harper.
Haldane, J. B. S. 1946. *Ann. Eugenics*, **13**: 197–205.
Haldane, J. B. S. 1949. *Evolution*, **3**: 51–56.
Haldane, J. B. S. 1954. *Proc. 9th Intern. Congr. Genet.*, **1**: 480–487.
Haldane, J. B. S. 1955. *Proc. Roy. Soc. (London)*, **B144**: 217–220.
Haldane, J. B. S. 1956. *Proc. Roy. Soc. (London)*, **B145**: 306–308.
Haldane, J. B. S. 1957a. *J. Genet.*, **55**: 218–225.
Haldane, J. B. S. 1957b. *Acta Genet. Statis. Med.*, **6**: 321–332.

Haldane, J. B. S.   1958.   *J. Genet.*, **55**: (in press).

Hall, G. O.   1935.   *Poultry Sci.*, **14**: 323–329.

Hardy, G. H.   1908.   *Science*, **28**: 49–50.

Harland, S. C.   1927.   *J. Genet.*, **18**: 55–62.

Haskell, G.   1954.   *Am. Naturalist*, **88**: 5–20.

Hayman, B. I.   1954.   *Genetics*, **39**: 789–809.

Hayman, B. I. and K. Mather.   1953.   *Heredity*, **7**: 165–183.

Hays, F. A. and Ruby Sanborn.   1939.   *Massachusetts Agr. Exp. Sta. Bull.* 307.

Hazel, L. N.   1943.   *Genetics*, **28**: 476–490.

Hazel, L. N., M. L. Baker and C. F. Reinmiller.   1943.   *J. Animal Sci.*, **2**: 118–128.

Hazel, L. N. and W. F. Lamoreux.   1947.   *Poultry Sci.*, **26**: 508–514.

Hazel, L. N. and J. L. Lush.   1942.   *J. Heredity*, **33**: 393–399.

Hazel, L. N. and C. E. Terrill.   1945.   *J. Animal Sci.*, **4**: 347–358.

Heberer, G., ed.   1954.   *Die Evolution der Organismen.*   Fischer.

Henderson, C. R.   1952.   *Heterosis* (Iowa State College Press), 352–370.

Herskowitz, I. H.   1952.   *Bibliography on the Genetics of Drosophila* (*Part 2*).   Commonwealth Agr. Bureaux.

Hexter, W. M.   1955.   *Genetics*, **40**: 444–459.

Hill, J. F. and A. W. Nordskog.   1956.   *Poultry Sci.*, **35**: 256–265.

Hollingsworth, M. J. and J. M. Smith.   1955.   *J. Genet.*, **53**: 295–314.

Horner, T. W., R. E. Comstock and H. F. Robinson.   1955.   *North Carolina Agr. Exp. Sta. Tech. Bull.* 118.

Howes, C. E. and F. B. Hutt.   1952.   *Poultry Sci.*, **31**: 360–365.

Howes, C. E. and F. B. Hutt.   1956.   *Poultry Sci.*, **35**: 1223–1229.

Hull, F. H.   1945.   *J. Am. Soc. Agron.*, **37**: 134–145.

Hurry, H. F. and A. W. Nordskog.   1953.   *Poultry Sci.*, **32**: 18–25.

Hutt, F. B.   1949.   *Genetics of the Fowl.*   McGraw Hill.

Hutt, F. B. and R. K. Cole.   1948.   *Offic. Rept. 8th World's Poultry Congr.*, **1**: 719–725.

Hutt, F. B. and R. K. Cole.   1952.   *Poultry Sci.*, **31**: 365–374.

Hutt, F. B. and R. K. Cole.   1953.   *Science*, **117**: 695–697.

Hutt, F. B. and R. K. Cole.   1954.   *Rept. 10th World's Poultry Congr.*, **2**: 197–201.

Hutt, F. B. and R. K. Cole.   1955.   *Poultry Sci.*, **34**: 271–283.

Huxley, J. S.   1955.   *Heredity*, **9**: 1–52.

Huxley, J. S., A. C. Hardy and E. B. Ford, eds.   1954.   *Evolution as a Process.*   Allen and Unwin.

Hyre, H. M.   1951.   *West Virginia Agr. Exp. Sta. Bull.* 346.

Hyre, H. M.   1955.   *West Virginia Agr. Exp. Sta. Bull.* 381.

Ives, P. T.   1950.   *Evolution*, **4**: 236–252.

Jaap, R. G. and J. F. Grimes.   1956.   *Poultry Sci.*, **35**: 1264–1269.

Jaap, R. G., J. F. Grimes and T. H. Coleman.   1954.   *Rept. 10th World's Poultry Congr.*, **2**: 42–45.

Jenkins, M. T.   1934.   *J. Am. Soc. Agron.*, **26**: 199–204.

Jennings, H. S.   1916.   *Genetics*, **1**: 53–89.

Jerome, F. N., C. R. Henderson and S. C. King.   1956.   *Poultry Sci.*, **35**: 995–1013.

Jerome, F. N., S. J. Slinger, C. M. Huntsman and W. F. Pepper.   1956.   *Poultry Sci.*, **35**: 488–489.

Johnson, A. S. and E. S. Merritt.   1955.   *Poultry Sci.*, **34**: 578–587.

Johnson, H. W., H. F. Robinson and R. E. Comstock.   1955.   *Agron. J.*, **47**: 477–483.

Jull, M. A.   1952.   *Poultry Breeding.*   3rd ed.   Wiley.

Kempthorne, O. 1955a. *Genetics*, **40**: 153–167.
Kempthorne, O. 1955b. *Cold Spring Harbor Symposia Quant. Biol.*, **20**: 60–75.
Kempthorne, O. 1957. *An Introduction to Genetic Statistics.* Wiley.
Kermack, H. A. 1954. *Phil. Trans. Roy. Soc. London*, **B237**: 375–428.
Kerr, W. E. and S. Wright. 1954. *Evolution*, **8**: 293–302.
Kheireldin, M. A. and C. S. Shaffner. 1954. *Poultry Sci.*, **33**: 1064.
Kimura, M. 1955a. *Cold Spring Harbor Symposia Quant. Biol.*, **20**: 33–51.
Kimura, M. 1955b. *Evolution*, **9**: 419–435.
Kimura, M. 1956a. *Evolution*, **10**: 278–287.
Kimura, M. 1956b. *Proc. Nat. Acad. Sci.*, **42**: 336–340.
King, D. F., R. K. Cole, F. B. Hutt and G. J. Cottier. 1952. *Poultry Sci.*, **31**: 1027–1029.
King, J. C. 1955. *Cold Spring Harbor Symposia Quant. Biol.*, **20**: 311–317.
King, S. C. 1954. *Rept. 10th World's Poultry Congr.*, **2**: 20–23.
King, S. C. and J. H. Bruckner. 1952. *Poultry Sci.*, **31**: 1030–1036.
King, S. C. and C. R. Henderson. 1954a. *Poultry Sci.*, **33**: 147–154.
King, S. C. and C. R. Henderson. 1954b. *Poultry Sci.*, **33**: 155–169.
Kislovsky, D. A. 1937. *Bull. Acad. Sci. URSS (Sci. math. nat.)*, **1937**: 121–173.
Knox, C. W. 1954. *Poultry Sci.*, **33**: 1064.
Krueger, W. F., G. E. Dickerson, Q. B. Kinder and H. L. Kempster. 1952. *Poultry Sci.*, **31**: 922–923.
Kushner, H. F. 1941. *Compt. rend. Acad. Sci. URSS*, **30**; 175–177.
Kushner, H. F. and S. V. Kameneva. 1954. *Zhur. Obshcheĭ Biol.*, **15**: 428–438.
Kyle, W. H. and A. B. Chapman. 1953. *Genetics*, **38**: 421–443.
Lambert, W. V. 1935. *Proc. Iowa Acad. Sci.*, **40**: 231–234.
Lamoreux, W. F. and F. B. Hutt. 1948. *Poultry Sci.*, **27**: 334–341.
Lamoreux, W. F., F. B. Hutt and G. O. Hall. 1943. *Poultry Sci.*, **22**: 161–169.
Landauer, W. 1951. *Storrs Agr. Exp. Sta. Bull.* 262.
Landauer, W. 1956. *J. Genet.*, **54**: 219–235.
Lerner, I. M. 1943. *J. Agr. Research*, **67**: 447–457.
Lerner, I. M. 1944. *Growth*, **8**: 33–41.
Lerner, I. M. 1946. *Poultry Sci.*, **25**: 204–209.
Lerner, I. M. 1950. *Population Genetics and Animal Improvement.* Cambridge Univ. Press.
Lerner, I. M. 1951. *Am. Naturalist*, **85**: 365–372.
Lerner, I. M. 1954. *Genetic Homeostasis.* Oliver and Boyd.
Lerner, I. M. 1955. *Am. Naturalist*, **89**: 29–34.
Lerner, I. M., V. S. Asmundson and Dorothy M. Cruden. 1947. *Poultry Sci.*, **26**: 515–524.
Lerner, I. M. and F. H. Bird. 1948. *Poultry Sci.*, **27**: 342–346.
Lerner, I. M. and Dorothy M. Cruden. 1948. *Poultry Sci.*, **27**: 67–78.
Lerner, I. M., Dorothy M. Cruden and L. W. Taylor. 1949. *Poultry Sci.*, **28**: 903–913.
Lerner, I. M. and E. R. Dempster. 1948. *Evolution*, **2**: 19–28.
Lerner, I. M. and E. R. Dempster. 1951a. *Heredity*, **5**: 75–94.
Lerner, I. M. and E. R. Dempster. 1951b. *Poultry Sci.*, **30**: 717–722.
Lerner, I. M. and E. R. Dempster. 1956. *Poultry Sci.*, **35**: 1349–1355.
Lerner, I. M. and C. A. Gunns. 1944. *Poultry Sci.*, **23**: 349–351.
Lerner, I. M. and C. A. Gunns. 1952. *Poultry Sci.*, **31**: 537–544.
Lerner, I. M. and L. N. Hazel. 1947. *Genetics*, **32**: 325–339.
Lerner, I. M., L. W. Taylor and J. R. Beach. 1950. *Poultry Sci.*, **29**: 862–869.

Lerner, I. M., L. W. Taylor and Dorothy C. Lowry. 1951. *Poultry Sci.*, **30**: 748–757.

Le Roy, H. L. and H. Lörtscher. 1955. *Z. Tierzücht. und Züchtungsbiol.*, **66**: 17–37.

Levene, H. 1953. *Am. Naturalist*, **87**: 331–333.

Lewis, D. 1948. *Heredity*, **2**: 219–236.

Lewis, D. 1954. *Heredity*, **8**: 333–356.

Lewontin, R. C. 1956. *Am. Naturalist*, **90**: 237–255.

L'Heritier, P. 1954. *Traité de Génétique*, v. 2. Presse Univ. France.

Li, C. C. 1955a. *Population Genetics*. Univ. Chicago Press.

Li, C. C. 1955b. *Am. Naturalist*, **89**: 281–295.

Li, C. C. 1956. *Biometrics*, **12**: 190–210.

Lillie, R. J., C. W. Knox and H. R. Bird. 1953. *Poultry Sci.*, **32**: 65–69.

Lörtscher, H. 1937. *Z. Zücht.*, **B39**: 257–362.

Lowry, Dorothy, C. 1955. *Biometrics*, **11**: 136–148.

Lowry, Dorothy, I. M. Lerner and L. W. Taylor. 1956. *Poultry Sci.*, **35**: 1034–1043.

Ludwig, W. 1954. *Die Evolution der Organismen* (Fischer), 662–712.

Lush, J. L. 1945. *Animal Breeding Plans*. 3rd ed. Iowa State College Press.

Lush, J. L. 1946. *Am. Naturalist*, **80**: 318–342.

Lush, J. L. 1947. *Am. Naturalist*, **81**: 241–261, 362–379.

Lush, J. L. 1948. *The Genetics of Populations*. (Mimeo notes, Dept. Animal Husbandry, Iowa State College).

Lush, J. L. 1949. *Proc. 8th Intern. Congr. Genet.*, 356–375.

Lush, J. L., W. F. Lamoreux and L. N. Hazel. 1948. *Poultry Sci.*, **27**: 375–388.

Mac Key, J. 1956. *Brookhaven Symposium Biol.*, **9**: 141–152.

Maddison, A. E. 1954. *Proc. Brit. Soc. Animal Prod.*, 109–115.

Malécot, G. 1948. *Les Mathematiques de L'Hérédité*. Masson.

Marble, D. R. 1943. *Poultry Sci.*, **22**: 61–71.

Martin, G. A., E. W. Glazener and W. L. Blow. 1953. *Poultry Sci.*, **32**: 716–720.

Mather, K. 1943. *Biol. Rev.*, **18**: 32–64.

Mather, K. 1949a. *Biometrical Genetics*. Methuen.

Mather, K. 1949b. *Proc. 8th Intern. Congr. Genet.*, 376–401.

Mather, K. 1953. *Symposium Exp. Biol.*, **7**: 66–95.

Mather, K. 1954. *Proc. 9th Intern. Congr. Genet.*, **1**: 106–123.

Mather, K. 1955. *Evolution*, **9**: 52–61.

Mather, K. and B. J. Harrison. 1949. *Heredity*, **3**: 1–52, 131–162.

Matthew, W. D. 1926. *Quart. Rev. Biol.*, **1**: 139–185.

Maw, A. J. G. 1935. *Sci. Agr.*, **16**: 85–112.

Maw, A. J. G. 1949. *Poultry Sci.*, **28**: 499–503.

Mayr, E. 1954. *Evolution as a Process* (Allen and Unwin), 157–180.

Mayr, E. 1955. *Cold Spring Harbor Symposia Quant. Biol.*, **20**: 327–333.

McClary, C. F. and I. M. Lerner. 1950. *Genetics*, **35**: 679.

McClintock, Barbara. 1956. *Cold Spring Harbor Symposia Quant. Biol.*, **21**: 197–216.

McLaren, Anne and D. Michie. 1956. *J. Genet.*, **54**: 440–455.

McLaury, D. W. and A. W. Nordskog. 1956. *Poultry Sci.*, **35**: 582–585.

Merrell, D. J. and J. C. Underhill. 1956. *J. Econ. Entomol.*, **49**: 300–306.

Merritt, E. S. and R. S. Gowe. 1956. *Can. J. Agr. Sci.*, **36**: 72–80.

Michie, D. 1955. *Proc. Roy. Soc. (London)*, **B144**: 241–259.

Michie, D. and Anne McLaren. 1955. *New Biology*, **19**: 48–80.

Milani, R. 1957. *Symposia Genetica*, **5**: 227–240.

Moree, R. 1953. *Science*, **118**: 600–601.

Morley, F. H. W.   1952.   *Australian J. Agr. Research*, **3**: 409–418.
Morley, F. H. W.   1955a.   *Australian J. Agr. Research*, **6**: 77–90.
Morley, F. H. W.   1955b.   *Australian J. Agr. Research*, **6**: 873–881.
Moultrie, F., G. J. Cottier and D. F. King.   1955.   *Poultry Sci.*, **34**: 458–461.
Moultrie, F., G. J. Cottier and D. F. King.   1956.   *Poultry Sci.*, **35**: 1345–1348.
Moultrie, F., D. F. King and G. J. Cottier.   1953a.   *Poultry Sci.*, **32**: 454–461.
Moultrie, F., D. F. King and G. J. Cottier.   1953b.   *Poultry Sci.*, **32**: 935–941.
Mueller, C. D.   1952.   *Poultry Sci.*, **31**: 166–170.
Munro, S. S.   1936.   *Sci. Agr.*, **16**: 591–607.
Nightall, E. W.   1956.   *Poultry Sci.*, **35**: 109–125.
Nordskog, A. W.   1948.   *Poultry Sci.*, **27**: 713–718.
Nordskog, A. W. and F. J. Ghostley.   1954.   *Poultry Sci.*, **33**: 704–715.
Nordskog, A. W. and A. J. Wyatt.   1952.   *Poultry Sci.*, **31**: 1062–1066.
Oliver, M. M., B. B. Bohren and V. L. Anderson.   1957.   *Poultry Sci.*, **36**: 395–402.
Olsen, M. W.   1951.   *Poultry Sci.*, **30**: 180–183.
Olsen, M. W. and S. J. Marsden.   1956.   *Poultry Sci.*, **35**: 674–682.
Osborne, R.   1952.   *Proc. Roy. Soc. Edinburgh*, **B64**: 445–455.
Osborne, R.   1954.   *Proc. Roy. Soc. Edinburgh*, **B65**: 285–298.
Osborne, R.   1957a.   *Heredity*, **11**: 93–116.
Osborne, R.   1957b.   *Proc. Roy. Soc. Edinburgh*, **B66**: 374–393.
Osborne, R. and W. S. B. Paterson.   1952.   *Proc. Roy. Soc. Edinburgh*, **B64**: 456–461.
Parker, J. E., F. F. McKenzie and H. L. Kempster.   1942.   *Missouri Agr. Exp. Sta. Research Bull.* 347.
Pearl R.   1912.   *J. Exp. Zool.*, **13**: 153–268.
Pearl, R.   1915.   *Am. Naturalist*, **49**: 595–608.
Pearson, K.   1931.   *Tables for Statisticians and Biometricians*.   Part II.   Biometric Laboratory, Univ. College.
Pease, M.   1948.   *Offic. Rept. 8th World's Poultry Congr.*, **1**: 33–42.
Pease, M. and F. Dudley.   1954.   *Rept. 10th World's Poultry Congr.*, **2**: 45–49.
Peeler, R. J., E. W. Glazener and W. L. Blow.   1955.   *Poultry Sci.*, **34**: 420–426.
Petrov, S. G.   1935.   *Poultry Sci.*, **14**: 330–339.
Pontecorvo, G.   1955.   *Proc. Roy. Soc. (London)*, **B144**: 171–177.
Prevosti, A.   1955.   *Cold Spring Harbor Symposia Quant. Biol.*, **20**: 294–299.
Rasmuson, Marianne.   1955.   *Acta Zool. (Stockholm)*, **36**: 1–49.
Rasmuson, Marianne.   1956.   *Hereditas*, **42**: 397–414.
Rasmusson, J.   1933.   *Hereditas*, **18**: 245–261.
Reeve, E. C. R.   1953.   *J. Genet.*, **51**: 520–542.
Reeve, E. C. R.   1955.   *Ann. Human Genetics*, **19**: 332–346.
Reeve, E. C. R. and C. H. Waddington, eds.   1952.   *Quantitative Inheritance*.   Agr. Reseach Council.
Reid, W. M.   1955.   *Poultry Sci.*, **34**: 30–35.
Rendel, J. M.   1943.   *Biometrika*, **33**: 48–58.
Rendel, J. M.   1953.   *Am. Naturalist*, **87**: 129–138.
Renwick, J. H.   1956.   *Ann. Human Genet.*, **21**: 159–169.
Rick, C. M.   1950.   *Evolution*, **4**: 110–122.
Robertson, A.   1952.   *Genetics*, **37**: 189–207.
Robertson, A.   1955a.   *Cold Spring Harbor Symposia Quant. Biol.*, **20**: 225–229.
Robertson, A.   1955b.   *Biometrics*, **11**: 95–98.
Robertson, A.   1956.   *J. Genet.*, **54**: 236–248.

Robertson, A. 1957. *Biometrics*, **13**: 442–450.

Robertson, A. and I. M. Lerner. 1949. *Genetics*, **34**: 395–411.

Robertson, F. W. and E. C. R. Reeve. 1952. *J. Genet.*, **50**: 414–448.

Robinson, H. F. and R. E. Comstock. 1955. *Cold Spring Harbor Symposia Quant. Biol.*, **20**: 127–135.

Robinson, H. F., R. E. Comstock and P. H. Harvey. 1955. *Genetics*, **40**: 45–60.

Rokizky, P. 1936. *Uspekhi Zootekhn. Nauk*, **2**: 161–202.

Rosenberg, M. M., J. E. Alicata and A. L. Palafox. 1954. *Poultry Sci.*, **33**: 972–980.

Sakai, K. 1955. *Cold Spring Harbor Symposia Quant. Biol.*, **20**: 137–157.

Sandler, L. and E. Novitski. 1957. *Am. Naturalist*, **91**: 105–110.

Scheinberg, S. L., Helen Ward and A. W. Nordskog. 1953. *Poultry Sci.*, **32**: 504–510.

Schmalhausen, I. I. 1949. *Factors of Evolution*. Blakiston.

Scossiroli, R. E. 1954. *Symposium on Genetics of Population Structure*. UIBS Publ., **B15**: 42–66.

Scossiroli, R. E. 1957. *Ricerca sci.*, **27** (Suppl.): 61–66.

Scossiroli, R. E. and P. Coen. 1958. *Ricerca sci.*, **28** (Suppl.): (in press).

Serebrovskaya, Raisa I. 1935. *Zool. Zhur.*, **14**: 465–480.

Serebrovsky, A. S. 1927. *Zhur. Eksp. Biol.*, **A3**: 62–146.

Serebrovsky, A. S. 1935. *Uspekhi Zootekhn. Nauk*, **1**: 85–140.

Shaklee, W. E. and C. W. Knox. 1956. *J. Heredity*, **47**: 211–212.

Shaklee, W. E. and C. S. Shaffner. 1952. *Poultry Sci.*, **31**: 935.

Sheppard, P. M. 1952. *Heredity*, **6**: 239–241.

Shoffner, R. N. 1948. *Poultry Sci.*, **27**: 448–452.

Shultz, F. T. 1953a. *Heredity*, **7**: 1–21.

Shultz, F. T. 1953b. *Biometrics*, **9**: 336–353.

Shultz, F. T. and W. E. Briles. 1953. *Genetics*, **38**: 34–50.

Siegel, P. B. and C. D. Mueller. 1955. *Poultry Sci.*, **34**: 1445–1446.

Simpson, G. G. 1953. *The Major Features of Evolution*. Columbia Univ. Press.

Skaller, F. 1954a. *Poultry Sci.*, **33**: 29–35.

Skaller, F. 1954b. *Poultry Sci.*, **33**: 316–321.

Skaller, F. 1954c. *Rept. 10th World's Poultry Cong.*, **2**: 59–64.

Skaller, F. and B. L. Sheldon. 1955. *Australian J. Agr. Research*, **6**: 171–185.

Skoglund, W. C. and A. E. Tomhave. 1949. *Delaware Agr. Exp. Sta. Bull.* 278.

Smith, C. A. B. 1957. *Ann. Human Genet.*, **21**: 363–373.

Smith, H. F. 1936. *Ann. Eugenics*, **7**: 240–250.

Smith, H. W. 1956. *Poultry Sci.*, **35**: 701–705.

Smith, J. M., Jean M. Clarke, and M. J. Hollingsworth. 1955. *Proc. Roy. Soc. (London)*, **B144**: 159–171.

Smith, R. M. and W. H. Wiley. 1950. *Arkansas Agr. Exp. Sta. Bull.* 499.

Snyder, E. S. 1945. *Ontario Dept. Agr. Bull.* 446.

Spector, W. S., ed. 1956. *Handbook of Biological Data*. Saunders.

Spurway, Helen. 1955. *J. Genet.*, **53**: 325–362.

Stephenson, A. B., A. J. Wyatt and A. W. Nordskog. 1953. *Poultry Sci.*, **32**: 510–517.

Sturtevant, A. H. 1918. *Carnegie Inst. Wash. Publ.* 264.

Stutts, E. C., W. E. Briles and H. O. Kunkel. 1956. *Poultry Sci.*, **35**: 727–728.

Tantawy, A. O. and E. C. R. Reeve. 1956. *Z. Induktive Abstammungs- und Vererbungslehre*, **87**: 648–667.

Taylor, L. W. 1946. *Poultry Sci.*, **25**: 610–615.

Taylor, L. W. and I. M. Lerner. 1938. *California Agr. Exp. Sta. Bull.* 626.

Taylor, L. W. and I. M. Lerner. 1939. *J. Agr. Research*, **58**: 383–396.

Taylor, L. W., I. M. Lerner, K. B. DeOme and J. R. Beach. 1943. *Poultry Sci.*, **22**: 339–347.

Taylor, L. W., Dorothy C. Lowry and L. G. Raggi. 1955. *Poultry Sci.*, **34**: 1036–1045.

Tebb, G. 1957. *Poultry Sci.*, **36**: 402–405.

Thoday, J. M. 1953. *Symposium Soc. Exp. Biol.*, **7**: 96–113. Cambridge University Press.

Tukey, J. W. 1954. *Statistics and Mathematics in Biology* (Iowa State College Press), 35–66.

Venge, O. 1950. *Acta Zool. (Stockholm)*, **31**: 1–148.

Vetukhiv, M. A. 1953. *Proc. Nat. Acad. Sci.*, **39**: 30–34.

Waddington, C. H. 1942. *Nature*, **150**: 563–565.

Waddington, C. H. 1953a. *Evolution*, **7**: 118–126.

Waddington, C. H. 1953b *Evolution*, **7**: 386–387.

Wallace, B. 1956. *J. Genet.*, **54**: 280–293.

Wallace, B. and J. C. King. 1951. *Am. Naturalist*, **85**: 209–222.

Wallace, B., J. C. King, Carol V. Madden, Bobbie Kaufmann and E. C. McGunnigle. 1953. *Genetics*, **38**: 272–307.

Wallace B. and M. Vetukhiv. 1955. *Cold Spring Harbor Symposia Quant. Biol.*, **20**: 303–309.

Warren, D. C. 1937. *Kansas Agr. Exp. Sta. Tech. Bull.* 44.

Warren, D. C. 1942. *Kansas Agr. Exp. Sta. Tech. Bull.* 52.

Warren, Katherine B., ed. 1955. *Population Genetics: The Nature and Causes of Genetic Variability in Populations.* (Cold Spring Harbor Symposia Quant. Biol., **20**). Long Island Biol. Assoc.

Warren, W. M. and G. E. Dickerson. 1952. *Missouri Agr. Exp. Sta. Research Bull.* 511.

Waters, N. F. 1954. *Rept. 10th World's Poultry Congr.*, **2**: 201–205.

Weber, F. and H. L. Le Roy. 1956. *Arch. Geflügelk.*, **20**: 1–14.

Weinberg, W. 1909. *Z. Induktive Abstammungs- und Vererbungslehre*, **1**: 377–392, 440–460; **2**: 276–330.

White, M. J. D. 1951. *Evolution*, **5**: 376–394.

White, M. J. D. 1957. *Australian J. Zool.*, **5**: 305–337.

Wigan, L. G. and K. Mather. 1942. *Ann. Eugenics*, **11**: 354–364.

Wilson, W. O. and H. Abplanalp. 1956. *Poultry Sci.*, **35**: 532–538.

Winters, L. M. 1952. *Heterosis* (Iowa State College Press), 371–377.

Wood-Gush, D. G. M. 1955. *Brit. J. Animal Behav.*, **3**: 81–110.

Woodworth, C. M., E. R. Leng and R. W. Jugenheimer. 1952. *Agron. J.*, **44**: 60–65.

Wright, S. 1921. *Genetics*, **6**: 111–178.

Wright, S. 1923. *J. Heredity*, **14**: 339–348.

Wright, S. 1931. *Genetics*, **16**: 97–159.

Wright, S. 1932. *Proc. 6th Intern. Congr. Genet.*, **1**: 356–366.

Wright, S. 1935a. *J. Genet.*, **30**: 243–256.

Wright, S. 1935b. *J. Genet.*, **30**: 257–266.

Wright, S. 1939. *Proc. Am. Soc. Animal Production*, **32**: 18–26.

Wright, S. 1940. *Am. Naturalist*, **74**: 232–248.

Wright, S. 1945. *Ecology*, **26**: 415–419.

Wright, S. 1950. *Moderne Biologie* (Peters), 275–287.

Wright, S. 1951. *Ann. Eugenics*, **15**: 323–354.
Wright, S. 1952. *Quantitative Inheritance* (Agr. Research Council), 5–41.
Wright, S. 1955. *Cold Spring Harbor Symposia Quant. Biol.*, **20**: 16–24.
Wright, S. 1956. *Am. Naturalist*, **90**: 5–24.
Wyatt, A. J. 1953. *Poultry Sci.*, **32**: 400–405.
Wyatt, A. J. 1954. *Poultry Sci.*, **33**: 1266–1274.
Yamada, Y. 1955. *Ann. Rept. Jap. Nat. Inst. Genet.*, **5**: 27–28.
Yoon, C. H. 1955. *Genetics*, **40**: 297–309.

Index of Names

Abplanalp, H., 149, 151, 187, 192–193, 200, 257, 265, 274, 283
Albada, M. van, 264, 274
Alicata, J. E., 242, 282
Allen, C. J., 264, 274
Allison, A. C., 103, 274
Anderson, E., 30, 274
Anderson, V. L., 68, 187, 240, 275, 281
Arvidson, R. B., 187, 274
Asmundson, V. S., 149, 151, 182, 227, 257, 274, 279

Bader, R. S., 100, 274
Baker, M. L., 149, 278
Bastian, J. W., 264, 274
Bateson, W., 19, 44, 226
Beach, J. R., 230, 244, 279, 283
Bell, A. E., 214, 217–218, 242, 274
Benzer, S., 20, 274
Berg, Raisa, 98, 274
Bernstein, F., 87, 274
Bird, F. H., 201, 279
Bird, H. R., 247, 280
Blow, W. L., 94, 149, 185, 211, 263, 274, 277, 280–281
Blunn, C. T., 270, 276
Blyth, Janet S. S., 183, 196, 211, 250, 264, 274
Bohren, B. B., 68, 187, 240, 274–275, 281
Bonnier, G., 264, 274
Bostian, C. H., 211, 277
Brieger, F. G., 217, 274
Briles, W. E., 72, 75, 103, 264, 274, 282
Brncic, D., 85, 274

Brown, R., 271, 274
Bruckner, J. H., 211, 279
Brunson, C. C., 256, 274
Buri, P., 104, 274
Burmester, B. R., 166, 244, 246, 274
Buzzati-Traverso, A. A., 85, 248, 266–267, 271, 274–275

Cain, A. J., 76, 275
Campbell, J. G., 242, 275
Card, L. E., 227
Carmon, J. L., 221–223, 275
Carroll, F. D., 241, 277
Caspari, E., 42, 275
Castle, W. E., 270, 275
Chai, C. K., 166, 275
Champion, L. R., 242, 264, 274–275
Chapman, A. B., 154, 170, 270, 275–276, 279
Chetverikov, S. S., 42, 70, 144, 204, 275
Clark, T. B., 255, 275
Clarke, Jean M., 98, 213, 275, 282
Clayton, G., 147, 154–155, 261, 275
Clough, Margaret, 87, 100, 275
Cochez, L. P., 187, 275
Cock, A. G., 87, 100, 103, 275
Cockerham, C. C., 48, 60, 221–223, 275
Coen, P., 242, 282
Cohen, C., 103, 275
Cole, L. J., 227
Cole, R. K., 190, 202, 211, 242–243, 245, 278–279
Coleman, T. H., 211, 275, 278
Coles, R., 242, 275

Comstock, R. E., 49, 52, 66, 102, 118, 211, 216–218, 221–223, 271, 275, 277–278, 282
Coonen, C. P., 153, 275
Cottier, C. J., 195–196, 202, 211, 242, 246, 279, 281
Craft, W. A., 270, 275
Crittenden, L. B., 68, 240, 275
Crow, J. F., 11, 66, 92, 104, 108, 217, 271, 275
Cruden, Dorothy M., 87, 149, 151, 182, 237, 257, 275, 279
    See also Lowry, Dorothy C.
Cunningham, C. J., 255, 275

Danielli, J. F., 271, 274
Darlington, C. D., 34, 97, 275
Darwin, C. R., 1, 5, 34, 42, 76, 85, 92, 99, 144, 146, 174, 273, 275
Davenport, C. B., 227
Dearstyne, R. S., 211, 277
Demerec, M., 42, 275
Dempster, E. R., 14, 51, 67, 75, 101, 117–118, 133–135, 139, 146, 152, 155, 184, 190–191, 193, 228, 233–234, 236–237, 262, 276, 279
DeOme, K. B., 244, 283
Dickerson, G. E., 117, 134, 148, 183, 193, 211, 214, 217–218, 223, 252, 262, 270, 275–277, 279, 283
Dobzhansky, Th., 3, 5, 13, 33–34, 70, 75, 85, 100, 103, 105, 108, 198, 218, 272–273, 276
Donald, H. P., 102, 216, 276
Dryden, J., 226
Dubinin, N. P., 42, 68, 71, 212, 276
Dudley, F., 211, 281
Dunn, L. C., 71, 227, 241, 276
Düzgüneş, O., 92–93, 187, 276

East, E. M., 102, 271, 276
Emerson, S., 102, 276
Essary, E. O., 211, 276

Falconer, D. S., 109, 114, 120, 145, 197, 200–201, 266, 270, 276
Farnsworth, G. M. Jr., 186, 276
Fischer, H., 68, 276

Fisher, R. A., 11, 20–21, 23, 78, 87, 113, 145, 272–273, 276–277
Fontes, A. F., 246, 274
Ford, E. B., 76, 271, 277–278
Fox, T. W., 216, 277
Francis, D. W., 242, 277
Fraps, R. M., 264, 277

Galton, F., 273
Garber, M. J., 103, 274
Garrison, F. H., 153
Gershenson, S., 68
Ghostley, F. J., 211, 281
Gilmour, D. E., 103, 277
Glazener, E. W., 94, 149, 185, 211, 263, 274, 277, 280–281
Godfrey, E. F., 216, 256, 277
Godfrey, G. F., 59, 120, 146, 149, 242, 255–256, 274, 277
Goff, O. E., 211, 276
Goldschmidt, R., 4, 270, 277
Goodale, H. D., 227, 248, 270, 277
Goodman, B. L., 120, 146, 149, 255–256, 274, 277
Goodwin, K., 214, 262, 277
Gordon, C., 68, 277
Gowe, R. S., 201–202, 277, 280
Gowen, J. W., 103, 199, 241, 271, 277
Graybill, F. A., 59, 277
Greenwood, A. W., 227
Gregory, P. W., 241, 277
Gregory, W. C., 266, 277
Griffing, B., 61, 277
Grimes, J. C., 174, 276
Grimes, J. F., 211, 257, 278
Grüneberg, H., 68, 277
Guhl, A. M., 266, 277
Gunns, C. A., 81–82, 133, 279
Gustafsson, Å., 266, 277
Gutteridge, H. S., 202, 277
Gyles, N. R., 134, 277

Hagberg, A., 271, 277
Haldane, J. B. S., 5, 12, 20, 23–24, 44, 75, 78, 81–82, 102–103, 114, 122, 147–148, 267, 272–273, 277–278
Hall, G. O., 228, 278–279
Halpin, J. G., 227
Hannah, Aloha, 270, 277

Hardy, A. C., 271, 278
Hardy, G. H., 18, 32, 46, 73, 271–272, 278
Harland, S. C., 239, 278
Harrison, B. J., 145, 261, 270, 280
Harvey, P. H., 52, 217–218, 282
Haskell, G., 145, 278
Hayman, B. I., 61, 87, 95, 212, 278
Hays, F. A., 227–228, 278
Hazel, L. N., 68, 89, 117, 145, 149, 154–155, 166, 177–179, 181, 193, 228, 243, 246, 260, 276, 278–280
Heberer, G., 271, 278
Henderson, C. R., 52, 61, 149, 187, 271, 278–279
Herskowitz, I. H., 98, 278
Hexter, W. M., 102, 278
Hill, J. F., 186, 202, 278
Hollingsworth, M. J., 75, 213, 278, 282
Horner, T. W., 49, 66, 278
Howes, C. E., 247, 278
Hull, F. H., 78, 217, 278
Huntsman, C. M., 257, 278
Hurry, H. F., 257, 278
Hutt, F. B., 190, 201–202, 211, 226–228, 242–243, 245, 247, 251, 256, 278–279
Huxley, J. S., 76, 271, 278
Hyre, H. M., 242, 246, 257, 278

Immer, F. R., 78, 276
Ives, P. T., 99, 278

Jaap, R. G., 211, 257, 275, 278
Jenkins, M. T., 221–223, 278
Jennings, H. S., 271, 278
Jerome, F. N., 52, 61, 149, 257, 278
Johannsen, W., 19, 37
Johnson, A. S., 149, 278
Johnson, H. W., 271, 278
Johnson, L. W., 103, 274
Jones, D. F., 271, 276
Jucci, C., 271, 275
Jugenheimer, R. W., 271, 283
Jull, M. A., 94, 146, 226–227, 242, 247, 251, 256, 278

Kameneva, S. V., 68, 279
Kaufmann, Bobbie, 42, 283

Kempster, H. L., 134, 183, 211, 264, 276–277, 279, 281
Kempthorne, O., 48, 50, 52, 72, 87, 182, 272, 279
Kermack, H. A., 148, 279
Kerr, W. E., 104, 279
Kheireldin, N. A., 242, 279
Kimura, M., 11, 15, 71, 75, 104, 275, 279
Kinder, Q. B., 134, 183, 211, 276–277, 279
King, D. F., 195–196, 202, 211, 242, 246, 279, 281
King, J. C., 42, 267, 269–270, 279, 283
King, J. W. B., 197, 266, 270, 276
King, S. C., 52, 61, 149, 186–187, 211, 216, 277–279
Kish, A. F., 242, 277
Kislovsky, D. A., 65, 279
Knight, G. R., 147, 275
Knox, C. W., 211, 227, 247, 258, 264, 280, 282
Kottman, R. M., 270, 276
Krider, J. L., 270, 276
Krueger, W. F., 103, 183, 211, 274, 276, 279
Kunkel, H. O., 264, 282
Kushner, H. F., 68, 263, 279
Kyle, W. H., 154, 170, 279

Lambert, W. V., 227, 243, 279
Lamoreux, W. F., 68, 166, 201, 214, 228, 243, 246, 262, 277–280
Landauer, W., 72, 227, 240, 279
Latyszewski, M., 201, 276
Leng, E. R., 271, 283
Lerner, I. M., 14, 42, 55, 61, 67–68, 79–83, 87, 89, 95–98, 100–101, 117–118, 131, 133–135, 139, 145–146, 149, 151–152, 154, 166, 182, 184, 190, 193, 200–201, 204, 216, 228, 230–231, 233–234, 236–237, 243–244, 250, 252, 254, 257, 264, 276, 279–280, 282–283
Le Roy, H. L., 44, 58, 280, 283
Levene, H., 75, 103, 276, 280
Lewis, D., 99, 102, 280
Lewontin, R. C., 100–101, 280

L'Heritier, P., 272, 280
Li, C. C., 23–24, 32, 54, 74–75, 107, 280
Lillie, R. J., 247, 280
Lörtscher, H., 58, 189, 280
Lowry, Dorothy C., 52, 146, 152, 200–201, 228, 231, 234, 236–237, 242–243, 254, 276, 280, 283
  See also Cruden, Dorothy M.
Ludwig, W., 272, 280
Lush, J. L., 24, 48, 58, 68, 88, 153, 155, 157, 161, 165, 177–179, 186, 243, 246, 260, 270, 272, 275, 278, 280
Lysenko, T. D., 268

MacArthur, J. W., 270
MacDowell, E. C., 271
Mac Key, J., 266, 280
Madden, Carol, 42, 283
Maddison, A. E., 184, 280
Malécot, G., 272, 280
Marble, D. R., 253, 280
Marsden, S. J., 268, 281
Martin, F., 59, 277
Martin, G. A., 185, 280
Mather, K., 6, 38–40, 51–52, 57, 85, 87, 95, 97, 145, 147, 212, 261, 270–271, 275, 278, 280, 283
Matthew, W. D., 148, 280
Maw, A. J. G., 211, 255, 280
May, H. G., 271
Mayr, E., 35, 103, 108, 268–269, 280
McClary, C. F., 166, 252, 280
McClintock, Barbara, 21, 280
McGunnigle, E. C., 42, 283
McKenzie, F. F., 264, 281
McLaren, Anne, 98, 100, 280
McLaury, D. W., 93, 280
Mendel, J. G., 19, 273
Merrell, D. J., 270, 280
Merritt, E. S., 149, 202, 278, 280
Michie, D., 98, 100, 148, 280
Milani, R., 270, 280
Moore, C. H., 214, 217–218, 274
Moree, R., 84, 280
Morgan, T. H., 19
Morley, F. H. W., 85, 152, 272, 281
Morris, J. A., 147, 154–155, 275
Morton, N. E., 104, 108, 275

Moultrie, F., 195–196, 211, 242, 246, 281
Mountney, G. J., 211, 276
Mueller, C. D., 211, 265, 281–282
Munro, S. S., 64, 281

Nightall, E. W., 242, 281
Nordskog, A. W., 93, 119, 185–186, 193–194, 202, 211, 257, 276, 278, 280–282
Novitski, E., 71, 282

Oliver, M. M., 187, 281
Olsen, M. W., 265, 268, 281
O'Neil, J. B., 202, 277
Osborne, R., 59, 158, 164, 173–176, 191, 200, 281

Palafox, A. L., 242, 282
Parker, J. E., 264, 281
Paterson, W. S. B., 59, 281
Pavlovsky, Olga, 105, 108, 276
Payne, F., 271
Pearl, R., 227–228, 270, 281
Pearson, K., 113, 281
Pease, M., 103, 211, 281
Peeler, R. J., 149, 263, 281
Pepper, W. F., 257, 278
Pero, R., 187, 275
Petrov, S. G., 228, 281
Piternick, Leonie K., 270, 277
Poisson, S. D., 104
Pontecorvo, G., 50, 102, 281
Prevosti, A., 147, 149, 281
Punnett, R. C., 226

Quisenberry, J. H., 216, 277

Raggi, L. G., 242–243, 283
Rapp, G. D., 187, 274
Rasmuson, Marianne, 217, 270–271, 281
Rasmusson, J., 51, 281
Reeve, E. C. R., 65, 87, 149, 270–271, 281–282
Reid, W. M., 242, 281
Reinmiller, C. F., 149, 278
Rendel, J. M., 81, 85, 281
Renwick, J. H., 147, 281
Rice, J. E., 226

Rick, C. M., 99, 281
Roberts, E., 227
Robertson, A., 68, 82–84, 89, 97–98, 109, 116, 125, 144, 147, 154–155, 193–194, 196, 219, 243, 261, 275–276, 281–282
Robertson, F. W., 270, 282
Robertson, W. H., 59, 277
Robinson, H. F., 49, 52, 66, 217–218, 271, 278, 282
Rokizky, P., 261, 282
Rosenberg, M. M., 242, 282

Sakai, K., 266, 282
Sanborn, Ruby, 228, 278
Sandler, L., 71, 282
Schaaf, K., 214, 277
Scheinberg, S. L., 186, 282
Schmalhausen, I. I., 6, 144, 282
Scossiroli, R. E., 65, 242, 261, 266–267, 270, 282
Serebrovskaya, Raisa, 261, 282
Serebrovsky, A. S., 70, 282
Shaffner, C. S., 242, 279, 282
Shaklee, W. E., 258, 264, 282
Sheldon, B. L., 200, 282
Sheppard, P. M., 76, 84, 275, 282
Shoffner, R. N., 94, 282
Shultz, F. T., 72, 75, 94, 103, 213–215, 253, 282
Siegel, P. B., 265, 282
Sierk, C. F., 270, 275
Simpson, G. G., 4, 6, 282
Skaller, F., 187, 200, 210–211, 282
Skoglund, W. C., 166, 282
Slinger, S. J., 257, 278
Smith, C. A. B., 59, 282
Smith, H. F., 145, 181, 282
Smith, H. W., 242, 282
Smith, J. M., 75, 98, 213, 275, 278, 282
Smith, R. M., 211, 282
Snyder, E. S., 251, 282
Snyder, L. A., 51, 276
Spector, W. S., 64, 282
Spencer, H., 85
Spurway, Helen, 14, 68, 277, 282
Stephenson, A. B., 119, 282
Stewart, H. A., 221–223, 275
Street, P. A. R., 68, 277
Sturtevant, A. H., 270, 282

Stutts, E. C., 264, 282

Tantawy, A. O., 65, 282
Taylor, L. W., 79–80, 200–201, 227–228, 230–231, 242–244, 250, 252, 254, 264, 279–280, 282–283
Tebb, G., 94, 187, 236, 283
Tedin, O., 78, 266, 276–277
Terrill, C. E., 89, 270, 275, 278
Thoday, J. M., 101, 283
Timofeeff-Ressovsky, N. W., 42, 271, 275
Tomhave, A. E., 166, 282
Trulsson, S., 264, 274
Tukey, J. W., 54, 283

Underhill, J. C., 270, 280
Urban, W. D., 214, 277

Venge, O., 166, 283
Vetukhiv, M. A., 33, 85, 269, 283

Waddington, C. H., 9, 81, 100, 268, 271, 281, 283
Wakely, W. J., 202, 277
Wallace, B., 33, 42, 100, 103, 267, 269, 276, 283
Walter, W. G., 246, 274
Ward, Helen, 186, 282
Warren, D. C., 214, 217–218, 227, 257–258, 274, 283
Warren, Katherine B., 271, 283
Warren, W. M., 223, 283
Warwick, E. J., 270, 276
Waters, N. F., 166, 227, 242, 244, 274, 283
Weber, F., 44, 283
Weinberg, W., 18, 32, 46, 73, 271–272, 283
Whatley, J. A., Jr., 270, 276
White, M. J. D., 34, 75, 283
Wigan, L. G., 145, 283
Wiley, W. H., 211, 282
Wilson, W. O., 265, 283
Winters, L. M., 118, 210–270, 275, 283
Wood-Gush, D. M., 266, 283
Woodworth, C. M., 271, 283
Woolf, B., 120

Wright, S., 5, 20, 23, 32–33, 47, 51,
    54–55, 57, 65–66, 68, 71, 73,
    78, 86–87, 90–91, 104–105, 108,
    123, 145, 155, 216, 272–273,
    279, 283–284
Wyatt, A. J., 119, 149, 181, 193–194,
    221, 281–283

Yamada, Y., 149, 283
Yao, T. S., 187, 276
Yates, F., 113, 277
Yoon, C. H., 100, 283

Zarrow, M. X., 264, 274
Zeleny, C., 271

Subject Index

Abnormal segregation ratio, 71, 241
Acquired characters, 9
Adaptive peaks, 73
Adaptive traits, as part of total phenotype, 13
Additively genetic value, *see* Genetic value
Additively genetic variance, *see* Genetic variance
Affinity, 148
Age structure of breeding population, in selecting for egg production, 118, 184
   related to selection response, 117
All-or-none traits, 19, 38
   epistatic variance of, 67
   examples of selection for, 130, 131, 244, 245
   heritability of, 68
Allele as a unit of hereditary transmission, 21
Allelic frequency, and dominance deviations, 47
   and the partitioning of genotypic variance, 48
   changes under selection, 23, 25
   distribution of, 105, 106
   effect of on selection coefficients, 24, 99
   equilibrium values of, 74, 76, 77, 78
   in a gene pool, 17
   sampling error of, 105, 107
Artificial selection, antagonistic to natural selection, 97, 125, 142
   as a purposeful process, 10

Artificial selection, by truncation, 7, 12
   confounded with natural selection, 12
   differs from natural selection, 10
   effects of on fitness, 127, 141
   efficiency of relative to natural selection, 14
   for broodiness, 11
   overefficient, 14
   purposes of, 109
   synergistic with natural selection, 10
Asymmetry of selection response, 119
   causes of, 121

Balance, between selection and mutation, 32, 73
   genetic, 39
   internal, 39
   of evolutionary forces, 73
   phenotypic, 144, 204
   polygenic, 40
   relational, 39
Balance sheet of hereditary variation, 85
Behavior, genetics of, 266
Biochemical approach to selection, 263
Biological organization, levels of, 2, 4
Biometric relations, between parents and offspring, 53
   between sibs, 53
   under inbreeding, 55
   underlying combined selection, 160, 169
   underlying family selection, 160
   underlying selection indexes, 160

Blood groups, advantage of heterozygotes for, 103
in chickens, 72, 75, 103, 264
Breeding population, structure of, in combined selection, 193
in family selection, 164
in selection for egg production, 118, 184
optimum, 191
related to selection response, 117
Broodiness, 239
hypothetical selection for, 11

C effects, see Environment, non-random
Canalization of development, 100
Coadaptation, 144, 225, 269, 278
and genetic homeostasis, 98
and luxuriance, 218
Darwin's usage of, 34
described, 33
following release of new variability, 95
in breeding practice, 205
in isolates, 108
internal, 34
levels of, 34
relational, 34
under selection, 110
Collective homeostasis, 100
Combined selection, and structure of breeding population, 193
biometric basis of, 160, 169
described, 169
efficiency of, 170, 174, 175
theory of, 169
weighting factors in, 171, 172, 173
Combining ability, see Selection, for cross-performance
Competition, interspecific, 13
Competitive ability, 265
Complementary dominance, 102
Complementary genes, 46
Controlling elements, 21
Corrections in selection, 187, 188
Correlated response, 42, 142, 146
causes of, 147
expectation of, 150
facultative, 147
illustrated, 143, 145, 146, 151
obligate, 145

Correlated response, quantitative aspects of, 145, 150
theoretical basis of, 145
Correlation of traits, between egg number and egg weight, 180, 183, 250
between egg number and viability, 146
between part and full egg production records, 147
consequences of, 148
evolutionary significance of, 148
origin of, 148
see also Correlated response
Crossbreeding, extent of in the United States, 198
for meat production, 258
legally defined, 206
literature on, 211
rotational, 210, 222
Cyclic selection, 75, 260
Cytoplasmic effects, 9, 20, 52, 165

Developmental homeostasis, model of, 101
Diallel crossing, 61
Directed evolutionary processes, 33
Directional selection, 6
concurrent with inbreeding, 94
interfered with by overdominance, 95
see also Artificial selection, Selection, etc.
Disassortative mating, 29, 84
Disease resistance, as an object of selection, 225
genetic basis of in poultry, 243
inheritance of, 241
of strain crosses, 214
Disruptive selection, 6
Domestication, 14, 239
Dominance, and allelic frequency, 47
and mutation rate, 98
defined, 45
merging into epistasis, 50
symbolization of, 78
Duplicate genes, 46
Dynamic selection, 6

Environment, changes of under domestication, 15

Environment, choice of by organisms, 14
  constancy of in experiments, 13
  defined, 71
  effects of on genotype, 9
  in relation to selection efficiency, 201
  non-random, 52, 54, 59, 165, 172
Environmental variance, as a component of phenotypic variance, 43
  changes in, 63, 102
  in relation to developmental homeostasis, 101
  of heterozygotes, 100
  partitioning of, 52
  under intense selection, 122
  under stabilizing selection, 109
Epistasis, and selection between inbred lines, 216
  defined, 45
  deviations due to, 47
  in all-or-none traits, 67
  in Bateson's usage, 45
  in traits with intermediate optima, 66
  interaction between heterozygotes, 75
  merging into dominance, 50
  partitioning of variance caused by, 45, 46, 47

Family, defined, 156
  genetic relation within, 157, 164
  standard deviation of average for, 158, 162
Family selection, and structure of breeding populations, 164, 193
  biometric basis of, 160
  efficiency of, 107, 163, 164, 167, 168, 175, 192
  expected gains from, 158
  on basis of progeny tests, 157
  theory of, 158
  under inbreeding, 161, 175
  when C effects are present, 167, 168
Family size, 162, 191, 192
Fitness, decline under selection of, 11, 146
  in relation to metric traits, 98
  in the Darwinian sense, 10
  measurement of, 10
  of artificially selected populations, 97, 126, 141, 237

Fitness, of heterozygotes, 100, 103
  rate of increase of under natural selection, 11
  under domestication, 239
  under inbreeding, 92
  when selection is suspended, 126, 137, 261

Gametic selection, 24
Gene, functions of, 21
  in current usage, 20, 36
  in Johannsen's usage, 19, 37
  operational features of, 37
Gene census, 70
Gene interaction, 42, 47, 49
Gene frequency, see Allelic frequency
Gene pool, coadaptation of, 33
  defined, 15
  in equilibrium, 32
  relation of to Mendelian population, 15
  schematic representation of, 17
  specification of in terms of allelic frequencies, 18
Genetic assimilation, 9, 268
Genetic correlation, and correlated response, 145
  attempts to modify, 263
  in index selection, 183
  in selection, 174
  literature on, 149
  origin of, 148
  statistical determination of, 149
Genetic homeostasis, and coadaptation, 98
  and heterozygosity, 98, 100
  as a by-product of individual homeostasis, 100
  model of, 96
  Robertson's analysis of, 83
Genetic inertia, 97
Genetic relationship, measurement of, 55, 88
  within families, 157, 164
  within inbred lines, 157
Genetic revolution, 35
Genetic value, defined, 21
Genetic variability, and disassortative mating, 84
  cryptic, 70

Genetic variability, exhaustion of, 111, 123, 197
  free, 40
  maintenance of, 71, 75, 83, 85, 264
  potential, 40
Genetic variance, and population size, 72
  converted to non-additive type, 123
  defined, 45
  due to sex-linked loci, 59
  of family averages, 158
  under inbreeding, 89
  under selection, 85
Genotype-environment correlation, 43
Genotype-environment interaction, and heterozygosity, 204
  and intense selection, 122
  defined, 43
  in poultry breeding practice, 200
  interfering with selection response, 123
Genotypic frequency, affected by inbreeding, 18
  and heterozygote superiority, 29
  changes in under selection, 25
  in Mendelian populations, 17
Genotypic selection, 5
Genotypic value, defined, 22
Genotypic variance, as a component of phenotypic variance, 43
  differs from genetic variance, 45
  partitioning of, 45, 48, 50

Hardy-Weinberg formula, see Population equilibrium
Heritability, changes of under selection, 65
  effect of on selection response, 62, 124, 155
  effective, 61
  in presence of genotype-environment interaction, 158, 161, 203
  of aggregate traits, 183
  of all-or-none traits, 67
  of family averages, 158, 161
  of multiple observations, 186
  sampling variance of, 59
  within inbred lines, 55, 59
Heritability estimates, biases in, 59, 60, 61

Heritability estimates, confidence limits of, 59
  corrected for inbreeding, 89
  for various traits, 64, 134, 236, 240, 242
  from diallel crosses, 61
  techniques of arriving at, 58
Heterosis, biochemical basis of, 102
  cumulative, 75
  in breeding practice, 198, 205
  literature on, 211
  origin of, 103
  produced by overdominance, 92
Heterozygote superiority, and allelic frequency equilibrium, 74
  and genotypic frequencies, 29
  and the homeostatic model, 83, 96, 100
  cumulative, 75
  in chickens, 103
  in humans, 103
  in phenodeviant inheritance, 68
  interference of, with directional selection, 95
    with inbreeding, 87, 95, 212
  of lethals, 77, 241
  selection curve for, 29
  see also Overdominance
Heterozygosity, and environmental variance, 100
  and fitness, 103
  enforcement of, 72
  in genotype-environment interaction, 204
  see also Genetic variability
Homeostatic strength, 97, 194
Hybridization, 30, 268

Immunogenetic approach to selection, 264
Inbred lines, and epistasis, 216
  genetic relationship within, 157
  legal definition of, 206
  selection between, 209, 214
  see also Inbreeding and Incrossbreeding
Inbreeding, affected by, domestication, 15
    population size, 91, 105
  and crises in reproduction, 213

Inbreeding, and family selection, 161, 175
as cause of decay of variability, 86
concurrent with selection, 94, 215, 216
corrections for, in heritability estimation, 89
in selection, 187
development of tolerance to, 99
effect of, on correlations between relatives, 55, 89
on genetic variability, 89
on genotypic frequencies, 18
on heritability, 55, 59
on selection response, 119
increase in homozygosity under, 90
interfered with by overdominance, 87, 95, 212
rate of, in commercial practice, 212
under intense selection, 122
Inbreeding coefficient, and genotypic frequencies, 18
changes of in a selected population, 91
computation of, 87
correlation between dams and daughters, 190
defined, 55, 86
under different mating systems, 90
Inbreeding depression, cause of, 92
causing asymmetrical selection response, 121
expressed by phenodeviants, 68
genetic basis of, 66
in poultry, 93
linearity of, 94, 119
of fitness, 92
of fitness components, 93, 98
Incrossbreeding, and combining ability, 219
commercial soundness of, 216
experimental results on, 215, 216
legally defined, 207
literature on, 211
prediction of results of, 220
schematized representation of, 209, 212
Index selection, and overdominance, 217
biometric basis of, 160, 181

Index selection, described, 177
efficiency of, 179, 182
experimentally tested, 257
illustrated, 178
in crossbreeding, 223
theory of, 181
see also Selection index
Individual homeostasis, 100
Intense selection, 122
Interaction, between genes, 42, 44, 45, 47, 50
of genotype and environment, 43, 122, 123, 200, 204
Intergeneration interval, 117
Intermediate optimum, Robertson's analysis of, 83
Wright's model of, 65
Intermittent selection, 260
Interpopulation selection, 24, 205, 213, 216
combined with intrapopulation selection, 30
schematic representation of, 31, 208, 209
Introgression, 30
Isoalleles, 18

Lethals, controlled by single genes, 41
elimination of, 240
in chickens, 240
maintained by heterozygote superiority, 77, 241
Linkage, and selection, 71
as cause of correlated response, 147
effect of on phenotypic variance components, 60
see also Correlated response and Polygenic blocks
Luxuriance, 198, 218

Macroevolution, 4, 267
Mass selection, see Artificial selection, etc.
Maternal effects, 9, 52, 165, 174
and estimation of heritability, 59
causing asymmetrical selection response, 121
examples of, 166
Meiotic drive, 71
Mendelian algebra, 15

Mendelian algebra, units of, 36
Mendelian inheritance, particulate nature of, 19
Mendelian population, as a coadapted entity, 33
  defined, 3
  genetic biography of, 14
  integration of, 34
  relation of to gene pool, 15
  schematic representation of, 17
  specification of, 18
Mesoevolution, 5
Microevolution, 4
Migration, 30, 31, 266
Modifiers, 71
Morphism, 6, 76, 80
Multiple-factor inheritance, 38
Multiple objectives, selection for, 124, 176
Mutation, 9, 21, 36
  artificial induction of, 261, 266, 267
  balancing selection, 32, 73
  interfering with selection response, 124
  maintaining genetic variability, 71
  role of, in selection, 30
Mutation rate, and dominance, 98
  variability of, 99
Mutual selection, 34

Natural selection, against lethals, 240
  antagonistic to artificial selection, 97, 125, 142
  attenuating the selection differential, 138
  based on total phenotype, 13
  defined, by Darwin, 5
    by Wright, 5, 33
  differs from artificial selection, 14
  efficiency of relative to artificial selection, 14
  for broodiness, 11
  for intermediate phenotypes, 81
  fundamental theorem of, 11
  measurement of, 114
  synergistic with artificial selection, 110
Normalizing selection, 81
Nutritional requirements, genetic differences in, 247

Overdominance, and genetic homeostasis, 98
  as cause of heterosis, 92
  based on multiple pathways, 102
  biochemical basis of, 102
  defined, 75
  equilibrium under, 74, 78
  evidence of, 102
  in breeding practice, 206
  maintaining lethals, 77
  origin of, 103
  schematic representation of, 49
  see also Heterozygote superiority

Partitioning, of environmental variance, 52
  of epistatic interactions, 45, 46, 47
  of genotypic variance, 45, 48, 50
  of phenotypic variance, 43, 51
Phenodeviants, crooked toes as an example of, 68
  described, 68
  in a poultry flock, 72
  under inbreeding, 68, 212
Phenotype determined by genotype and environment, 8
Phenotypic distributions, continuous vs. discontinuous, 19
Phenotypic selection, 5
Phenotypic variance, partitioning of, 43, 51
Physiological approach to selection, 260, 264
Physiological limits, 121
Pleiotropy, as cause of correlated response, 146
  obligate on phenotypic level, 42
Polyallel crossing, 61
Polygenic blocks, acting as Mendelian units, 41
  in balanced genotypes, 39
  maintained by selection, 71
  pleiotropic effects of, 42
  properties of, 37
Polygenic inheritance, and correlated response, 145
  and major genes, 42
  conversion of to monogenic inheritance, 41
  defined, 38

Polygenic inheritance, Mather's theory of, 39
Polymorphism, 6, 76, 80
Population equilibrium, 18, 73
defined, 32
under selection, 79
when heterozygotes are favored by selection, 74, 76
Population genetics, historical literature of, 271
in relation to other disciplines, 3
levels of, 4
Population size, and genetic variability, 72
and inbreeding, 91, 105
and the selection differential, 194
effect of on selection efficiency, 193
effective, 104
Progeny testing, antiquity of, 153
as a method of family selection, 157
Protective genes, 72
Pseudo-overdominance, 75

Quasi-continuous variation, 68

Random drift, 104
interacting with selection, 108
Random evolutionary processes, 33
Recurrent reciprocal selection, 209, 218
Repeatability, 185, 202
Reproductive rate, and enforcement of heterozygosity, 72
and structure of breeding populations, 191
effect of on selection progress, 25, 28
Reversed selection, 13, 75

Scale transformation, 56
Segregating units, number of, 51
Selection, against heterozygotes, 75
against phenodeviants, 69
and fitness, 11, 97, 126, 237
as synonym for choice, 5
balancing mutation, 32, 73
by independent culling levels, 177
concurrent with inbreeding, 215, 216
defined, 5
effect of, on genetic correlations, 152
on genetic variability, 71, 85
on heritability, 65

Selection, for all-or-none traits, 130, 131, 244, 245
for close linkage, 71
for cross-performance, 209, 217, 220, 221
for dominant alleles, 27
for heterozygotes, 29, 68, 74, 76, 95
for long-range objectives, 124, 176
for recessive alleles, 28
for record-breaking individuals, 110
for sex-limited traits, 158, 163, 176
in a gene pool, 17
in absence of dominance, 26
interacting with drift, 108
maintaining genetic variability, 71, 74, 78, 83
under conditions of stress, 265
using corrections, 187, 188
with a constant tester, 219
Selection accuracy, 63
see also Heritability
Selection aids, 184
Selection coefficient, 23
affected by allelic frequency, 24, 99
Selection differential, affected by population size, 194
attenuation of by natural selection, 138
cumulative, 120
defined, 25, 113
expected, 113, 139
in family selection, 159
realized, 113, 139, 140
related to selection intensity, 112, 114, 115
Selection efficiency, affected by population size, 193
and environment, 201
artificial vs. natural, 14
criteria of, 122
in presence of interaction, 200, 203
of combined selection, 174, 175
of family selection, 163, 164, 167, 168, 175, 176
of index selection, 179, 182
related to family size, 192
Selection experiments in poultry, blood spots in eggs, 252, 254
body size, 256
breast width, 257

Selection experiments in poultry, comb
    shape, 79
  crooked keels, 257
  crooked toes, 130
  disease resistance and susceptibility,
    243, 244, 245
  egg number, 62, 227
  egg quality, 251
  egg shape, 253
  egg shell thickness, 252
  egg weight, 62, 215, 251
  growth rate, 120, 255
  meat production traits, 254
  of historical interest, 226
  persistency of production, 249
  resistance to riboflavin deficiency, 201
  sexual maturity, 129
  shank growth ratio, 128
  shank length, 132
  viability, 195, 246
Selection index, construction of, 171
  efficiency of, 171
  for conformation of broilers, 182
  for egg production, 183
  in combined selection, 171, 173
  see also Index selection
Selection intensity, defined, 112
  effect of on selection response, 115,
    124
  related to the selection differential,
    112, 114, 115
  under multiple-objective selection,
    177
Selection limits, 265
Selection literature, 270
Selection pressure, absence of, 124
  measurement of, 23
Selection response, affected by repro-
    ductive rate, 25, 28
  asymmetric, 119, 121
  attenuated by natural selection, 125,
    127, 237
  controls in measurement of, 262
  dependence of, on genetic variance,
    73
    on heritability, 62, 115, 124, 155
    on selection intensity, 115, 124,
      155

Selection response, factors affecting,
    111, 115, 123
  genetic basis of, 23
  long-term prediction of, 155
  maximum possible rate of, 156
  measured   by,   allelic   frequency
    changes, 23
    genotypic frequency changes, 25
  of single loci, 24, 25
  per unit of time, 117
  prediction of, 111, 115, 116, 155
  schematic representation of, 17, 127
  theoretical model of, 126
  under inbreeding, 119
  validation of theory of, 154
Selection types, 7
Selfing, obligate, 99
Self-sterility, 99
Sex-limited traits, selection of, 158, 163,
    176
Sex-linkage of polygenic traits, 59
Sexual selection, 13
Somatic assortment, 91
Stabilizing selection, 6, 81, 83, 109
Stress in selection practice, 265
Strain crossing, 209, 211, 214, 222
Superdominance, see Overdominance
Survival of the fittest, 85
Suspended selection, effect of, on fit-
    ness, 126, 137
  on gains attained, 126, 133, 134,
    194, 195
  experiments on, 132, 195, 261

Tandem selection, described, 177
  efficiency of, 179
  illustration of, 178
Topcrossing, 210, 211
Total-score selection, see Index selec-
    tion

Unique events in evolution, 33, 35, 108
Units in heredity and evolution, 20, 36

Weighting factors, in combined selec-
    tion, 170, 171, 172, 173
  in selection indexes, 181